Anatomy
of the
Ship

THE HEAVY CRUISER
TAKAO

The Anatomy
of the Ship
series

THE HEAVY CRUISER
TAKAO

JANUSZ SKULSKI

CONWAY
MARITIME PRESS

Frontispiece: Takao outside Tokyo Bay, 14 July 1939, on trials after her main rebuilding. She reached maximum speed of 34.25kts at 14,894 tons displacement and 133,100shp. (*Fighting Ships of the Imperial Japanese Navy*)

© Janusz Skulski 1994

First published in Great Britain in 1994 by
Conway Maritime Press
an imprint of Brassey's (UK) Ltd,
33 John Street,
London WC1N 2AT

British Library Cataloguing-in Publication Data

Skulski, Janusz
Heavy Cruiser 'Takao'. – (Anatomy of the Ship Series
I. Title II. Series
623.8

ISBN 0 85177 628 0

Designed by John Leath, MSTD
Typeset by Dorwyn Ltd, Rowlands Castle, Hants
Printed and bound in Great Britain, by the Bath Press, Bath

Contents

Acknowledgements

I would like to express my sincere thanks to those who have helped both directly and indirectly in collecting materials and information for this book.

I am would also like to thank the friends who have offered advice on reconstructions and drawings. Their help had made this book possible.

I am especially grateful to Mr Hasegawa Tohichi, Mr Kawai Tokio, Mr Kamakura Takumi and Mr Uchiyama Mutsuo.

JANUSZ SKULSKI
Krakow, March 1994

Main sources for the Introduction
Report of the US Naval Technical Mission to Japan
Warship International 1977–84
Maru Special
Maru
Rengo Kantai

Introduction

The origins of the modern Japanese cruiser can be traced back to the early 1920s. On 31 July 1923 the light cruiser *Yubari* entered service in the Imperial Japanese Navy. This ship differed greatly in her appearance, profile and in innovatory technical features from light cruisers of the earlier *Tenryu*, *Kuma*, *Nagara* and *Sendai* classes. She was not a large vessel, even compared to contemporary light cruisers, with a standard displacement of 3387 tons (4075 tons at two-thirds trial displacement). Officially described as an 'experimental light cruiser', the ship was built to test the concept of a cruiser of high speed and relatively high firepower, on the smallest possible displacement.

The originator of this new cruiser design was Naval Constructor Hiraga Yuzuru, head of Fundamental Design, part of the 4th Shipbuilding Section of the Navy Technical Department. In the summer of 1921 he proposed the building of a cruiser with a standard displacement of 7500 tons, 35kts speed, armed with six new type 20.3cm (8in) 50cal guns in single mountings, and six twin 61cm broadside torpedo tubes. The installation of such a large armament in relation to the displacement was made possible because of the following radical weight reduction measures:
– the side and deck armour was worked as longitudinal strength members for the hull,
– a flush deck from bow to stern with an unusual undulating sheer line,
– continuous upper deck, which made the longitudinal strength members very effective and, at the same time, reduced structural weight.
However, such a complex structure necessarily complicated the construction of the hull.

In October 1921 the building of an experimental 'small' cruiser was approved by the Naval General Staff, based on the design of the proposed 7500-ton cruiser. Under Hiraga's supervision, Fujimoto Kikuô, Hiraga's assistant, worked out the design of *Yubari*. Construction took fourteen months, from June 1922 to July 1923. At the same time, the general outline of the basic design of the 7500-ton cruiser (known later as the *Furutaka* class) was approved by the naval authorities in August 1921. As for *Yubari*, the design was the work of Hiraga Yuzuru, assisted by Fujimoto Kikuô, and was intended to surpass the US *Omaha* and British *Hawkins* classes. The building of two cruisers was approved in February–March 1922, and work commenced in November–December 1922.

In the meantime an important conference took place, which increased interest in the cruisers' building. This was the Washington Naval Conference of 12 November 1921 to 6 February 1922. The resulting treaty limited the number of capital ships – battleships and aircraft carriers – but did not limit the number of ships up to 10,000 tons (10,160 tonnes), which were defined as 'auxiliary surface combat craft'. This placed a limit of 10,000 tons standard on the displacement of cruisers. The standard, or Washington, displacement was the tonnage of the ship ready for sea, with full stores, ammunition and complement but without fuel, reserve feed water and lubricating oil.

Prior to the Washington Naval Treaty the Japanese Navy used the normal displacement (in British tons) corresponding to the ship ready for sea, but with only a quarter of the fuel, three-quarters of the ammunition, a half to two-thirds of the stores and lubricating oil, and no reserve feed water. After 1920, however, ships were designed in trial condition: two-thirds trial displacement (in metric tonnes), that is, in full load condition minus a third of the full load fuel oil, lubricating oil, potable and reserve feed water, and stores.

As a signatory of the Treaty, Japan was forced to abandon her ambitious '8–8 Programme' – the construction of eight modern battleships and eight battlecruisers. On 3 July 1922 the new 'Naval Limitation Programme' was approved. This comprised fifty-nine ships, including the building of two cruisers with a standard displacement of 7100 tons (medium type) and four with a standard displacement of 10,000 tons (large type). Fujimoto Kikuô undertook the design of the two medium-type cruisers, while Hiraga was abroad.

Under pressure from the Naval General Staff, Fujimoto altered the armament of these cruisers, installing three twin 20.3cm (8in) gun turrets (compared with six single 20.3cm gun turrets in *Furutaka* and *Kako*), four single 12cm (4.7in) HA gun mounts (four single 8cm (3.2in) HA gun mounts in *Furutaka* and *Kako*) and a new type of catapult. The torpedo armament in both types of cruiser (twelve broadside torpedo tubes) was not changed. Named *Aoba* and *Kinugasa*, the new cruisers had an increased displacement at two-thirds trial of about 320 tons (*Kinugasa* 9930 tons). The additional topside weight reduced stability compared with the *Furutaka* type, and Hiraga protested strongly against that decision on his return to Japan.

At the end of 1922 the Naval General Staff presented Hiraga with the requirements for a new cruiser design of 10,000 tons displacement and 20cm (7.8in) guns. The requirements of the Naval General Staff were as follows:

1. An armament of eight 20.3cm (8in) guns in twin turrets, three turrets forward and one aft.
2. Anti-aircraft armament of four single 12cm (4.7in) HA guns.
3. Eight broadside 61cm (24in) torpedo tubes.
4. Protection of ship's vitals against indirect hits by 20.3cm (8in) cm shells and both direct and indirect hits by 15cm (6in) shells.
5. Protection along machinery space by 'bulges' (anti-torpedo and anti-mine).
6. Maximum speed over 35kts.
7. Range 10,000nm at 14kts.
8. Equipped to carry two floatplanes.

Hiraga did not entirely agree with the basic requirements, suggesting an increase of the main armament to ten 20.3cm (8in) guns (the point being to obtain an advantage over foreign equivalents, which usually had eight 20.3cm guns); an extention of anti-torpedo protection by fitting longitudinal armoured bulkheads inside the 'bulges'; a reduction of range to 8000nm at 14kts; and omission of the torpedo tubes as both unnecessary and dangerous (the likelihood of explosion if hit in action).

Early in 1923 Fujimoto, under the supervision of Hiraga, began work on the design, taking into account the changes suggested by Hiraga. However, during Hiraga's next posting abroad Fujimoto bowed to the pressure of the Naval General Staff, adding eight broadside 61cm (24in) torpedo tubes and increasing the number of 12cm (4.7in) HA guns from four to six (during construction the number of torpedo tubes was further augmented to twelve). In 1924 building started on the cruisers designated No 1 to No 4, later named *Myoko*, *Nachi*, *Ashigara* and *Haguro*. The displacement of the *Myoko* class cruisers was as follows:

Standard 10,980 tons (11,156 tonnes)
Two-thirds trial 13,071 tons (13,280 tonnes)
Nachi 13,090 tons (13,300 tonnes).

In March 1927, after discussions with and under pressure from the Naval General Staff, and as a result of the approval by the US Congress of a programme to build eight new cruisers of 10,000 tons displacement, the new shipbuilding programme (*Shôwa 2 Nendo Kantei Seizô Shinhojû Keikaku* – '1927 Shipbuilding New Replenishment Programme') was signed during the 52nd session of Parliament, held from 18 January to 26 March 1927. This programme comprised the building of twenty-seven ships during 1927–32, including four 10,000-ton cruisers.

Design

The cruiser design and preliminary work had begun in 1925. The design was to be an improved version of the *Myoko* class. The requirements of the Naval General Staff were as follows:

1. *Primary task:* Advance protection of the home support force and the driving back of enemy support forces. In addition, prime responsibility for fleet reconnaissance.
2. *Main opponents:* US and British heavy cruisers.
3. *Fire power:* Ten 20.3cm (8in) guns capable of anti-aircraft (HA) fire, eight 61cm (24in) torpedo tubes on the upper deck level (main deck level on *Myoko*) and anti-aircraft armament as for the *Myoko* class.
4. Protection against indirect 20.3cm (8in) shells and against direct and indirect 15cm (6in) shells.
5. Speed: Over 33kts. Range: 8000nm at 14kts.
6. To operate three floatplanes.
7. Equipment of the ship as a fleet flagship in peacetime and squadron flagship in wartime.

Design work began under the direction of Fujimoto at the beginning of 1925 and final plans were approved by Hiraga on his return from Great Britain in 1926. The overall design, including hull construction, armour system and powerplant, was based on the *Myoko* class and was designated the 'Improved *Myoko* design', despite a number of alterations and improvements, the most important being:

1. Heavier protection around the ammunition magazines.
2. Extensive use of Ducol steel, aluminium and electric welding.
3. A large, castle-like tower bridge.
4. New E2 type twin 20.3cm (8in) gun turrets with a maximum 70-degree elevation angle.
5. Rotating twin 61cm (24in) torpedo tubes in a torpedo room at upper deck level.
6. Fitting of two catapults.

Alterations 1, 2 and 4 were introduced following the recommendations of Hiraga, who had obtained information on the latest British designs, including the *Kent* class 10,000-ton cruisers. However, the installation of two catapults was the result of an assessment from the Intelligence Service that the new US 'Washington' (10,000-ton) cruisers were to be fitted with two catapults.

The '1927 Shipbuilding New Replenishment Programme' designated the new cruisers Nos 5 to 8 Large Type cruisers, and were later given a provisional classification as Nos 9 to 12 'A' class cruisers. The total building costs for the four cruisers were estimated at 113.48 million yen, *ie* 28.37 million yen per cruiser (compared with 281.54 million yen for the battleship *Yamato*, or about ten times more than the cost of one cruiser).

The four cruisers were named after mountains:

– On 23 June 1927 No 9 cruiser was named *Takao* after Takaosan, east of Kyôtô; No 10 cruiser was named *Atago* after Atagosan, in the Kyôtô region,
– On 13 April 1928 No 12 cruiser was named *Chokai* after the Chokaisan mountains in Ugo province, Yamagata prefecture,
– On 11 September 1928 No 11 cruiser was named *Maya* after Mayasan in the Hyôgô prefecture.

TABLE 1: Building dates and yards

	Takao	Atago	Maya	Chokai
Programme	No 5	No 6	No 7	No 8
Designation	'Large Type Cruiser' (Dai Gata Junyōkan)			
Ordered	Early 1927	Early 1927	Early 1928	Early 1928
Estimates	1928–28	1927–28	1928–29	1928–29
Provisional Designation	No 9	No 10	No 11	No 12
	'A Class Cruiser' (Kō-kyū Junyōkan)			
Named	23 Jun 1927	23 Jun 1927	11 Sept 1928	13 Apr 1928
Laid down	28 Apr 1927	28 Apr 1927	4 Dec 1928	26 Mar 1928
Launched	12 May 1930	16 Jun 1930	8 Nov 1930	5 Apr 1931
Commissioned	31 May 1932	30 Mar 1932	30 Jun 1932	30 Jun 1932
Building yard – hull and machinery	Yokosuka Kaigun Kôshô	Kure Kaigun Kôshô	Kawasaki Dockyard Co, Kôbe works	Mitsubishi Shipbuilding & Eng Co, Nagasaki works
Yard number	–	–	550	455

The four ships were henceforth designated *Takao* class cruisers and given the names of previous warships of the Imperial Japanese Navy.

The *Takao* class cruisers were the largest warships of their type in the Japanese Navy. They had a characteristically shaped hull and profile, large tower bridge and highly original arrangement of funnels and masts, all features introduced by the famous Japanese constructors Hiraga and Fujimoto. Their design was the culmination of a development in Japanese cruisers which had begun with the experimental vessel *Yubari*. The aim of the constructors was to create a warship that would outclass contemporary foreign vessels, especially those of the USA and Britain, even by breaching the displacement limits imposed by the Treaty. This had the negative effect of reducing metacentric height and decreasing stability. These aspects were corrected during the main phase of modernisation in 1938–39.

Like the earlier *Myoko* class, the *Takao*s became a prototype for the next five (later four) ships, designated the 'Improved *Takao* class'. In April 1927 the Americans started to build another six cruisers (CL–26 to CL–31), as a result of which the Japanese Naval Staff began preparations to push through the '1927 Shipbuilding New Replenishment Programme'. Four new cruisers were to be built, in pairs: two in 1930–34 and two in 1931–35, at a cost of 27.41 million yen each. All the necessary figures were estimated from the *Takao* class, and alterations included the installation of four new type 12.7cm (5in) HA guns and the upgrading of armour, especially around the ammunition magazines and anti-torpedo protection.

Presentation of the new plans to Parliament was, however, postponed when the Japanese Government received information from the British Prime Minister on 7 October 1929 about a naval disarmament conference which was to begin in January 1930. The signing of the London Naval Treaty by Japan on 22 April 1922 limited the number of 'A' class cruisers to twelve, thereby cancelling the building of the four ships of the 'Improved *Takao* class'. However, design of the 'B' class cruisers was started, and later they were built as the *Mogami* and *Tone* classes.

The fathers of the modern Japanese cruiser were Hiraga and Fujimoto; Fujimoto began as Hiraga's assistant and became his successor. Hiraga, who designed the capital ships of the '8–8 Programme' and the above-mentioned cruisers, and who later was responsible for the battleship

TABLE 2: Japanese 'A' class cruisers compared with contemporary foreign heavy cruisers

Completion Name	1926 Furutaka	1927 Aoba	1929 Myoko	1932 Takao	1930 (USA) Northampton	1930 (GB) Norfolk	1930 (Fr) Suffren	1931 (It) Zara
Displacement – Standard	8100 (8230)	8300 (8432)	10,980 (11,156)	11,350 (11,532)	9050 (9195)	9925 (10,084)	11,290 (11,471)	11,870 (12,060)
– Trial ⅔ tons (tonnes)	9400 (9551)	9665 (9820)	13,709 (13,929)	14,035 (14,260)	FULL LOAD:→ 12,150 (12,344)	13,450 (13,666)	12,780 (12,984)	14,530 (14,762)
	–	–	–			–	–	
Dimensions 1oa × b × d(m)	185.17 × 16.5 × 5.6	185.17 × 16.5 × 5.6	203.7 × 19.0 × 6.23	203.7 × 19.0 × 6.57	183 × 20.1 × 7.3	192.4 × 20.2 × 6.6	196 × 20.3 × 7.5	182.7 × 20.6 × 7.2
Armament	6 × 20cm 4 × 8cm 2 × 7.7mm	6 × 20cm 4 × 8cm 2 × 7.7mm	10 × 20.3cm 6 × 12cm 2 × 7.7mm	10 × 20.3cm 4 × 12cm 2 × 40mm 2 × 7.7mm	9 × 20.3cm 4 × 12.7cm 8 × 12.7mm	8 × 20.3cm 8 × 10.2cm 8 × 12.7mm	8 × 20.3cm 8 × 7.5cm 8 × 37mm 16 × 13mm	8 × 20.3cm 16 × 10cm 4 × 40mm
Torpedo tubes	12 × 61cm	12 × 61cm	12 × 61cm	8 × 61cm	6 × 53.3cm	8 × 53.3cm	12 × 55cm	–
Aircraft catapults	1 AIRCRAFT / 1 CATAPULT	1/1	1/1	2/2	4/2	1/1	2/2	2/1
Protection side/deck(mm)	76/48	76/48	102/35	127/32+47	75/50	25/35–38	54–60/54–60	100–150/70
Power plant (shp)	102,000	106,000	131,800	139,525	107,000	80,000	90,000	118,000
Speed (max. kts)	34.5	34.5	35.25	35.6	32.5	32.25	31.0	34.2
Range (nm/kts)	6000/14	7000/14	7000/14	8000/14	10,000/15	10,400/14	5000/15	5630/16
Crew	627	643	764	761	621	700	773	830

Yamato, was the most successful constructor in the Imperial Japanese Navy. Because he spent a good deal of time abroad, he was able to keep abreast of the latest developments in international shipbuilding. He introduced unique ideas in an effort to improve on his opponents' ships. However, he did not submit to pressure from the Naval General Staff, which requested an excessive amount of armament and equipment for the ships.

The same cannot be said of his successor, Fujimoto, whose ships included the *Mogami* class cruisers. A talented naval architect, Fujimoto became head of the 'Basic Design Section'. He often had to submit his designs to the pressures of the Naval General Staff for increases in armament, with a consequent loss in stability due to a rise in the ships' centre of gravity (CG). This overloading culminated in the capsize of the torpedo boat *Tomozuru* on 12 March 1934, for which Fujimoto was held responsible and relieved of his position in November 1934. Deeply shaken by his dismissal, he died suddenly – when a Rear Admiral – in January 1935.

Summary of service
Built by Yokosuka Kaigun Kôshô Shipyard.
28 Apr 1927: Laid down.

1930
12 May: Launched.

1932
31 May: Commissioned. *Takao, Atago, Maya* and *Chokai* registered at the *Yokosuka Chinjufu* (Naval District). Designated (until 1 Dec) as 1st Reserve Ships (*No 1 Yobikan*) and used for training purposes.
1 Dec–15 Nov 1935: Takao class formed *Sentai 4* of *Kantai 2* (*sen* = line, *tai* = formation, *kan* = warship) as replacement for *Myoko* class which went into reserve.

1933
Apr: Sentai 4, together with *Sentai 5* (comprising *Kako, Aoba, Kinugasa*) took part in night artillery gunfire exercises.

1935
Nov: Takao class transferred to reserve and attached to *Yokosuka Keibi Sentai* (Guard Squadron).

1936
Oct to Jul 1937: Takao modernised.
1 Dec: Takao and *Maya* formed into *Sentai 4* of *Kantai 2*.

1937
Autumn: After joining *Chokai* on 7 Aug, *Sentai 4* of *Kantai 2* operated in the Ryojun region (Port Arthur).
15 Nov: Takao joined *Atago* in Yokosuka before going into reserve for major refit.

1938
May–31 Aug 1939: Takao's major refit at the *Yokosuka Kaigun Kôshô*. (*Atago*

underwent a similar reconstruction from Apr to Oct 1939.) During modernisation the cruisers were in reserve.

1939
15 Nov: Takao and *Atago* re-formed as *Sentai 4* of *Kantai 2*, with *Takao* as flagship.

1940
Mar: Takao ships cruising in South China region.

1941
Feb–Mar: Sentai 4 again cruising in South China region, then returned to home waters.
20 Sept: Maya replaced *Takao* as flagship.
15 Aug: Takao class began preparations for war. *Takao* and *Atago* docked at Yokosuka (*Takao* 15–22 Sept). Embarked fuel and ammunition and sailed for their base. *Takao* and *Atago* sailed from Yokosuka to join *Maya* and *Chokai* in Saseki Bay.
29 Nov: Sailed for Makô, Pescadores Islands, arriving 2 Dec. *Atago* hoisted flag of Vice-Admiral Kondo Nobutake, Commander of *Nan Hômen Butai* (Southern Area Force).
Dec: 'First stage operations' – *Takao* class and *Ashigara* operated in South China Sea. *Takao* and *Atago*, together with *Sentai 3* (comprising the battleships *Kongo* and *Haruna*), formed the 'main body' of Southern Area Force as distant cover for Malaya and Borneo operations.

1942
Jan–mid Feb 1942: Takao, Atago and *Maya* remained at Palau to carry out anti-submarine patrols in the area.
16 Feb: Takao and *Maya* left Palau to act as distant cover for the carrier force that attacked Port Darwin on 19 Feb, arriving at Staring Bay, near Kendari, on 21 Feb.
25 Feb: Takao, Atago and *Maya* left Staring Bay to act as part of the 'Southern Striking Force' that intercepted Allied shipping south of Java during 2–5 Mar, returning to Staring Bay on 7 Mar.
11 Mar: Takao and *Maya* sailed from Staring Bay to Yokosuka (arriving 18 Mar) for refit (the addition of twin 12.7cm [5in] HA gun mounts). After refit the four *Takao*s trained as *Sentai 4* in home waters.
2 May: Between Yokosuka and Hachirajima, *Takao* rescued 472 survivors from *Miduho*, sunk the previous night off Omaezaki by the submarine USS *Drum*.
20 May: Takao and *Maya*, as the second section of *Sentai 4*, were attached to the Second Mobile Force, with the carriers *Junyo* and *Ryujo*.
22 May: Left Kure to support the Aleutians operation during the strikes on Dutch Harbor on 3–5 June.
7 Jun–5 Jul: Cruised south of the Aleutians, returning to Hachirajima on 13 July.
10 Aug: After US forces landed on Guadalcanal, *Sentai 4* (*Takao, Atago* and *Maya*) and *Sentai 5* (*Myoko* and *Haguro*) left Hachirajima under the command of Vice Admiral Kondo Nobutake to sail for Truk, arriving 17 Aug.

24 Aug: Admiral Kondo's squadron, together with Admiral Nagumo's carrier force, made contact with the US Task Force 61, resulting in the Battle of the Solomons.

9–23 Sept: Kondo's and Nagumo's squadrons cruised north of the Solomons.

26 Oct: Both squadrons engaged in a night battle with US forces and sank the burning hulk of the aircraft carrier USS *Hornet* in the Battle of Santa Cruz Island.

14–15 Nov: Third Battle of the Solomons or Battle of Guadalcanal. During the night *Takao, Atago* and the battleship *Kirishima* engaged the US battleships *South Dakota* and *Washington. South Dakota* was hit by at least sixteen *91 Shiki* 20.3cm (8in) shells from *Takao* and *Atago* at a distance of 5000m. *Kirishima* was sunk, *Takao* was not hit, and *Atago* suffered light damage.

22 Nov: *Takao* left Truk and sailed to Yokosuka, arriving 27 Nov.

19 Dec: After a small refit (addition of 25mm MG mounts) *Takao* left Yokosuka and arrived at Truk on 24 Dec, based there until 21 July 1943.

1943

31 Jan–9 Feb: *Takao* sailed with *Sentai 5* north of the Solomons to act as distant support for the evacuation of Guadalcanal.

21 July: *Takao* and *Atago* left Truk and arrived Yokosuka on 26 July for refit (addition of *21 Gô* radar, triple 25mm (1in) MG mounts).

17 Aug: After re-forming as *Sentai 4, Takao* and *Atago* left Yokosuka with army troops for Truk, arriving 23 Aug.

26 Aug: Left Truk for Rabaul. Returned 29 Aug.

18 Sept: Left Truk, to Eniwetok.

25 Sept: Returned to Truk as a result of the US carrier force raid on the Gilberts.

17 Oct: After US carrier raids on Wake, *Sentai 4* left Truk with the Combined Fleet, put in at Eniwetok 19–23 Oct, and returned to Truk 26 Oct.

3 Nov: *Sentai 4* and other ships left Truk for Rabaul, arriving 5 Nov. Anchored ships attacked by aircraft from Task Force 38. *Takao* hit by a bomb on the upper deck, starboard of No 2 20.3cm (8in) gun turret. The explosion pierced the upper deck, damaging No 2 turret barbette and the starboard side of No 1 20.3cm gun turret directed to starboard at the time. Twenty-three crew killed by explosion. On same day, *Takao* and *Atago* left for Truk, arriving 7 Nov.

11 Nov: Both cruisers left Truk for Yokosuka, arriving 15 Nov. Remained there for repairs until 29 Jan 1944 (to fit 25mm MG and *22 Gô* radar).

1944

29 Jan: *Takao* left Yokosuka for Truk, but diverted en route to escort the damaged aircraft carrier *Unyo* back to Yokosuka.

15 Feb: *Takao* left Yokosuka once again, for Palau, arriving 20 Feb.

4 Mar: Ships of *Sentai 4* and *Sentai 5* organised into the 'First Mobile Fleet' – No 1 *Kido Butai* – and left Palau 29 Mar, remaining at Davao 1–4 Apr before anchoring in Lingga Roads 9 Apr.

11 May: *Sentai 4* left Lingga Roads for Tawi-Tawi, Borneo.

13 Jun: *Sentai 4* left Tawi-Tawi to participate in Battle of the Marianas 19–20 June.

24 Jun: All ships returned to the Inland Sea and Hachirajima Bay, with one call at Okinawa on 22 June.

8 Jul: *Takao* and *Atago* as cruisers of *Sentai 4* left Kure after modification, reaching Singapore on 16 July.

26 Jul–8 Aug: *Takao* docked in Kure.

26 Jul: *Sentai 4's* four *Takao*s were to be part of No 1 Strike Force – *No 1 Yugeki Butai* – under the command of Vice-Admiral Kurita Takeo, making preparations for Operation 'SHO Go'.

30 Aug: *Takao* and *Atago* arrived Singapore. All ships then remained in readiness and for training, at Lingga Roads.

18 Oct: After the commencement of Operation 'SHO Go', the Battle of the Philippine Islands (or Battle for Leyte Gulf), *Sentai 4* left Lingga Roads for Brunei, arriving 20 Oct.

22 Oct: *Sentai 4's Takao*s left Brunei for San Bernardino Strait.

23 Oct: *Takao* hit at 0634hrs by two (of a salvo of four) torpedoes from the US submarine *Darter* at a distance of 1400m (from stern torpedo tubes, after firing at *Atago* from bow tubes). First torpedo (21in Mark 14) hit starboard frame 180, flooding No 4, No 6 and No 8 boiler rooms; second torpedo hit starboard frame 335, damaging the rudder and both starboard propellers, and reducing the power of both engines. The explosions started an oil fuel fire, and the ship came to a stop with a 10-degree list to starboard. Counterflooding the port boiler rooms corrected the list and the fire was extinguished. Seriously damaged, the cruiser set out for Brunei that night, escorted by the destroyers *Akishimo* and *Naganami*, sailing at low speed and arriving in port on 25 Oct.

23 Oct: *Atago* and *Maya* sunk, *Atago* by four torpedo hits from USS *Darter, Maya* by four torpedos from USS *Dace*.

25 Oct: *Chokai* sunk after heavy bomb damage and finally scuttled by a torpedo from the destroyer *Fujinami*. After emergency repairs, *Takao* left Brunei for Singapore, arriving 12 Nov.

15 Nov: *Takao* attached to *Sentai 5*.

20 Dec: *Atago, Chokai* and *Maya* deleted from the Navy List.

1945

1 Jan: Remaining cruisers of *Sentai 5* (*Takao, Myoko, Haguro*) transferred to the South West Area Force (*Ashigara* was attached to *Kantai 5*.) *Takao* underwent provisional repair after her damage, but without the necessary major repairs, which could only be undertaken in Japan, she was not able to take part in the naval operations of the time. After many reshuffles in the course of 1945, *Takao*, along with *Myoko, Ashigara* and *Haguro*, formed the First South Expeditionary Fleet.

5 Feb: First South Expeditionary Fleet attached to No 10 Area Fleet. After *Ashigara* and *Haguro* sank, *Takao* and *Myoko* were retained in Seletar Base, Singapore, for use as floating anti-aircraft batteries. *Takao* suffered more damage as a result of aircraft attacks. Since the condition of *Takao* and *Myoko* was not fully known to the Allied authorities, the British planned to attack the cruisers with midget submarines (X-Craft) brought via Panama by the depot ship HMS *Bonaventure* to Subic Bay, Borneo. The midget submarine *XE-3*, commanded by Lt I E Fraser and towed by the submarine HMS *Stygian*, was to attack *Takao*. *XE-1*, commanded by Lt J E Smart and towed by HMS *Spark*, was to attack *Myoko*. As *XE-1* was unable to locate *Myoko*, both midget submarines proceeded to attack *Takao*. A one-ton charge and six 35kg limpet mines were attached to her hull; though the charge failed to explode, some of the mines succeeded (at 2130hrs, 31 July), blowing a hole 7m long and 3m wide (21 by 9ft) in the hull bottom, to starboard and parallel with the keel, between frames 113 and 116. This caused flooding of the compartments below the lower deck: No 1 and No 2, with 12.7cm (5in) HA ammunition magazines and 25mm (1in) MG magazines, and the plotting room.

21 Sept: Takao surrendered to British forces at Seletar Base.

1946

Early months: Takao used by the South East Area Forces as base ship for communications, repairs and accommodation. Later the British authorities made the decision to scuttle *Takao* (and *Myoko*), at a depth of over 150m, in the Malacca Strait, off Port Swettenham.

27 Oct: Takao left Seletar Base at 0730hrs, towed by HM Fleet tugs *Griper* and *Assiduous* and escorted by the cruiser HMS *Newfoundland* (possibly to increase towing power). *Nitto Maru*, the ex-submarine hunter *No 17*, accompanied them, to take *Takao*'s Japanese crew back to Singapore after the scuttling. She was scuttled at noon, position 03°05'05"N, 100°41'00"E (near *Myoko*) – the end of the last of the 'A' class Japanese cruisers.

1947

3 May: Takao deleted from the Navy List.

Hull structure

The hull of the *Takao*s was based on the earlier vessels of 7100 and 10,000 tons displacement, and upgraded with Hiraga's design amendments, which were as follows:

1. Upper deck: flush type with undulating sheer line; high freeboard at bow (7600mm, 4403mm amidships) and low at stern (3350mm), which became known as *Suihei Kanpan Gata* (horizontal deck type). This design made the longitudinal strength members continuous, for greater effect, and at the same time reduced structural weight; but it evidently caused severe complications during building. It was calculated that thanks to these weight-saving measures, the hull weight would amount to only 32 per cent of the two-thirds trial displacement.

2. Armour plates, on both the side belt and middle deck, were worked as both protection and as longitudinal strength members. The side plates contributed 100 per cent on the compression side and 65 per cent on the tension side; the deck plates 100 per cent on the compression side and 80 per cent on the tension side.

The structure and shape of the hull were based mainly on the *Myoko* class design, to which were made the following important changes: Ducol steel was used instead of HT steel, and the maximum breadth was located further forward, just abaft No 1 fore funnel, frame 174. The plans were

TABLE 3: **Hull characteristics**

	As designed, 1926	As completed, 1932
Length, pp	192.540m	192.540m
overall	203.759m	203.759m
waterline	201.663m*	201.900m**
Beam, maximum (below waterline)	18.999m	18.999m
waterline	18.030m*	18.200m**
Depth, upper deck side	10.973m	10.973m
Draught, fore-aft	6.114m	6.570m
Freeboard, bow	8.056m	7.600m
admidship	4.859m	4.403m
stern	3.806m	3.391m
Displacement, standard	9850 tons	11,350 tons
	(10,008 tonnes)	(11,532 tonnes)
normal	–	12,532 tons
		(12,732 tonnes)
⅔ trial	12,781 tons	14,035 tons
	(12,986 tonnes)	(14,260 tonnes)
Hull coefficients for ⅔ trial displacement:		
Block coefficient (Cb)	0.542	0.552
Prismatic coefficient (Cp)	0.618	0.627
Midship coefficient (Cm)	0.877	0.822
Waterline coefficient (Cw)	–	0.721
Maximum amidship submerged area	101.8m²	110.0m²
Length/beam ratio (L/b)	11.25	11.095
Draught/length ratio (D/l)	0.0303	0.0326
Beam/draught (B/d)	2.933	2.776
Deadrise	1.143m	
Camber, upper deck	0.254m	
Bilge keel	60m long, 1.40m wide	
Rudder	Balanced rudder of 19.83m² surface	

Waterline length and beam, draught and freeboard are given at ⅔ trial condition displacement
Note: *on waterline; **on ⅔ trial condition waterline

worked out for the first time in metric units; previously, ship design was in English Imperial units.

Hull weight and stability

When the project was begun, none of the earlier 'A' class cruisers had run trials, and the problem of excessive weight had not yet come to light. Savings on weight through the application of electric welding above upper deck level, and the use of aluminium (for internal structures and equipment), were insufficient to compensate for very heavy upper superstructures and as completed *Takao*'s two-thirds trial displacement increased by more than 10 per cent from the designed 12,986 tonnes to 14,260 tonnes.

The increase in displacement reduced the freeboard, impaired seakeeping, and reduced both maximum speed and endurance. Moreover, it lowered the metacentre (M) and resulted in a reduction of the metacentric height (GM), despite an advantageous centre of gravity (CG) located below the waterline (negative OG), at least in the two-thirds trial condition. The addition of various topside fittings between 1932 and 1938 resulted in a further slight increase in displacement, which further reduced GM and, in consequence, the range of stability. Only with the major refit of 1938–39, in which 'large type bulges' were added and superstructure weight reduced, was the stability improved.

TABLE 4: **Weight distribution for *Takao* as completed 1932**			
	Tons	*(Tonnes)*	*Per cent*
Hull structure	4086.7	(4151.4)	29.0
Armour and protective plates	2368.2	(2406.1)	16.8
Fittings	521.7	(530.0)	3.7
Equipment, 'fixed'	179.8	(182.7)	1.3
Armament, total weight	1728.7	(1756.4)	12.3
Guns	1166.4	(1185.1)	8.3
Torpedo armament	166.9	(169.6)	1.2
Electrical equipment	359.2	(364.9)	2.6
Aircraft equipment	30.7	(31.2)	0.2
Navigation equipment	5.5	(5.6)	–
Machinery	2670.6	(2713.3)	19.0
Oil fuel (⅔)	1754.6	(1782.7)	12.5
Reserve feed water (⅔)	104.7	(106.4)	0.7
Light oil lubrication oil (⅔)	56.3	(57.2)	0.4
Underwater protection	213.0	(216.4)	1.5
Unknown	68.9	(70.0)	0.5
Total weight	14,066.7	(14,292.0)	100.0

TABLE 5: **Stability data for *Takao* 1932–41**						
	Displacement (tons)	Draught (m)	KG (m)	OG (m)	GM (m)	Range
2.3 trial condition						
1932	14,109	6.51	6.37	–0.14	1.20	88°
1937	14,579	6.68	6.50	–0.18	1.08	84°
1941	14,838	6.316	6.437	+0.121	1.505	89°
Normal value	–	–	–	0	>1.30	>85°
Light conditions						
1932	11,406	5.49	7.18	+1.69	0.38	73°
1937	11,523	5.51	7.37	+1.87	0.17	68°
1941	12,171	5.423	7.176	+1.834	1.46	73°
Normal value	–	–	–	<1.50	>1.0	>75°

KG height of centre of gravity (CG) above keel
OG height of centre of gravity above waterline
GM metacentric height
Range angle of inclination from upright at which righting moment vanishes and ship capsizes

Hiraga opted for a large GM in order to limit the angle of heel after damage when a machinery space on one side was flooded and the flooding remained unilateral owing to the presence of the longitudinal centreline bulkhead. The GM had to be sufficient to allow the flooding of two machinery spaces on the same side without capsizing. The large GM was also needed to limit the angle of the heel (to less than the accepted 13 degrees) during high-speed turns (at 8/10 maximum power with helm at 35 degrees).

Protection

The armour was to protect the ship's vitals against indirect 20cm shells and against direct and indirect 15cm shells. It formed an armoured box which protected the ammunition magazines, boiler and engine rooms. The dimensions of the armoured box were: 123.60m between fore and aft bulkheads (No 1 to No 5 barbettes) at store deck level (frame 62 to 292); 119.80m for the total length of the main side belt (frame 70 to 292).

Vertical protection
The NVNC steel side belt had a 12-degree inwards angle and covered both the machinery space and the barbettes enclosing ammunition magazines. The central part of the belt extended slightly over the machinery space and was 82.40m long (frame 116 to 258), with a uniform thickness of 102mm and height of 3.5m. Its upper edge connected with the armoured middle deck. The extremities of the belt extended fore and aft to enclose the gun turret bases and their magazines up to the lower deck. The belt extended straight downwards to about 1.70m below the store deck and its NVNC steel plates were tapered.

The upper 2.5m of the belt was 127mm thick and the lower strake reaching to about 1.7m below the store deck level was tapered, from 76mm at the upper edge to 38mm at the lower edge. The extension of the belt armour downwards, where there was no anti-torpedo bulkhead, was intended to protect the magazines against 'diving' shells. This protection system was further extended in subsequent designs (for *Mogami*, *Tone* and *Yamato*) to replace the curved anti-torpedo bulkheads over the machinery spaces.

At two-thirds trial displacement there was a resulting increase in draught, leaving only 1.3m of the belt above the waterline amidships (the belt around the fore and aft magazines was at waterline level). At 15,490 to 15,697 tons (15,738 to 15,948 tonnes) full load displacement during 1937–38, with a draught over 7.0m, the main belt was only about 0.8m above the waterline.

76mm thick NVNC steel transverse bulkheads enclosed the machinery space and the No 4 turret barbette on the lower deck side; below the lower deck, 102mm thick NVNC steel bulkheads enclosed the bases of No 1 and No 5 gun turrets.

The after bulkhead was straight and the forward one angled. The barbettes of the main 20.3cm gun turrets were protected above the lower deck by 76mm NVNC steel; however, to save weight, the 'shadow' caused by the adjacent barbettes was used as protection and the thickness was reduced to 38mm within an angle of 30 degrees on each side of the centreline. Additional vertical protection was provided along the middle deck side by 25mm thick Ducol steel plates, and within the main belt by 9mm and 25mm plates.

Horizontal protection
The flat middle deck, with a camber extending 254mm over the machinery space, had a thickness of 35mm NVNC steel, except for the outer strake of 1.52m where it was 32mm. This outer strake was connected to the upper edge of the main belt. The lower deck covering the magazines was connected to the upper edges of the fore and aft belt parts by 47mm of NVNC steel. The upper deck was reinforced by two layers of Ducol steel plates amidships, the lower 16mm thick and the upper 12.5 to 25mm thick.

Other protection

The funnel uptakes were protected by 88.5mm thick (70mm on the centreline) NVNC steel plates up to 1830mm above the armoured middle deck. The steering gear spaces were protected by 50mm thick NVNC steel plates at the sides, 38mm at the ends (fore and aft side) and by 25mm at the middle deck level. The conning tower (middle bridge deck) was protected against enemy aircraft machine-gun fire and against splinters by 16mm Ducol steel plates.

Underwater protection

Protection against torpedoes and mines consisted of submerged 'bulges' and longitudinal bulkheads. The bulges were about 93m long and 2.5m deep. The inner side of the bulges was formed by a curved longitudinal bulkhead consisting of two 29mm Ducol steel plates, giving 58mm of protection. This anti-torpedo system was based on the one introduced by Hiraga in the capital ships *Nagato* and *Kaga* and in subsequent designs. It was calculated that it could provide protection against the contact explosion of a 200kg Shimose (picric acid explosive) charge.

Machinery

The Naval General Staff requirement for 35kts meant an increase in power to 130,000shp. The Navy Technical Department designed a powerplant that was directly derived from the one developed for the cancelled *Amagi* class battlecruisers designed under Hiraga in 1919. This powerplant was already installed in the *Myoko* class cruisers, but in *Takao* the generators – electric motors fitted on *Myoko* to run the inner propellers and so reduce the drag during cruising – were omitted. In addition, two small 'induction' turbines were provided to move the inner shafts in order to switch more rapidly from cruising conditions to higher speeds, for instance during combat to help start the after turbines and hence accelerate and ease the transition from two- to four-shaft propulsion. The turbines were driven by the steam exhausted from the cruiser turbines. Errors during coupling resulted in very high rotation speed and repeated accidents, leading to the 'induction' turbines being removed during the 1938–39 refit.

Turbines

The main forward turbines were single-flow impulse *Kansei Honbu* or Kanpon type, developing 130,000shp at 320rpm on four shafts (32,500shp per shaft). Four sets of turbines were fitted, two forward and two aft, separated by longitudinal and transverse bulkheads. Each set comprised four forward turbines, two low-pressure and two high-pressure, geared down to one shaft via a four-pinioned helicoidal gear, and two astern turbines located in the low-pressure turbine casing. Each of the forward sets also included a cruising turbine connected to the outer high-pressure turbine via a reduction gear (current use). The turbine rotors were hardened steel with stainless steel 'B' blades.

The cruising turbine output was 3100shp at 5439rpm, reduced to 1600shp by the cruising gear. The overall turbine output, including cruising, outer high-pressure and low-pressure turbines, was 7050shp at 170rpm after reduction in the main gear, or 14,000shp for port and starboard turbines.

In cruising conditions the turbine sets of the after engine rooms freewheeled, or could be disconnected at the gearing. In other conditions the live steam was admitted to both outer and inner high-pressure turbines, the cruising turbine being bypassed and disconnected at the cruising gears.

The after engine room turbine sets driving the inner shafts each comprised two high-pressure and two low-pressure turbines and a small 'induction' turbine. Each of the eight low-pressure turbine casings contained an astern turbine of 4500shp (or 36,000shp in total) at 180rpm.

The steam pressure at the inlet was 17.25kg/cm² and 0.155kg/cm² at the exhaust.

Condensers

There were eight single-flow 'Uniflux' type condensers, four to the sides and four beneath the low-pressure turbine casings. Each condenser had a 762m² cooling surface and a Weir dual type air pump of 96 tons/hr capacity and a two-cylinder reciprocating circulating pump.

Boilers

There were twelve boilers of the three-drum water tube Kanpon *Shiki RO-gô* type for oil fuel use only. The saturated steam pressure (working pressure) was 20kg/cm². Each boiler had eleven No 2 type oil burners with a total capacity of 5.5 tons/hr, and four No 4 oil burners with a capacity of 1.2 tons/hr. The boiler's heating surface was 970m². Each set of four boilers had a funnel uptake, and each boiler had a Weir type oil fuel pump with a capacity of 10.5 tons/hr, and two forced geared-drive type draught fans with a capacity of 1150m³/hr each.

A *RO-gô* type Donkey boiler (14kg/cm² pressure) was fitted on the upper deck centreline (frame 182), which was later removed from *Takao* during the 1938–39 refit.

Auxiliary machinery

The total output of the electric generators was 1225kW. The electric current (225 volts) was provided by five generators, four 250kW driven by internal combustion engine and one 225kW diesel engine (at lower deck level forward of the port boiler rooms. Each engine room had two exhaust and suction fans driven by an electric Sirocco type motor.

Four Weir type fire and bilge pumps were fitted, two in the engine rooms (total capacity 59 tons/hr) and two in the boiler rooms (total capacity 155 tons/hr).

Machinery weight

The overall weight of the powerplant was 2660 to 2670 tons (2703–2713 tonnes) = 48.8hp/ton. The weight distribution was as follows:

Main engines 681 tons (692 tonnes)
Boilers 592 tons (601 tonnes)
Funnels and uptakes 96 tons (97.5 tonnes)

Shafts and propellers 245 tons (249 tonnes)
Tubes and pipe systems 236 tons (240 tonnes)
Auxiliary engines 170 tons (173 tonnes)
Various 126 tons (128 tonnes)
Oil fuel and water in boilers, pipes, etc, 412 tons (419 tonnes).
Maximum fuel capacity was 2645 tons (2687 tonnes) of oil. Maximum endurance was 8000nm at 14kts, but with overloading effective endurance was 7000nm at 14kts. The maximum design speed was 35.5kts from 130,000shp at 320rpm. During trials off Tatayama on 31 March 1932 *Takao* reached 35.6kts with 139,525shp at 12,175 tons (12,370 tonnes) displacement. Propeller diameter was 3.86m (12ft 9in), pitch 4.2m, with a developed area of 9.15m².

Main armament

The armament comprised ten 20.3cm/50cal guns, officially designated '50cal 3 Nendo Shiki 2 Gô 20cm guns', with an effective bore of 203.2mm (8in). These were approved on 25 July 1931 and mounted for the first time in the *Takao* class ships.

TABLE 6: **Characteristics of the 20.3cm/50 gun**

Calibre of bore	20.3cm (8in)
Length in calibre	50 cal
Construction	Monobloc, radially expanded
Breech mechanism	Normal swinging (hand or hydraulic)
Length oa	10.310m
Weight with breech	19.0 tons (19.3 tonnes)
Grooves, number	48
Chamber, length	1.348m
volume	68 litres
Muzzle velocity	835m/sec
Bore pressure (max)	31.4kg/mm²
Life of barrel	About 320 rounds
Firing rate	4–5 rounds/min (effective 2–3rpm)
Max range at 45°	29,400m (vertical range 9500m)
Max vertical range	12,000m at 55° and 70°
Max depression	–5°
Shell weight (all types)	125.85kg
Charge weight (common)	33.8kg
NVNC steel penetration at:	
15,000m	150mm
20,000m	125mm
Cruiser's all-gun firing:	
Fire rate/min (effective)	50 shells/min (30 shells/min)
Broadside weight (effective)	6293kg (3776kg)

Characteristics of the gun mountings and turrets
The *Takao* class cruisers were equipped with a new type of gun turret known as model 'E', designed (as were the guns) by Engineer C Hada, who went on to design the gun turrets for the battleship *Yamato*. The turret design was inspired by the British 8in mounts for the *Kent* class 10,000-ton cruisers, which theoretically were capable of anti-aircraft fire. Model 'E' was designed for a 70-degree elevation, but due to the light weight of the elevating and recoil mechanism, effective maximum eleva-

tion was 55 degrees. (Redesigned model 'E₁' turrets installed on *Maya* had a maximum elevation of 55 degrees.)

The gun cradles were fitted with hydraulic recoil cylinders and pneumatic run out rams, using hydraulic power both to absorb the recoil energy (brake cylinders) and to return the guns to the firing position. The pneumatic rams made part use of the adiabatic compression (during recoil) and expansion (for run-out) of the air.

The loading position was +5 degrees for surface firing, top speed (elevation and depression) was 12 degrees/sec, and maximum training speed was 4 degrees/sec. The distance between gun barrels was 1.9m. Turret dimensions were: length 8.25m, width 6.0m and height 2.15m. The external diameter of the roller path was 5.029m. Turret protection was limited to 25mm thick Ducol steel plates on the sides, face, rear and roof surfaces; in addition they were protected from all sides by anti-heat protection made of thin steel sheets with about 10–15cm of airspace between the armour and steel sheets, which served as a sun screen in tropical climates. The overall weight of the model 'E' turret was 171 tons (173.7 tonnes).

Power supply to gun mounts and turrets
Each turret was fitted with two hydraulic pumps (A-ends) driven by two 100hp electric motors located in the lower chamber of the turret's engine room. The hydraulic pressure was 35kg/cm². The turrets used hydroelectric power, with mineral oil as fluid, for various operations: for training the turret via a set of cylindrical worm and wormwheels (maximum 4 degrees/sec), for elevating and depressing the guns via piston type gears (maximum 12 degrees/sec), and for moving the rammer and actuating the ammunition hoists.

Ammunition supply
Model 'E' mounts had two hoists per gun, one for low-angle (surface) fire and one for high-angle (anti-aircraft) fire. For low-angle fire the shells were carried by hand on a shell bogie from the shell room on the lower deck to the shell-handling room. A 'pusher' type hoist carried the shells (a maximum of four per minute) to the turret, where they were loaded and rammed hydraulically at a fixed elevation of +5 degrees. The shell fuse setting was done manually on the loading tray. Additional hoists for anti-aircraft fire were fitted to the front of the turret trunk to provide a better rate of fire.

The powder charges were carried by hand from flash-tight canisters in the powder magazines below the store deck to the powder-handling room, and put into 'bucket' type hoists (at a maximum rate of four complete charges per minute) for carrying up to the turret, where they were then loaded by hand. Flash-tight rotating powder scuttles were positioned between the powder magazines and the powder-handling rooms, and all powder and shell hoists were fitted with flash-tight doors at both lower and upper ends.

Gun drill was as follows:

1. The Trainer positioned the turret, as indicated by the gun director; the Layer positioned the gun to a loading angle of +5 degrees.

2. No 1 Gunner opened the breech and flushed the inside of the barrel with compressed air to lessen the risk of backfire.

3. No 3 Gunner carried the sheel loading tray, containing a sheel brought up by the 'pusher' hoist, towards the breech and placed the shell partly in the chamber. No 2 Gunner rammed the shell (hydraulically) into the chamber.

4. No 4 Gunner took a powder charge bag from the 'bucket' hoist and passed it to No 5 Gunner who placed it on the loading tray. No 2 Gunner dispatched it hydraulically into the powder chamber. The second powder bag was dispatched in the same manner. Then No 2 Gunner positioned the firing capsule (primer).

5. No 1 Gunner closed the breech. Loading was then complete.

6. The Layer relaid the gun as indicated by the gun director. The gun was then ready for firing.

The complement of the gun turret consisted of forty-two officers and men, twenty-three men on the turret compartment, nine in the shell room and ten in the powder magazine.

Ammunition for 20.3 guns

SHELLS

1. Capped *91 Shiki 'Hibô Tetsukôdan'* AP shell with 3.11kg of *91 Shiki* explosive (TNA), *13 Shiki 4 Gô* base fuses (length 906mm, weight 125.85kg). Colours were white with a red band. The shell was called '*Suichû dan*' ('underwater, or diving, shell') and was fitted with a wind/water shield. It could pierce a 165mm thick NVNC plate at a 30-degree striking angle and a velocity of 474m/sec. According to range, its NVNC plate piercing capability was 190mm at 10,000m, 120mm at 18,000m, and 74mm at 29,400m (maximum range).

2. HE (high explosive) *91 Shiki 'Tsûjôdan'* common shell with 8.17kg of *91 Shiki* explosive (TNA), *91 Shiki* nose time fuse. Colours were brown with a yellow band.

3. *O Shiki 'Tsûjôdan'* common shell with sharper nose profile (replaced after 1940 by the *91 Shiki* common shell) with 8.17kg of *91 Shiki* explosive (TNA), *91 Shiki* nose time fuse. Colours were brown with a yellow band. Length 880mm, weight 125.85kg. This could be used as an anti-aircraft shell, with a maximum height of trajectory of 10,000m and effective destruction radius of 29.3m.

4. *3 Shiki 'Sankaidan'* common shell, an incendiary or fragmentation shell used after 1939 (see illustration). It was filled with 198 incendiary tubes and 48 stays, with *91 Shiki* nose time fuse. Colours were red with a yellow band. Length 860mm, weight 125.85kg. Officially classified as a common shell. The shell burst was initiated by the time fuse, the incendiary tubes igniting about 0.5sec later and burning for 5sec at 3000 degrees Celseuis with a flame of about 5m. The effective burst diameter was about 100m. This shell was more efficient than the normal common shell (*O Shiki* or *91 Shiki*).

5. Illuminating 'B' shell ('*Shomeidan B*'), a starshell with parachute and double ejection charge, approved in about 1937, with *91 Shiki* nose time fuse. Colour red, weight 125.85kg. This shell was fired with a reduced charge with a muzzle velocity of 710m/sec, and was filled with 5.13kg of

pyrotechnics, mainly magnesium, barium nitrate and beeswax. Its maximum range was 22,600m and effective range 16,000m, with an illuminating power of 1.6 million candlepower.

6. Timed exercise shell with *91 Shiki* nose time fuse. Colours were black with a yellow band.

7. Exercise shell without fuse. Colour black.

All of these shells used three types of powder charge:

1. 'Common' charge. Weight 33.8kg with $80C_2$, $70C_2$, 60DC or 53DC powder.
2. 'Reduced' charge, with $70C_2$, 60DC or 53DC powder.
3. 'Light' charge, with $35C_2$ powder.

Ships were provided with a maximum of 1200 20.3cm shells, *ie* 120 shells per gun.

The percentage hit probabilities of the 20.3cm gun salvos were:

1932–34: 11.5 at 10,000m, 6.7 at 15,000m, 5.1 at 17,000m, 3.0 at 20,000m and 1.5 at 23,000m.
1935–40: 15.0 at 10,000m, 10.2 at 15,000m, 8.4 at 17,000m, 6.0 at 20,000m and 4.0 at 23,000m.

The mean spread of the 20.3cm gun salvos (at a range of 20,000m) was 480m in 1933, 425m in 1937 and 380m in 1940.

High angle guns

10 Nendo Shiki 12cm HA 45cal gun

Between 1932 and the 1942 refit, *Takao* was fitted with four 12cm HA guns designed by Engineer C Hada. The guns were mounted in single shielded and electro-hydraulically actuated model 'B_2' gun mountings at a high angle gun deck level.

12cm ammunition

SHELLS:

1. HE common shell, '*Tsûjôdan*', containing 1.7kg of Shimose (picric acid explosive with *91 Shiki* nose time fuse). Colours were maroon with a white top.
2. Marker or target shell, '*Mokuhyodan*', with a 30sec time fuse. Colour was green.
3. Illuminating starshell, '*Hoseidan*', which had no parachute and a short burning time. After 30 March 1938 it was renamed '*Shomeidan A*'. Colour was bluish grey.
4. Timed exercise shell, '*Jigen Enshudan*', with 91 time fuse. Colours were black with a white top.
5. Exercise shell, '*Enshudan*', without fuse. Colours were black with a yellow top.

Types of charge, in brass cartridge case:

1. 'Common' charge, with 5.06kg of $35C_2$ or 5.5kg of 30DC powder.
2. 'Reduced' charge, with $35C_2$ or 30DC or $20T_2$ powder.
3. 'Light' charge, with $20C_2$ or $20C_3$ powder.

Type 89 Model A-1 12.7cm HA 40cal gun
Four twin mounts replaced the 12cm single HA gun mountings during the 1942 refit. These guns were designed by Engineer C Hada and approved on 6 February 1932.

TABLE 7: **Characteristics of the 12cm/45 AA gun**

	Approved 1926
Calibre of bore	12.0cm (4.7in)
Length of calibre	45cal
Construction of barrel	Built up (Mk IX$_2$)
Breech	Horizontal sliding breech
Length oa	5.604m
Weight with breech	2980kg
Grooves, number	34
Chamber, length	0.656m
volume	10.77 litres
Muzzle velocity	825m/sec
Bore pressure (max)	26.5kg/mm^2
Life of barrel	700–1000 rounds
Firing rate	10–11 rounds/min
Max range	15,600m
Max vertical range	10,065m
Effective vertical range	8450m
Max elevation	75°
Max depression	−10°
Shell weight	20.45kg
Total weight of round:	
shell + brass case	34.0 to 32.5kg
Total weight of mount	10.0 tons
Training, max speed	10°/sec
Elevation and depression, max speed	6.5°/sec

TABLE 8: **Characteristics of the 12.7cm/40 HA gun**

Calibre of bore	12.7cm (5in)
Length in calibre	40cal
Construction	Monobloc, autofrettaged, radially expanded
Breech mechanism	Horizontal sliding
Length oa	5.284m
Length of barrel	4.930m
Weight with breech	3060kg
Grooves, number	36
Chamber, length	0.534m
volume	9.0 litres
Muzzle velocity	725m/sec
Bore pressure (max)	25.0kg/mm^2
Life of barrel	800 to 1500 rounds
Firing rate (max)	14 rounds/min
Effective firing rate	11 to 12 rounds/min
Max range	14,800m
Max vertical range	9400m
Max elevation	90°
Max depression	−8°
Shell weight	23.45kg
Assembled round weight, shell + cartridge	34.32kg
Total weight of mount	20.3 tons
Training, max speed	6°/sec
Elevation and depression, max speed	12°/sec

12.7cm ammunition
All shells weighed 23.05kg, with a length of 43.68cm. Each was fitted with a brass cartridge containing 3.98kg of 21DC powder. The full length of the assembled round was 0.9708m, the cartridge being 0.583m.

SHELLS:
1. HE common shell,'*Tsûjôdan*', containing 1.778kg of Shimose (picric acid) explosive, with *91 Shiki* time fuse. In anti-aircraft firing it had an 18.8m effective destruction radius. Colours were brown with a white top.
2. *3 Shiki* incendiary (fragmentation) common shell, '*Sankaidan*', containing 43 incendiary tubes and 23 stays (as in the 20.3cm shell). Its effective burst diameter was about 54m in anti-aircraft firing. Colour was red.
3. Illuminating shell 'B$_1$', '*Shomeidan B$_1$*', containing 1.1kg of illuminating powder. Its muzzle velocity was 720m/sec, maximum range 14,500m, effective range 8000m, illumination 680,000 candlepower. Colour was red.
4. Timed exercise shell, '*Jigen Enshudan*', with *91 Shiki* time fused head. Colours were black with a white nose.
5. Exercise shell, '*Enshudan*', not fused. Colours were black with a yellow nose.

All guns had 250–300 shells per barrel.

Light anti-aircraft armament 1932–38

40mm single MG mount
Vickers type single anti-aircraft automatic guns were fitted on platforms on each side of the rear funnel. It was designated the '*HI*' *Shiki 40mm 62cal Kiju*, actually an imported Vickers-built mount based on the Mk VIII.

TABLE 9: **Characteristics of the 40mm/62 AA gun**

Calibre of bore	40mm
Length of calibre	62cal
Length of gun (total)	2.5m
Length of barrel	1.58m
Weight of gun (total)	281kg
Total weight of gun + mount	941kg (mount 660kg)
Muzzle velocity	600m/sec
Firing speed max	200 rounds/min
Normal firing rate	6 to 100 rounds/min
Max range	13,000m
Max vertical range	7000m
Action range	3500m
Effective range	2500m
Max elevation	80°
Max depression	−10°
Ammunition:	
Shell weight	0.907kg (common type)
Cartridge weight	1.300kg
Round weight	2.207kg
Loading	Feeding belt with 50 rounds or magazine with 20 or 25 rounds
Remaining data	Manual training and elevation, water-cooled gun barrel, Vickers type recoil mechanism

7.7mm Lewis type machine-gun

Two of these were fitted on both sides of the fore funnel during 1932–38. The machine-gun was imported from Britain and approved in 1925. It was 1.283m long, weighed 11.8kg (unloaded), with a firing rate of 550 rounds/min, muzzle velocity of 745m/sec and a maximum effective range of about 1000m.

Light anti-aircraft armament 1939–45

The 25mm machine-gun

The 25mm machine-gun was a very successful weapon and was the principal anti-aircraft gun of the Imperial Japanese Navy. It was based on the French-built Hotchkiss gun developed in 1930. It was approved in Japan on 6 August 1936 and designated the *96 Shiki 25mm Kiju 1 Gata* twin mount. The triple mounts were fitted in 1941 and single mounts in 1943.

TABLE 10: **25mm machine-guns mounted on *Takao***

Date	Mounting	Total
May 1938–31 Aug 1939	4 twins on both sides of fore and aft funnels	8
Autumn 1941	2 twins replaced 13mm MG on tower bridge	12
26 Jul–17 Aug 1943	2 triples added, frame 202	18
15 Nov 1943–29 Jan 1944	8 singles added	26
24 Jun–8 Jul 1944	4 triples and 22 singles added	60

TABLE 11: **Characteristics of 25mm gun**

Calibre of bore	25mm
Length in calibre	60cal
Construction of barrel	Monobloc
Mechanism (breech)	Gas operated
Gun length oa	2420mm
Length of barrel	1500mm
Grooves, number	12
Weight of barrel	43kg
Weight of breech	72kg
Weight, total of gun	115kg
Muzzle velocity	900m/sec
Max bore pressure	27kg/mm²
Life of barrel, max	15,000 rounds
Firing rate max	260 rounds/min
Firing rate standard	220–240 rounds/min
Effective firing rate	110–120 rounds/min
Max horizontal range (50°)	7500m
Max vertical range (80°)	5250m
Max AA fighting range	3500m
Effective AA range	1500m
Max elevation	80°
Max depression	−10°
Max training speed	18°/sec
Max elevation speed	12°/sec
Total weight of twin mount	1100kg
Total weight of triple mount	1800kg
Total weight of single mount	785kg
Magazines for 15 rounds	

TABLE 12: **Ammunition for the 25mm gun**

Type	Weight	Explosive	Colour
Common '*Tsûjôdan*'	243.2g	13.2g Trotyl	Brown
Incendiary Common '*Shoi Tsûjôdan*'	250.7g	11.3g 2 *Shiki*	Orange
AP '*Tetsukôdan*'	262.0g	–	White
Tracer '*Eiryôdan*'	252.0g	2 *Shiki*	Unknown

Cartridge was filled with 102g powder
Total weight of round was about 680g
One of 5 shells was a tracer shell
Visual ammunition supply was 2000 rounds barrel
Crew: for twin mount, 7, for triple mount, 9

The ammunition cartridge contained 102g of powder. The overall weight of the round was about 680kg. One of the five shells was a tracer round. The normal ammunition supply was 2000 rounds per barrel. The twin mounting had a seven-man crew and the triple mounting nine.

93 Shiki 13mm machine-gun

Two twin machine-gun mountings were fitted during the 1938–39 major refit, on both sides of the tower bridge, and were subsequently removed in autumn 1941 (replaced by two twin 25mm machine-gun mounts on bigger platforms). These guns, a Japanese version of the Hotchkiss, were approved in 1935.

AMMUNITION
Ammunition consisted of 30-round magazines, each round weighing 120g. The cartridge had 15g of powder. Supply was 2500 rounds per barrel.

TABLE 13: **93 *Shiki* 13mm MG characteristics**

Calibre of bore	13.2 mm (0.52in)
Length in calibre	76cal
Construction of barrel	Monobloc
Breech mechanism	Gas operated
Gun length oa	1597mm
Length of barrel	1000mm
Grooves, number	8
Weight of barrel	19.8kg
Weight of breech	22.0kg
Weight total of gun	41.8kg
Muzzle velocity	800m/sec
Max bore pressure	29kg/mm²
Firing rate max	475 rounds/min
Firing rate standard	450 rounds/min
Effective firing rate	250 rounds/min
Max horizontal range	6500m at 50° elevation
Max vertical range	4500m at 85° elevation
Max elevation	85°
Max depression	−4°
Max AA fighting range	2500m
Effective AA range	1000m
Total weight	355kg

Ammunition:
Magazines of 30 rounds, weight of round 120g, cartridge with 15g powder

TABLE 14: 13mm MG ammunition

Type	Weight	Round weight	Filling
Incendiary	49.6g	116.7g	Phosphore 3.5g
Common	44.5g	12.6g	Pentrit and Hexogen
Tracer (yellow paint)	46.0g	113.0g	Mixture
AP	51.8g	118.5g	–
Exercise	51.8g	118.5g	–

Ammunition supply – 2500 rounds per barrel

TABLE 15: Torpedo armament 1932–38

Torpedo tube mount	89 *Shiki* twin mount
Total weight (without torpedoes)	14,500kg
Electro-hydraulic power	15hp (motor 600rpm, 220V)
Rotating speed	4.5°/sec
Rotating angle	105°
Length oa	9100mm
Distance between tubes	1200m
Torpedoes	61cm 90 *Shiki* compressed air-propelled torpedo
Length	8550mm
Weight, total	2540kg
Warhead weight	390kg of 91 *Shiki* (TNA) explosive
Range	7000m at 46kts
	10,000m at 42kts
	15,000m at 35kts
Propulsion	Two-cylinder, double-acting reciprocating Whitehead engine using compressed air (225kg/cm² pressure), kerosene and water as fuel

Torpedo armament

The earlier 'A' class ships *Furutaka*, *Aoba*, and *Myoko* were fitted with torpedo tubes in the hull at middle deck level, on fixed broadside mounts. They were designed primarily as gunfire ships, but were later fitted with 61cm long-range torpedoes, which changed their original character.

The *Takao* design had incorporated the two tactical advantages of superior gun power and torpedo armament, the latter enhanced by the positioning of the torpedo tubes in rotating mounts at upper deck level. Hiraga was very much aware of the dangers of carrying torpedoes, which could explode accidentally during battle. To lessen this risk, his design incorporated torpedo tubes outside the hull proper (above the upper deck and below the high-angle gun deck) and positioned at a maximum angle away from the hull (about 90 degrees in relation to the hull axis), so that the torpedo warheads were well away from the side of the ship. In addition, the warheads were protected with 50mm Ducol steel casings before loading.

Torpedo tubes 1932–38

Four partly shielded rotating 89 *Shiki* twin mounts, approved in 1931, were fitted on the upper deck. The original design allowed for twelve torpedo tubes (four triple tubes), but these were abandoned due to weight and space limitations. The mounts were trained hydraulically but this could be done manually in emergencies.

The torpedoes were fired by compressed air, with an additional powder charge if necessary. To compensate for the reduced number of tubes, the mount was fitted with a device for rapid reloading of reserve torpedoes. A system of aerial rails, fitted to the deckhead of the high-angle gun deck above, was fitted with tackles to allow the reserve torpedoes to be moved to any of the tube mounts. The torpedoes were lowered on to rails abaft the torpedo tubes, from where they could then be loaded easily into the tubes by a motor-driven endless chain device, which meant that reloading could be done in about three minutes.

Sixteen torpedoes were usually carried, eight stowed on the rails (where the warheads were protected by a Ducol steel casing), and another eight stowed in pairs on both sides of the funnel uptakes, with similar protection.

There were special openings in the ship sides, between the torpedo tube apertures, for the torpedoes to be loaded using a derrick and small bogie

Torpedo armament after 1938–39 refit

Four quadruple 92 *Shiki* 1 *Gata* *Modif* 1 'Hasshakan' torpedo tube mounts were fitted. They were trained by a 10hp compressed-air motor, or manually in emergencies. The torpedoes were fired by compressed air, each tube being fitted with its own air bottle. Torpedo launching speed was 11–12m/sec. In emergencies they could also be launched with a 600g black powder charge. The overall weight of the quadruple mount was 15,000kg. Twenty-four (93 *Shiki*) torpedoes were carried, sixteen in tubes and eight in casings on each side of the funnel uptakes, the warheads protected by 25mm Ducol steel. They were moved into position by an aerial rail system.

TORPEDOES:

The *93 Shiki Gyôrai 1 Gata*, a second-modification torpedo known later as

TABLE 16: Torpedo characteristics after 1938–39 refit

Torpedo: 61cm 93 *Shiki* oxygen-propelled

Length oa	9000mm
Total weight	2700kg
Negative buoyancy	480kg
Volume oxygen vessel	980 litres
Pressure	225kg/cm²
Oxygen weight	299kg
Kerosene weight	106kg (128 litres)
Engine power	200hp at 36–38kts
	300hp at 40–42kts
	520hp at 48–50 kts at 1200rpm
Fuel consumption	2.65kg/hp/hr
Explosive charge	490kg (97 *Shiki* explosive)
Range	20,000m at 48–50kts
	32,000m at 40–42kts
	40,000m at 36–38kts
Wander max (left or right)	500m 20,000m
	1000m 32,000m
	1500m 40,000m
Engine	Two double-acting cylinders horizontally in line (standard Whitehead design), cylinder bore 142mm, stroke 180mm

'Long Lance', was approved for the fleet on 28 November 1935. These oxygen-propelled, wakeless, high-speed, heavy warhead torpedoes were, with later alterations, to become the most powerful torpedoes of the Second World War.

Fire control

Bridge structure

Takao class cruisers had a huge, castle-like tower bridge with a greater cubic capacity than any cruiser before or since. The huge superstructure was a result of the need to accommodate numerous compartments: gunnery, torpedo, navigation, transmission, electrics and optics. This facility to house so many command centres was one of the reasons why the ship was later used as a fleet flagship.

A full-sized wooden model of the upper part of the ship's bridge, including all fittings, was built to test the design functions, *ie* fire control, look-out positions, and so on, and tests were carried out from June to December 1930 which resulted in numerous alterations to the original design, although these did not alter the cubic capacity of the tower bridge.

Fire control installation

The 'follow the pointer' system for firing 20.3cm guns was approved. To direct fire, and for target range and speed data, a *14 Shiki* main gun director and a *13 Shiki Sokutekiban* were mounted on the upper part of the bridge, and an auxiliary *14 Shiki* main gun director and main armament command room were fitted above the aircraft hangar, abaft the mainmast.

To direct the 12cm HA gun anti-aircraft fire, two *91 Shiki Kosha Sochi* towers were mounted on each side of the tower bridge at compass bridge level. Two *14 Shiki* 3.5m rangefinders were fitted on each side of the tower bridge at upper bridge deck level.

The torpedo firing station was fitted with an *89 Shiki* torpedo firing director. Two were installed on each side of the fire command platform, with two auxiliaries above the hangar (frame 216–218).

Rangefinders

Three 6m rangefinders were mounted on No 1, No 2 and No 4 20.3cm gun turrets, one 4.5m main rangefinder high on the tower bridge, and two 4.5m rangefinders on each side above the hangar. Both were used primarily to determine high-angle range but could also be used for surface-fire ranges. Two sets of 3.5m and two 1.5m rangefinders were fitted on the tower bridge. All rangefinders were fitted with the *14 Shiki* model binocular coincidence system. They supplied target range data to the *Shagekiban*, with a range error of 235m at 25,000m and 191m at 20,000m.

Searchlights

In 1932 four *'SU' Shiki* 110cm searchlights were fitted in *Takao* for night action. They were mounted on four protected 'searchlight towers', on each side of the fore and after funnels.

In 1936 they were replaced by the new *92 Shiki* 110cm searchlights.

20

TABLE 17: **Searchlights**

	'SU' Shiki	92 Shiki
Diameter (cm)	110	110
Approved	1922	6 Mar 1933
Tension (V)	75	76–82
Current (A)	150	200
Light intensity (Candela/m²)	9000 (blue-white light)	12,800 (blue-white light)
Elevation	−15° to +100°	−10° to +100°
Inherent scatter angle	1°50'	1°30'
Max range	6000	8000
Effective range	5000	Over 6000
Concentrated light of two, range (m)	8000	10,000

The searchlight control positions and control table in the searchlight command room were fitted at fire command platform (VI) level and communicated with the main gun command platform to co-ordinate the activities of the searchlights in support of the ship's gunfire.

Radars

The *21 Gô* air search radar was fitted in *Takao* after the Solomons campaign, during the 26 July–17 August 1943 refit at Yokosuka. Its official designation was *2 Shiki 2 Gô Denpa Tanshingi 1 Gata Kai 2* or *21 Gô Dentan Kai 2*.

TABLE 18: *21 Gô radar characteristics up to Apr–Aug 1943*

Antenna 'Mattress' type radars were fitted for receiving and transmitting.

Antenna	Type A Model 6
Transmitter type	Oscillator circuit with two T-310 tubes
Power output	5kW (max)
Wave length	1.5m
Pulse length	10 microsec
Pulse rate	1000/sec
Receiver	Detector type UN-953 RE 3
Max detection range:	
Aircraft group	100km ± 1 to 2km
Single aircraft	70km ± 1 to 2km
Bearing error	5–8°
Min detection range	5km
Weight of set	840kg
Operators	4–5 men, 2 to operate radar and 2–3 to operate telephones

The *13 Gô* air search radar was fitted in *Takao*, abaft the foremast, in July 1944 during the 24 June–8 July modification at Yokosuka. Its official designation was *3 Shiki 1 Gô Denpa Tanshingi 3 Gata* or *13 Gô Dentan*.

The *22 Gô* surface search radar was fitted in January 1944 during the 17 December 1943–29 January 1944 refit. The two twin horn antennas were located below the main 6m rangefinder on the tower bridge, and radar installation was housed in the aft part of the *Sokuteki* room. This radar could only be used for surface search, not for fire control. Its official designation was *2 Gô Denpa Tanshingi 2 Gata Kai 4* or *22 Gô Dentan Kai 4*.

TABLE 19: *13 Gô* radar characteristics

Antenna Ladder type broadside array, separated set for transmission and receiving. Each set had four steps of two elements.

Development	Sept 1943
Receiver	Detector type UN-954
Transmitter type	2C-Oscillating circuit with two T-311 tubes
Wave length	2.0m
Power output	10kW (max)
Pulse length	10 microsec
Pulse rate	500/sec
Max detection range:	
Aircraft group	100km
Single aircraft	50km
Range error	± 2 to 3km
Bearing error	±10°
Min detection range	5km
Weight of set	110kg
Operators	4 men, 2 to operate radar and 2 to operate telephones

TABLE 20: *22 Gô* radar characteristics

Development	Dec 1942–Dec 1943
Antenna	Two electro-magnetic horns, the upper for receiving, the lower for transmitting
Transmitter type	Water cooled Magnetron type M-312-A
Wave length	10cm
Power output	2kW (max)
Receiver	Autodyne circuit with crystal detector and Magnetron type M-60-S as local oscillator
Max detection range:	
Battleships	35km ±700m
Cruisers	20km ±700m
Destroyers	17km ±700m
Bearing error	±5°
Min detection range	1500m
Weight of set	320kg
Operators	4–6 men, 2–3 to operate radar and 2–3 to operate telephones

Aircraft equipment

Catapults 1932–38

Two Kure type No 2 Model 3 catapults (*Kure Shiki 2 Gô Shashutsu 3 Gata*) gunpowder-propelled catapults were fitted, with an overall length of 19.35m and an effective launching length of 15.4m. Launch speed was 28m/sec. The catapult could launch a weight up to 3000kg with an acceleration of 2.7g.

Catapults after main 1938–39 refit

The earlier catapults were replaced by two heavier *Kure Shiki 2 5 Gata* catapults, approved on 21 October 1938. Overall length was 19.6m and it could launch a weight up to 4000kg. At the same time a special casing was built to stow four 250kg and forty-four 60kg bombs for floatplanes, together with a special hoist for 250kg (and 60kg) bombs.

TABLE 21: **Nakajima E4N2, Navy Type 90-2 Reconnaissance Floatplane**

Two planes were embarked from Dec 1932 to Dec 1936

Length	8.869m
Span	10.976m
Height	3.967m
Max speed	232km/hr
Powerplant	460hp at 1500m Nakajima 'Jupiter' 9-cylinder air-cooled radial engine
Armament	2 × 7.7mm MG and 2 × 30kg bombs
Crew	2

TABLE 22: **Kawanishi E7K1, Navy Type 94 Reconnaissance Floatplane**

One plane was embarked from Dec 1934 to May 1938

Length	10.41m
Span	14.0m
Height	4.81m
Wing area	43.6m²
Max speed	239km/hr at 500m
Power plant	600hp at 1500m, 12-cylinder W liquid-cooled Hiro Type 91 engine, driving four-blade wooden propeller
Weight (empty)	1970kg
Weight (loaded)	3000kg
Armament	3 × 7.7mm MG and 4 × 30kg or 2 × 60kg bombs
Crew	3

TABLE 23: **Kawanishi E7K2, Navy Type 94 Reconnaissance Floatplane characteristics**

Allied codename 'Alf'. One plane embarked from Aug 1939 to autumn 1942

Length	10.50m
Span	14.0m
Height	4.81m
Wing area	43.6m²
Max speed	276km/h at 2000m
Cruising speed	185km/h at 1000m
Power plant	870hp 14-cylinder air-cooled radial Mitsubishi Zuisei 11 engine, driving two-blade metal propeller
Weight (empty)	2100kg
Weight (loaded)	3300kg
Endurance	11hr 30min
Armament	3 × 7.7mm MG and 4 × 30kg or 2 × 60kg bombs
Crew	3

Complement

The original design allowed for a crew of 48 officers and 679 men (total 727) but, as a result of modernisation, during 1932–38 the crew comprised 743 to 761 men.

Ventilation and other systems

Compared with earlier cruisers, the ventilation system was considerably improved and modified for operation in tropical climates, with subse-

TABLE 24: Nakajima E8N2, Navy Type 95 Reconnaissance Floatplane

Allied codename 'Dave'. Two planes were embarked from Dec 1936 (replaced E4N2) to autumn 1942

Length	8.81m
Span	10.98m
Height	3.84m
Wing area	26.5m²
Max speed	300km/hr at 3000m
Cruising speed	185km/hr
Powerplant	580hp 9-cylinder air-cooled radial Nakajima Kotobuki 2 Kai 1 engine, driving two-blade propeller
Weight (empty)	1320kg
Weight (loaded)	1900kg
Armament	2 × 7.7mm MG and 2 × 30kg or 2 × 60kg bombs
Range	890km
Crew	2

TABLE 25: Mitsubishi F1M2, Navy Type 'O' Reconnaissance Floatplane

Allied code name 'Pete'. Two planes were embarked from autumn 1942 to end of war (replaced E8N2)

Length	9.5m
Span	11.0m
Height	4.0m
Wing area	29.54m²
Max speed	370km/h
Cruising speed	193km/h
Powerplant	875hp 14-cylinder air-cooled radial Mitsubishi Zuisei 13 engine, driving three-blade propeller
Weight (empty)	1928kg
Weight (loaded)	2550kg
Armament	3 × 7.7mm MG and 2 × 60kg bombs or as experimental installation one 250kg bomb
Range	740km
Crew	2

TABLE 26: Aichi E13A1, Navy Type 'O' Long Range Reconnaissance Floatplane

Allied code name 'Jake'. One plane was embarked from autumn 1942 to end of war

Length	11.3m
Span	14.5m
Height	7.4m
Wing area	36m²
Max speed	375km/hr
Cruising speed	222km/hr
Powerplant	1080hp 14-cylinder air-cooled radial Mitsubishi Kinsei 43 engine, driving three-blade metal propeller
Weight (empty)	2642kg
Weight (loaded)	3640kg
Armament	1 × 7.7mm MG and 1 × 250kg or 4 × 60kg bombs
Range	2090km
Crew	3

quent health advantages for the crew. The officers' living quarters were situated in the bow and the crew were accommodated in the stern, away from the boiler and engine rooms on middle deck, so they were not too hot. In peacetime the *Takao* cruisers were equipped to serve as fleet flagships, with extensive communication and radio installations and a large tactical command room. In wartime they served as squadron flagships, with accommodation for the Chief of Staff, his aides-de-camp, and the musicians of the squadron's band.

Modernisations 1933–44

1933–34: Improvements to the ventilation. Ventilation cowls were extended on both sides of the tower bridge below the 60cm signal searchlight platforms, on the rear part of the bridge below the signalling platform, and on the main gun platform under the main 4.5m rangefinder. New compartments (larger on the starboard side) were added on each side of the fore funnel.

1935–36: The 20m mainmast boom with guys was replaced by a modern, lattice jub revolving crane.

1936–37: Refit. Major changes were:

1. Shortening of the foremast and fitting of an additional platform in the quadrupod lattice mast, with a goniometer antenna fitted to the fore topmast.
2. Removal of the blast screens from the searchlight towers and replacement of the *SU Shiki* 110cm searchlights with *92 Shiki* 110cm searchlights.
3. Removal of the protective shields from four searchlight control positions (at fire command platform level).
4. Enlargement of the fore part of the *Sokuteki* room.
5. New shields for the *91 Shiki* HA director and *14 Shiki* main armament director tower.
6. Removal of the three protected look-out positions from the forward part of the tower bridge, those remaining with new type shields. New radio wiring tube on the fore lower part of the tower bridge.
7. Bamboo storage on both sides of the funnels.
8. Modernisation of the lower and upper aft parts of the hangar superstructure.
9. Improvement of longitudinal strength-members – 1.5m Ducol steel plates were added along the bottom of each side of the keel (16mm thick) to increase resistance to the bottom extension, and 19mm plates were added on the upper deck to resist deck compression.

Major modernisation, Yokosuka Kaigun Kôshô, May 1938–31 August 1939
Modification plans were begun in 1937 and completed in April 1938.

1. The weight of the upper part of the tower bridge was reduced, above the upper bridge deck, and the superstructure completely modified. A new tripod foremast was built, with the torpedo fire control station on top, and a *93 Shiki* goniometer antenna and compartment in the central part of the mast.
2. The midship superstructure was rebuilt, and the mainmast moved towards the stern, behind the new aircraft and boat decks.
3. The crew was increased to 55 officers and 780 men, a total of 835 at the end of 1939. By 1941 the number had increased to 920 (970 including the

Kantai staff). The cabins of the more senior officers were rebuilt and the number of cabins, including those for lower rank officers, increased to eighteen. Crew quarters were also extended.

4. Communication facilities were increased and updated. A new emergency command centre was installed in the lower part of the bridge.

5. A new flooding and drainage system, with appropriate command room, was installed. Some of the athwart fuel tanks fore and aft at store deck level were transformed into watertight compartments to correct bow and stern flooding, while watertight compartments in the new bulges could be used to correct heel. The power capacity of the drainage and fuel transfer pumps was increased.

6. 'Large' type bulges were fitted in the hull to improve stability and anti-torpedo and anti-mine protection. The maximum beam was increased to 20.726m. The upper part (at waterline level) of the bulges was filled with water-tight steel tubes to improve buoyancy and increase protective strength. The remaining bulge compartments were used as fuel tanks and the water-tight compartments for counterflooding. New 60m long, 1.4m wide bilge keels were fitted on the bulges.

The bulges improved stability greatly by increasing the metacentric height (GM) above 1.5m (formerly 1.08–1.20m) and by improving the range of stability in both two-thirds trials (89 degrees) and in a light condition (73 degrees). Bulges also improved the longitudinal strength members. The resulting increase in beam after fitting the bulges reduced the draught at the two-thirds trial displacement.

7. Powerplant modernisation:
The 'induction' turbines were removed, and for cruising conditions the exhaust steam of the cruising turbines was introduced directly into the aft high-pressure turbines so that cruising took place on four shafts. A new type of more powerful burner was fitted on to the boilers to reduce fuel consumption. On trials off Tatayama on 14 July 1939 *Takao* reached 34.25kts with 133,100shp at 309.5rpm and 14,989 tons displacement. Maximum fuel capacity was reduced from 2645 to 2318 tons, but thanks to the new burners and new cruising arrangement the radius was increased to 8500nm at 14kts (reaching 5049nm at 18kts).

8. For the main armament the 20.3cm gun barrels were renewed and the forward parts of the turrets (ports) improved. The surface fire control installation was modernised by fitting the main *94 Shiki* low-angle director tower on the rebuilt upper part of the tower bridge and an auxiliary director abaft the rear funnel. A 6m *14 Shiki* rangefinder removed from No 1 20.3cm gun turret was fitted on top of the tower bridge. A *92 Shiki Sokutekiban* (to caluclate the target course and speed) was fitted in the new *Sokuteki* room and a *92 Shiki* computer was installed in the plotting room below the bridge.

9. Anti-aircraft armament:
The after 12cm HA gun mounts (No 3 and No 4) were moved about a metre further aft (until March 1942). Two new *94 Shiki Kosha Sōchi* high-angle directors (replacing the *91 Shiki* ones) were fitted on the bridge forward of the *91 Shiki* 4.5m rangefinders (a replacement from the hangar superstructure) at the compass platform level. Four twin *96 Shiki* 25mm machine-gun mounts were installed on both sides of the fore and rear funnel, and two *95 Shiki Kiju Shojun Sōchi* towers (machine-gun directors) were fitted abaft the fore funnel. Two twin *93 Shiki* 13mm machine-gun mounts were fitted on the forward part of the tower bridge (up to autumn 1941).

10. Torpedo armament:
Four quadruple *92 Shiki 1 Gata Modif 1* mounts were fitted for the new *93 Shiki* torpedoes, and the broadside salvo increased to eight 'Long Lances'. The two *93 Shiki Sokutekiban* and two *93 Shiki Hoiban* (to calculate target course and speed) for torpedo fire control were repositioned in the bridge at the *Sokuteki* room and compass platform level.

11. Aircraft equipment:
A new heavier and larger type of catapult (the *Kure Shiki No 2 5 Gata*) was fitted, about 10m further forward than the previous position, on both sides of the new 'aircraft deck'.

Autumn 1941 refit
The two twin *93 Shiki* 13mm machine-gun mounts were replaced by two twin *96 Shiki* 25mm mounts on the larger platforms of the tower bridge.

TABLE 27: **Displacement and dimensions after major refit (Oct 1939)**

At ⅔ trial condition:

Displacement	14,838 tons (15,075 tonnes)
Draught	6.316m
Waterline length	201.72m
Waterline beam	19.52m

At full condition:

Displacement	15,875 tons (16,129 tonnes)
Draught	6.672m
Standard displacement	13,400 tons (13,615 tonnes)

TABLE 28: **Effective weight distribution after refit** (changes compared with May 1932 in parentheses)

Hull structure	4571 tons (+484 tons)	[4644 tonnes (+492 tonnes)]
Armour and protective plates	2393 tons (+25 tons)	[2431 tonnes (+25 tonnes)]
Fittings	564 tons (+44 tons)	[573 tonnes (+45 tonnes)]
Armament: total weight	1997 tons (+248 tons)	[2029 tonnes (+252 tonnes)]
Guns	1248 tons (+82 tons)	[1268 tonnes (+83 tonnes)]
Torpedo	203 tons (+36 tons)	[206 tonnes (+37 tonnes)]
Electric equipment	426 tons (+67 tons)	[433 tonnes (+68 tonnes)]
Aircraft equipment	82 tons (+51 tons)	[83 tonnes (+52 tonnes)]
Navigation equipment	18 tons (+12 tons)	[18 tonnes (+12 tonnes)]
Machinery	2746 tons (+75 tons)	[2789 tonnes (+76 tonnes)]
Equipment, fixed	198 tons (+18 tons)	[201 tonnes (+18 tonnes)]
non-fixed	402 tons (+88 tons)	[408 tonnes (+89 tonnes)]
Oil fuel ⅔	1563 tons (−192 tons)	[1588 tonnes (−195 tonnes)]
Reserve feed water ⅔	105 tons, no change	[107 tonnes, no change]
Light oil and lubrication oil ⅔	64 tons (+8 tons)	[65 tonnes (+8 tonnes)]
Underwater protection: steel tubes + unknown weight	253 tons (−29 tons)	[257 tonnes (−30 tonnes)]
Total	14,838 tons (+771 tons)	[15,075 tonnes (+783 tonnes)]

18 March–2 May 1942 refit
The single 12cm 45cal HA gun mounts were replaced by twin 12.7cm HA 40cal gun mounts, together with changes to the ammunition magazines and hoists, and the installation of an anti-aircraft command platform above the compass bridge (with wind baffles on the shield).

Autumn 1942 refit
Two Mitsubishi F1M1 and one Aichi E13A1 floatplanes were taken on board to replace the E8N2 and E7K2 floatplanes.

26 July–17 August 1943 refit
Two additional triple *96 Shiki* 25mm machine-gun mounts were fitted on new platforms on both sides of the auxiliary *94 Shiki* low-angle director tower (frame 202). The *21 Gô* air search radar 'Mattress' type antenna was installed on top of the foremast. The radar room was located in the former goniometer room (centre of the tripod foremast).

15 November 1943–29 January 1944 refit
Eight single *96 Shiki* 25mm machine-gun mounts were installed in the waist of the cruiser. The *22 Gô* surface search radar was installed under both sides of the main 6m rangefinder tower on top of the bridge.

24 June-8 July 1944 refit
The *13 Gô* air search radar was fitted on the rear part of the foremast. Four triple *96 Shiki* 25mm machine-gun mounts were added on the quarter deck (frame 330) and on both sides of the after funnel, on the tops of the new standby rooms for the extra anti-aircraft gun crew. Twenty-two single *96 Shiki* 25mm machine-gun mounts were fitted – the total number of 25mm machine-gun barrels then amounted to sixty.
In July 1944 the full complement was about 970 (maximum 1050).

Colour schemes

1. Warship grey was used on the hull above the waterline, the super-structures, all metal decks, the gun turrets, the topside fittings, the boats' sides (external), boats' cabins and bottom surfaces of the open ones. The grey varnish, and the black and white was semi-gloss in finish. The colour of Imperial Japanese Navy ships varied in shade but was based on regulation colours and made up according to a standard paint mixture formula consisting of: 15 per cent black, 75 white, 6 brown, 4 blue.
2. A reddish brown (*aka aji ga katta chairo*) was used for the hull below the waterline and consisted of: 20 per cent red, 65 brown, 10 black, 5 white.
3. The linoleum used on the surface of the upper deck was a dark yellow-ish brown (ochre – *odo*) in a pale 'milk chocolate' shade. The linoleum sheets were 4m long by 2m wide and the contact edge of the sheets were joined by brass strips. From 1943 the linoleum was taken out of the inner decks of the hull because of fire risks in closed areas, but was retained on open decks to the end of the war.
4. Up to the outbreak of the Pacific War, white canvas was used for blast bags, reel covers, torpedo opening covers, etc.

The fore funnel had white bands (see illustration):

1 December 1932–15 November 1935: three bands
No bands until spring 1936, then: one band
Summer 1936: two bands (one 60cm, one 120cm)
1937 after refit: two bands (two 60cm)
December 1937–15 November 1939: no bands
15 November 1939 to end of 1941: one band
White was also used for the stripes on the upper part of the mainmast, and for the inscriptions on the boat sides (forward part) – *hiragana* (ship's name) or numerals 100mm wide.

5. Light brown canvas replaced white canvas in wartime.
6. A natural wood colour was used on the inside thwarts of the boats, the motorboat decks, and the gratings (anti-aircraft defence platform above the compass bridge, 110cm searchlight platforms, in the *Sokuteki* and compass rooms, etc).
7. Gold was used for the chrysanthemum crest on the bow and the *hiragana* (ship's name) on the stern.
8. A semi-gloss black was used for the upper part of the funnels and the mainmast.
9. Aircraft colours:
1932–36: The floatplanes were silver (a natural finished metal or alumin-ium) with a black *katakana* (ship's name) and numeral (1 to 3) on the wings (upper and lower surfaces). The name and numeral were painted in white on the vertical fin plane. Red was used for the *Hinomaru* and fin and tailplane and for the stripes on the floats (under the propeller) and on the aft part of the body (black letters or numerals were painted with a thin white border on red background only). The cowling was black (see illustration).
1937–38: The upper surfaces of the wings and body were painted sea green with brown camouflage markings, and the lower surfaces were light grey with a red fin and tail plane. The inscription was white with a metallic-red border.
After November 1939: All floatplanes were painted sea green N-1 on the upper surfaces, gull grey N-2 on the lower surfaces, orange stripes on the wing leading-edges (F1M2 and E13A1 only) and red and white stripes on the floats (under the propellers).
The inscriptions on the F1M2 and E13A1 floatplanes (vertical fin plane) were: (1942) E III-1 to E III-3 red with a white border, (after August 1944) 242–02 blue or white numerals.
Hinomaru was red with white borders over a green or brown background. All versions had white stripes on the upper surface of the tailplanes (5-degree angle space) for the rear gunner.

The Photographs

Takao, photographed on 5 May 1930,
shortly before her launch on 12 May 1930.
(*Maru Special*)

Takao in November 1930 with a full size
wooden model of the upper part of the
bridge, viewed from aft. Note the opening
for the funnel uptakes on the upper deck.
(*Maru Special*)

Takao, 21 September 1931. The fore funnel is under construction. (*Maru Special*)

Takao before her launch in May 1930. A view of the side bulges and bilge keel. (*Maru Special*)

Takao photographed on 20 November 1930 in the Koumi Basin of Yokosuka Kaigun Kōshō. The upper deck of the hull is fitted with a full size wooden model of the upper part of the bridge on a wooden scaffold. Several modifications were introduced before the definitive shape was adopted. Note the 12cm HA gun shields on the quay. (*Maru Special*)

Takao photographed in Kuomi Basin in October 1931 during construction of the tower bridge structure.

Takao, a port side view on 20 November 1931, 90 per cent completed. (*Sekai-no Kansen*)

Takao, 20 December 1931. A view of the tower bridge and forecastle deck before the lookout, director and rangefinder towers were fitted to the bases. (*Sekai-no Kansen/ Ships of the World*)

Takao in December 1931. A view of the hangar superstructure and rear upper deck. The small superstructure on the hangar has just been fitted. (*Sekai-no Kansen*)

Takao's HA gun deck, 20 February 1932. (*Maru Special*)

Takao, 20 February 1932. (*Maru Special*)

Takao in trials off Tatayama on 31 March 1932. On this day she reached her maximum speed of 35.6kts at 12,175 tons displacement. (*Maru Special*)

A forward view of turrets 1 and 2 and the tower bridge during *Takao*'s trials in March 1932. Not all of the equipment of the bridge has been fitted. Note the tripod of the awning stanchion (left) and the side awning stanchions (right). (*Fighting Ships of the Imperial Japanese Navy*)

A view of *Takao*'s tower bridge structure on 23 May 1932, eight days before her commissioning on 31 May 1932. (*Maru Special*)

Takao, at Yokosuka on 20 May 1932, ten days before being commissioned. (*Sekai-no Kansen*)

Takao, 1 February 1934, the forecastle deck. Visible are numbers 1 and 2 turrets, at left a section of the roof of the *Sokuteki* room and below the turret the roof of the compass bridge. (*Maru Special*)

Takao, 8 December 1932, a view of the 20.3cm turrets and the tower bridge. (*Sekai-no Kansen*)

Atago, hangar, 1934. Note the canvas cover coiled in the upper part. (*Sekai-no Kansen*)

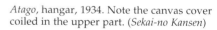

Takao in Saiki Bay, 29 April 1934. Note the three white bands of the fore funnel. (*Sekai-no Kansen*)

Takao, 1934. Note the blast protection (shield) with canvas roof for the 110cm searchlight and the Nakajima E4N2 type 90–2 floatplane on catapult. (*Maru Special*)

Takao, 1936. Note the two white bands on the fore funnel (the upper is 120cm, the lower 60cm wide). (*Maru Special*)

Below left:
Takao, photographed around about spring 1936. Note the one white band on fore funnel. (*Maru Special*)

Below:
Takao after refitting in 1936–37 with a shortened foremast. The upper photograph, taken in June or July 1937, shows two white bands on the fore funnel; in the lower photograph, taken after July 1937, the funnel is without white bands. (*Maru Special*)

軍艦高雄艦橋改装前（前部）

Takao, 1 May 1938. A forward view of the
the tower bridge before the 1939
rebuilding. (*Maru Special*)

Takao's bridge superstructure as in
October–November 1937. (*Sekai-no Kansen*)

Takao's hangar superstructure during refitting, 1936–37. (*Maru Special*)

Chokai, fore funnel, 1938. In the lower left of the photograph there is bamboo storage on both sides of the funnels. On the right, a fragment of the 110cm searchlight tower with the 5m derrick for boats. (*Rengo Kantai*)

The middle part of *Takao*'s superstructure shortly before the start of the main rebuilding programme (May 1938 to 31 August 1939). (*Maru Special*)

A port side view of *Takao* taken on 1 May 1938. (*Maru Special*)

Takao, a profile view, 21 December 1939. (*Author's collection*)

Takao's 110cm searchlights, rear funnel, mainmast, catapult and 4.5m rangefinder. *Maya* (right) and *Chokai* can be seen from the deck. (*Maru Special*)

Takao, the tower bridge structure after rebuilding, 21 December 1939. (*Fighting Ships of the Imperial Japanese Navy*)

Takao, 21 December 1939. A forward view of the tower bridge after rebuilding. Note the connections of the wireless antennae above and to the left of the scuttles. (*Maru Special*)

Above left:

Takao, 21 December 1939, after her rebuilding. In the centre of the aircraft deck a Kawanishi E7K2 'Alf' floatplane is visible, fixed on a trolley to the deck. At the sides can be seen the wingtips of two Nakajima E8N2 'Dave'. In the lower part of the photograph, on the boat deck (upper deck) there are boat crutches, an Admiralty pattern anchor, ventilators and the open doors of the aircraft stores. Visible behind the mainmast is a 20m crane with No 4 turret directed to starboard. (*Maru Special*)

Above:

Takao, 21 August 1939, a starboard side view of the aircraft deck, mainmast and turret No 4. On the deck two floatplanes are visible: right, E8N2 'Dave' and left, E7N2 'Alf'. Under the mainmast on aircraft deck is the bamboo storage area and lower down, between the aircraft deck and upper deck, the gas bottle storage area. (*Maru Special*)

Atago, hoisting the ensign at Singapore, March 1942. On the aircraft deck are two Nakajima E8N2 'Dave' floatplanes. Note the 60kg bombs under the lower wings. (*Maru*)

Atago, 25 March 1942, the crew at morning exercises. Visible are the catapult's wooden formers under canvas and, at right, the lower part of the mainmast with the 20m crane. Also on the deck is a trolley with the catapult's cradle for a float seaplane. (*Maru*)

Below left:
Atago, 3 December 1941. A view forward from the aircraft deck. At the sides are Nos 3 and 4 12cm HA guns, 110cm searchlights on platforms and in the centre part of the tower of the auxiliary low angle director (*94 Shiki Hoiban Shojun Sochi*). (*Maru*)

Below right:
Atago in the Solomon Sea, September 1942. In the lower part of the photograph are visible the twin 25mm MG and the 110cm searchlights protected by sisal ropes. Visible below the far searchlight is the *95 Shiki* MG fire control tower (*Kiju Shageki Sochi*) open position (on *Takao* it was a closed tower) and, on the catapult, a Nakajima E8N2 'Dave' floatplane. (*Maru Special*)

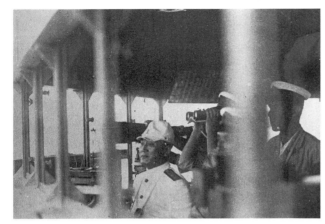

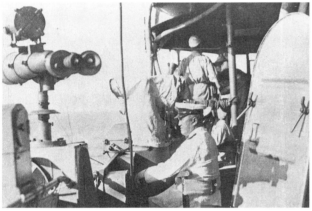

Top: *Atago*'s compass room, a detail of the
fore windows, 1942. (*Maru*)
Bottom: *Atago*, Sokuteki, the port side
platform. At left, the 12cm binoculars with
the signal lamp. (*Maru*)

Atago, 1942–43. A view from the tower
bridge on the mainmast and stern part. At
right, a fragment of the foremast with the
radio (UHF) antenna. In the lower part of
the photograph is the rear funnel and, on
the catapult, an Aichi E13A1 'Jake'
floatplane. (*Maru*)

Atago, 2 June 1942, a view of the forward
20.3cm turrets and the bridge structure.
Note the anti-splinter protection of sisal
ropes on the upper part of the bridge.
(*Maru*)

Takao, July 1942. A view of the port side part of the aircraft deck with two Nakajima E8N2 floatplanes and Nos 4 and 5 turrets on right and, at left, the deck washer. (*Maru Special*)

Refuelling at sea (*Takao* and *Mogami* class cruisers) as seen from *Atago*, 16 September 1942. At left is the compass bridge with 1.5m navigation rangefinder. (*Sekai-no Kansen*)

Takao, main gun firing exercise, circa 1940–41. (*Maru*)

The author's scale 1:1000 model of *Takao*.

The Drawings

A General arrangement

A1   *TAKAO* AS COMPLETED, MAY
          1932
A1/1   *External profile (scale 1/450)*
A1/2   *Plan (scale 1/450)*

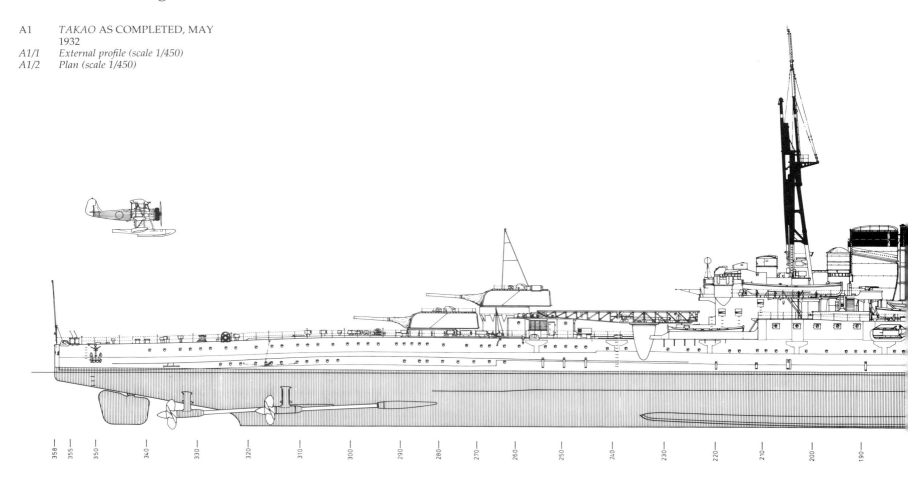

A1/1

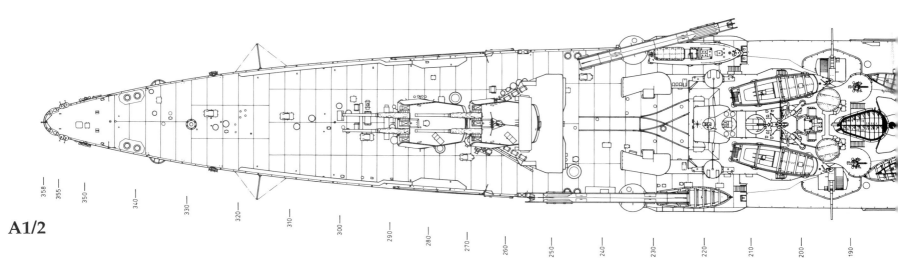

A1/2

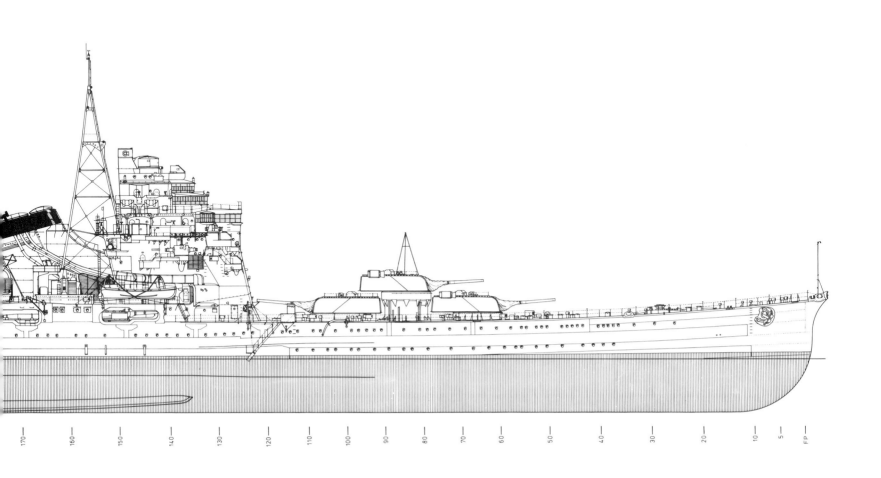

170 160 150 140 130 120 110 100 90 80 70 60 50 40 30 20 10 5 FP

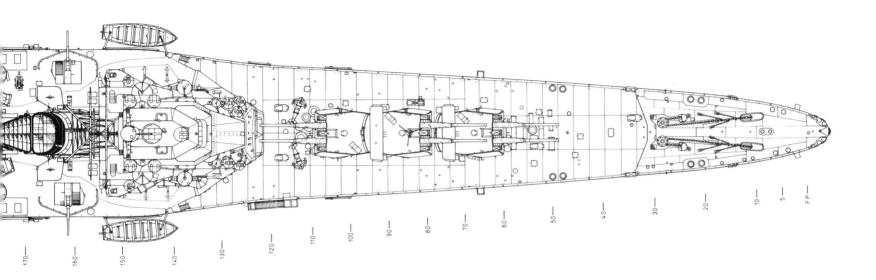

170 160 150 140 130 120 110 100 90 80 70 60 50 40 30 20 10 5 FP

A General arrangement

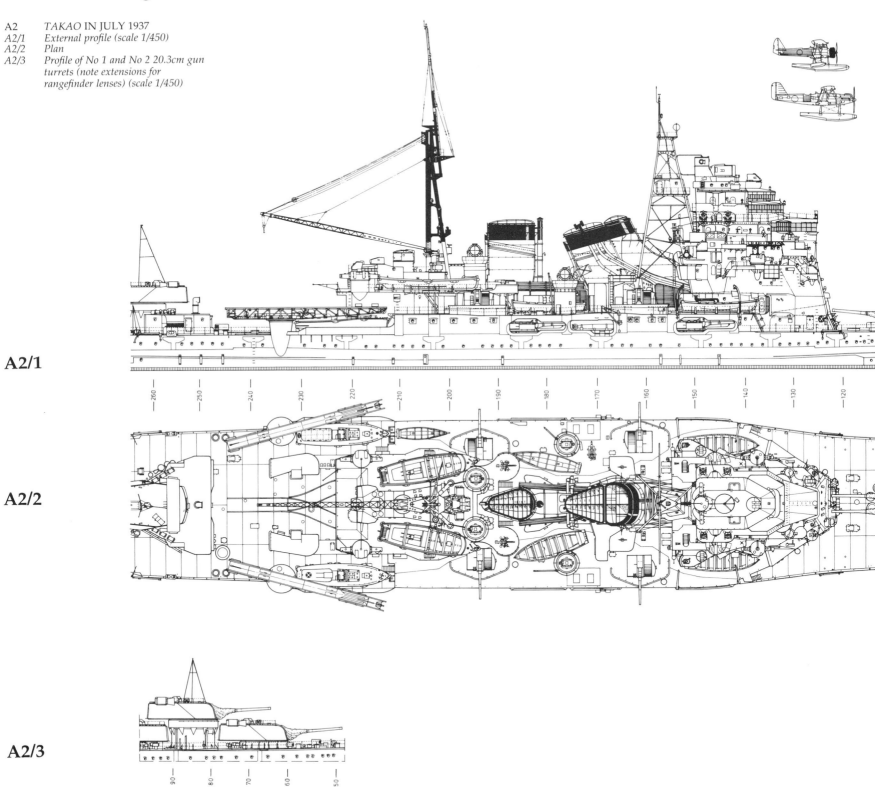

A2/1

A2/2

A2/3

A3   SCHEMES OF RIG
A3/1   *Scheme of rig 1932–38 (no scale)*
A3/2   *Scheme of rig 1939–45 (no scale)*

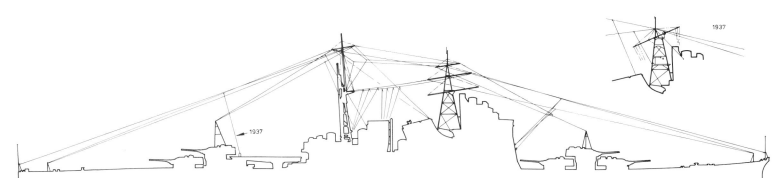

A3/1

A3/2

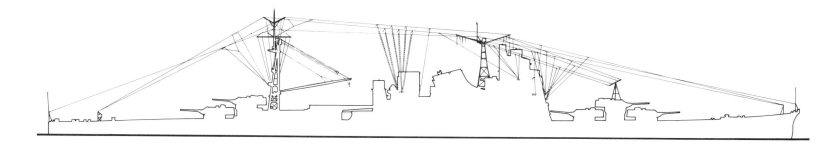

A General arrangement

A4   *TAKAO* IN AUGUST 1939 AFTER
             MODERNISATION
A4/1   *External profile (scale 1/450)*
A4/2   *Plan (scale 1/450)*
A4/3   *Port side hull view 1932–38 with rails*
             and awning stanchions (scale 1/450)

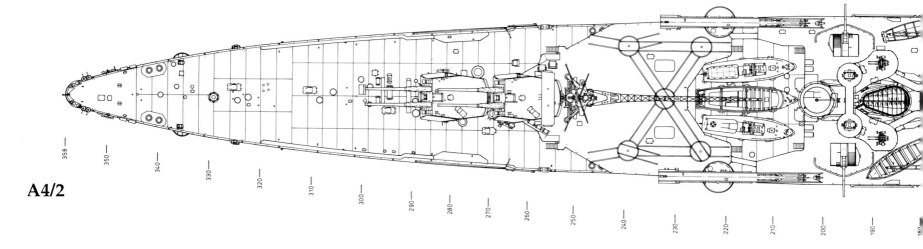

A4/1

A4/2

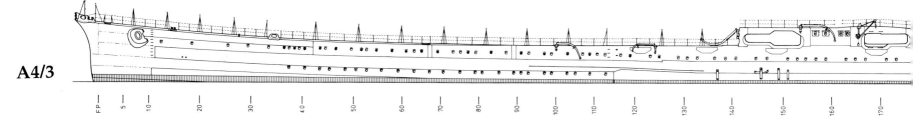

A4/3

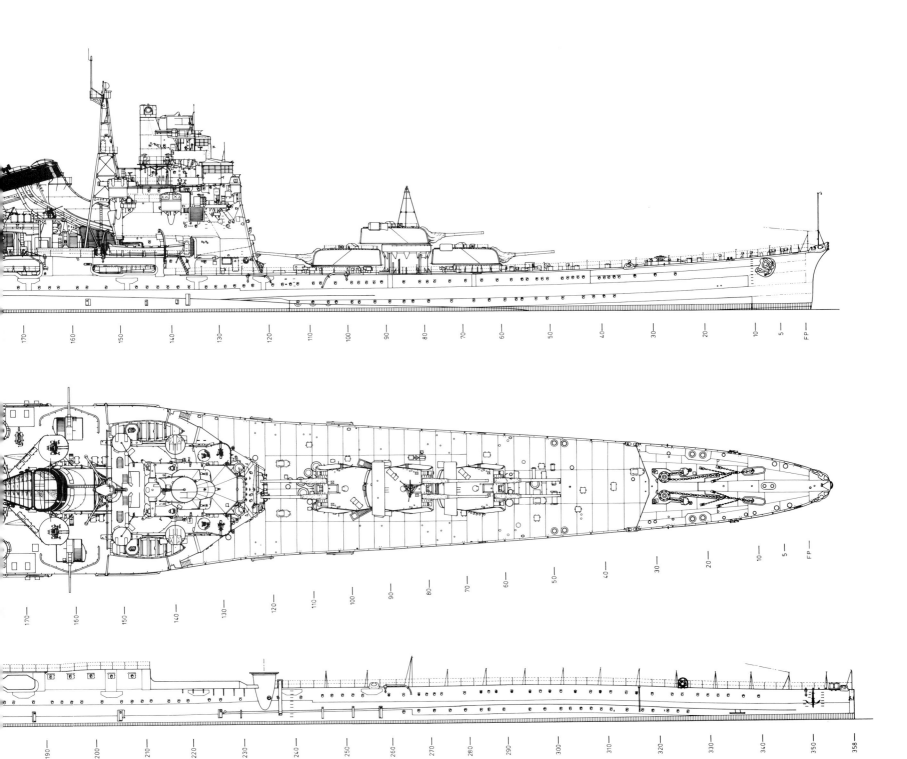

170   160   150   140   130   120   110   100   90   80   70   60   50   40   30   20   10   5   FP

170   160   150   140   130   120   110   100   90   80   70   60   50   40   30   20   10   5   FP

190   200   210   220   230   240   250   260   270   280   290   300   310   320   330   340   350   358

51

A General arrangement

A5   *TAKAO* IN SEPTEMBER 1944
A5/1   *External profile (scale 1/450)*
A5/2   *Plan (scale 1/450)*

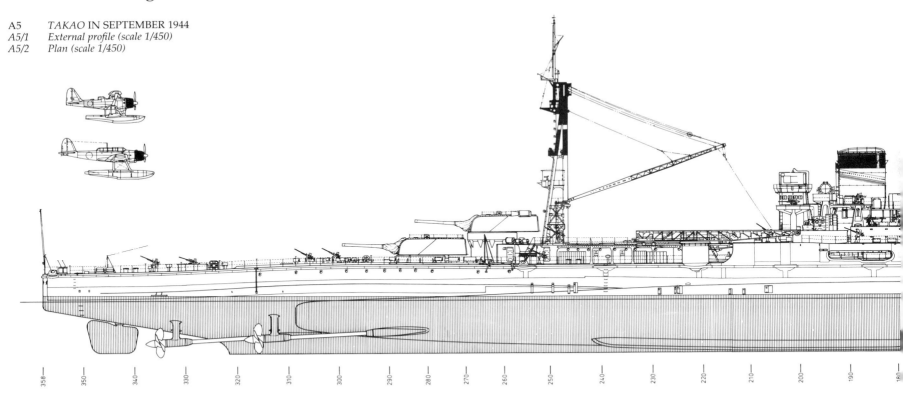

A5/1

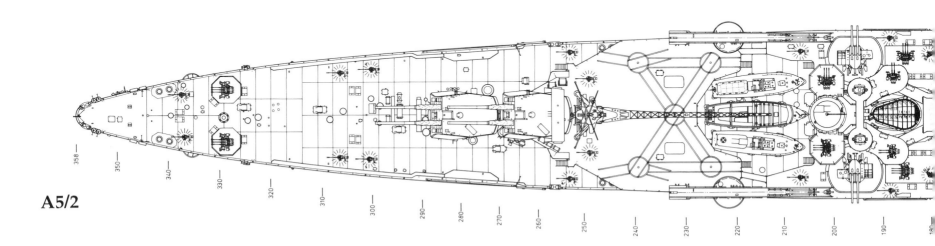

A5/2

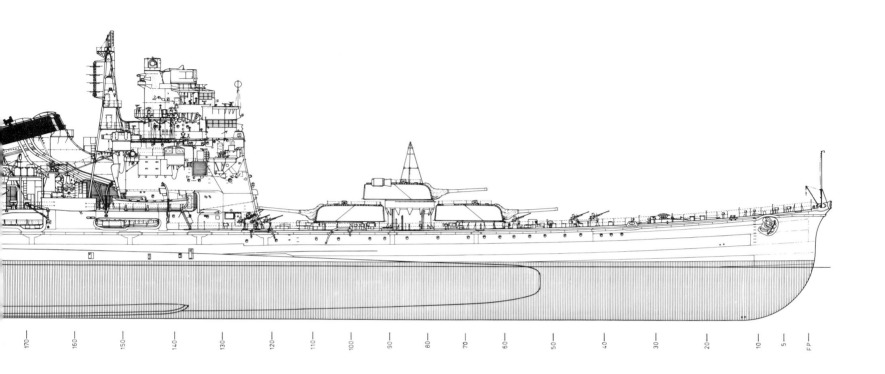

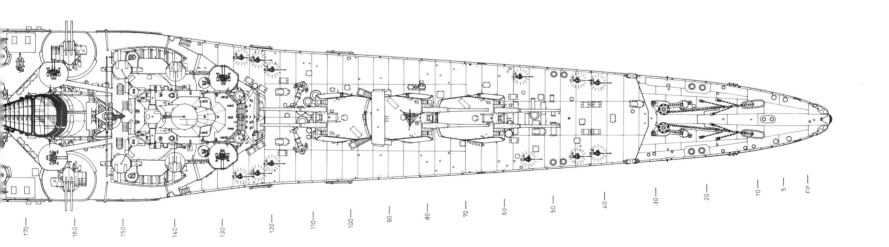

A General arrangement

A6 INTERNAL ARRANGEMENTS, 1932

A6/1 Profile (scale 1/450)

1 Canned food store
2 Food store with soya sauce store
3 No 1 rice and wheat store
4 No 4 rice and wheat store
5 Bilge pump room
6 Trim tank
7 Capstan machinery room
8 Cable locker (anchor cable locker)
9 Second officer's office
10 Warrant officer's food store
11 Sonar compartment
12 Admiral's cabin
13 Passage
14 Oil fuel tank
15 Reserve oil fuel tank
16 20.3cm powder handling room
17 No 1 turret shell room
18 No 1 turret powder magazine
19 No 2 turret shell room
20 No 3 turret shell room
21 Officer's cabin
22 Passage to diver's room
23 Lower radio room
24 No 1 12cm HA ammunition magazine
25 4.5m *14 Shiki* rangefinder tower
26 *14 Shiki* main armament director control tower
27 Survey telescope tower
28 Crew standby room
29 Officer's standby room
30 Main armament command communication installation
31 Optical ordnance store
32 Upper electrical circuit room
33 *Sokuteki* (target course and speed computer) store and standby room
34 Communication installation for the *Sokutekiban*
35 13 *Shiki Sokutekiban* – target course and speed computer
36 Action command station
37 No 1 headquarters (*shireibu*) store
38 No 1 navigation store
39 Bridge with compasses and binoculars – compass platform
40 No 1 emergency action command station
41 Passage
42 Tactical command centre
43 Chart room
44 Signal platform
45 Commanding officer's standby room
46 No 2 communication battery room
47 Passage
48 Communications command station
49 Navigation store
50 High angle gun command station
51 Protected wheelhouse
52 Navigation officer's room
53 No 3 telephone room
54 Forward radio room
55 No 1 boiler room
56 No 2 boiler room
57 Reserve watertank
58 Funnel No 1
59 Funnel No 2
60 Workshop – machine-shop
61 Boiler room ventilation supply
62 Casting house (forge)

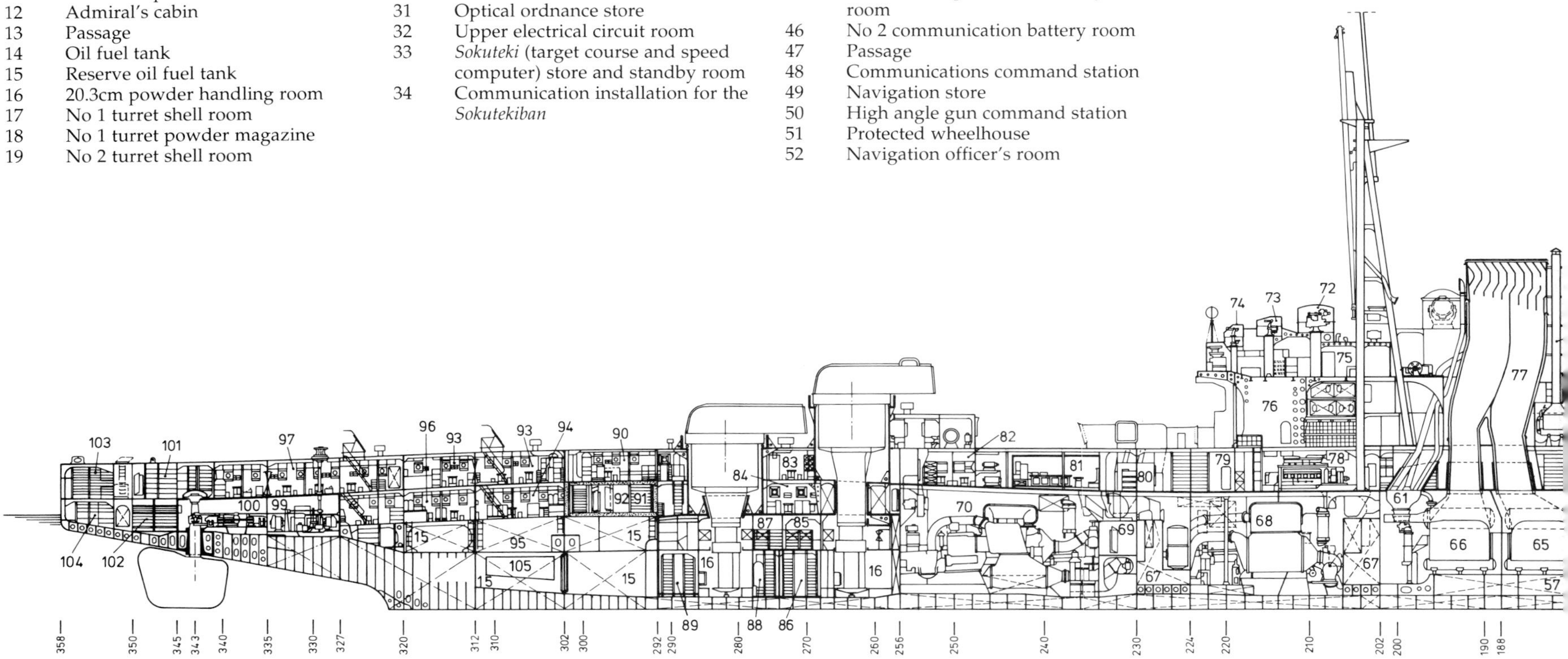

A6/1

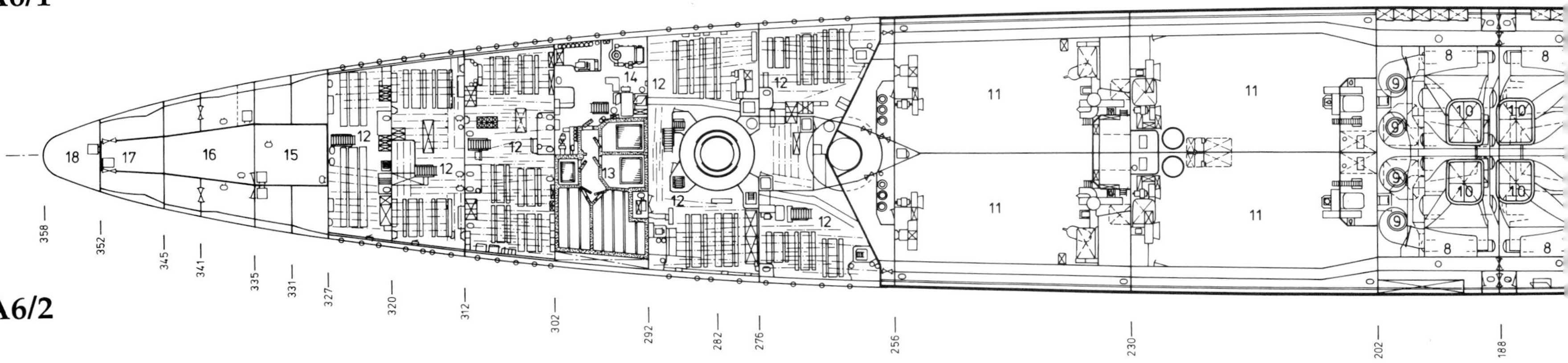

A6/2

63	No 3 boiler room	72	Main armanent auxiliary command room with *14 Shiki* director
64	No 5 boiler room		
65	No 7 boiler room	73	Searchlight control position
66	No 9 boiler room	74	Protected lookout position
67	Water supply tank	75	Radio room
68	Forward engine room	76	Seaplane hangar
69	Main engines control room	77	After funnel – funnel No 3
70	After engine room	78	250kW generator room – internal combustion engine
71	Smoke outlet of donkey boiler located at upper deck level		
		79	Paymaster's store and kitchen office
		80	Lubricating oil store
		81	Radio room
		82	Electric motor room to power wireless
		83	No 5 crew quarters
		84	No 9 crew quarters

85	No 4 turret shell room
86	No 4 turret powder magazine
87	No 5 turret shell room
88	No 5 turret powder magazine
89	No 5 turret powder magazine
90	No 6 crew quarters
91	Food stores – cold stores for meat and fish
92	Ice store
93	No 7 crew quarters
94	Crew quarters
95	Oil fuel tank (after 1939 dry food stores for rice and wheat)
96	No 12 crew quarters
97	No 8 crew quarters
98	No 13 crew quarters
99	Rudder engine room
100	Steering rudder room
101	Food store – rice and wheat
102	Canvas stores

103	No 2 administration department stores
104	Store – after 1939 depth charge magazine
105	Petrol (gasoline tank)
A6/2	*Lower deck (scale 1/450)*
1	Food store – soya sauce
2	No 4 rice and wheat store
3	Cable locker
4	Second officer's office
5	Officer's living quarters with cabin
6	Passage
7	Generator room
8	Boiler rooms
9	Forced draught fans – two per boiler
10	Funnel uptake
11	Engine room space
12	Crew living quarters
13	Refrigeration rooms
14	Distilling plant compartment
15	Rudder engine room space
16	Steering rudder room space
17	Canvas stores
18	Store – after 1939 depth charge magazine

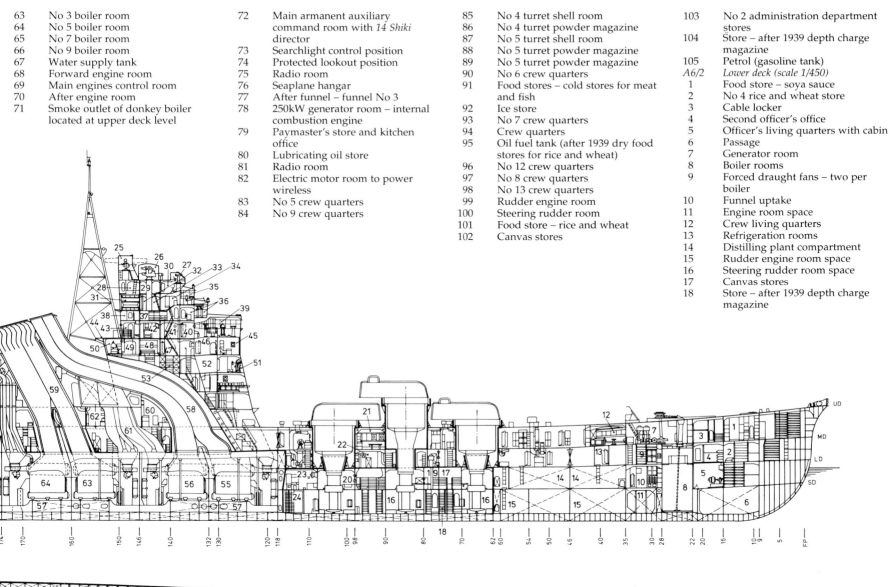

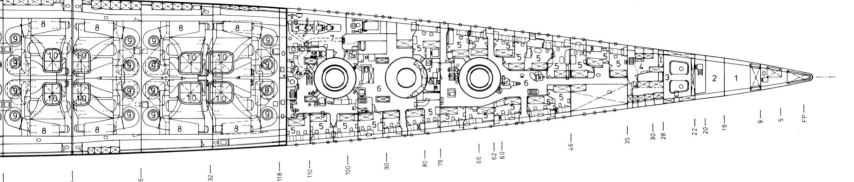

A General arrangement

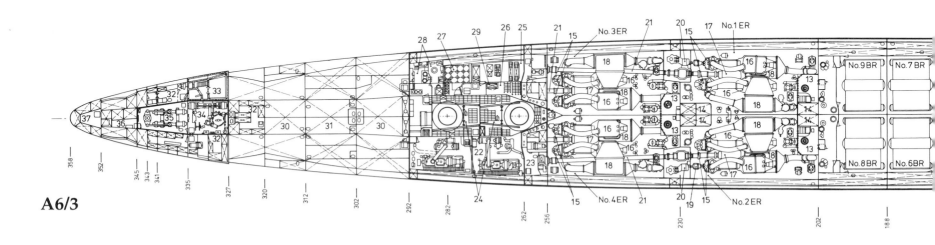

A6/3

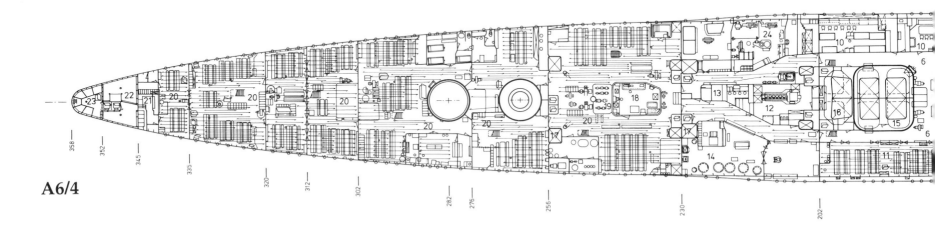

A6/4

28	Transformer room	36	Canvas stores	8	Officers' mess	17	Ventilation fan
29	Hoist	37	Store	9	WC	18	After radio room
30	Reserve oil fuel tanks	A6/4	*Middle deck – 1939 (scale 1/450)*	10	Petty officers' living quarters	19	Telecommunication generator
31	Oil fuel tank rice and wheat store	1	Canned food store	11	Crew living quarters		room
	1939	2	No 1 rice and wheat store	12	250kW generator room	20	Crew living quarters
32	Miscellaneous stores	3	Capstan machinery room	13	Paymaster's store and kitchen	21	Miscellaneous stores
33	Refrigeration room	4	Admiral's cabin		office	22	Rice and wheat store
34	Rudder engine room with winch	5	Officer's cabin	14	Kitchen	23	No 2 administration department
	engine and emergency helm	6	Passage	15	Funnel hatch (uptake)		stores
35	Rudder room with hydraulic rams	7	Paymaster's office	16	Ventilation fan for boiler room	24	Workshop

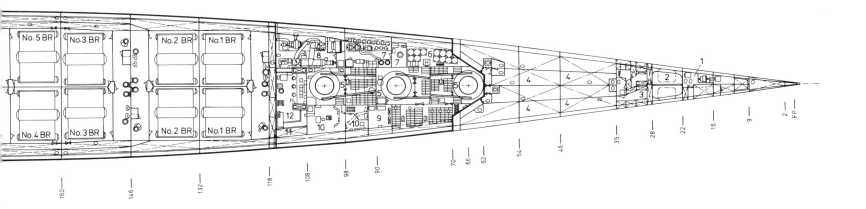

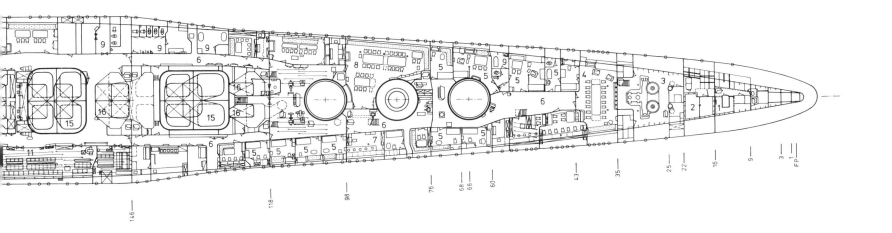

A General arrangement

A6/5 Internal profile after modernisation, August 1939 (midship) (scale 1/400)

1 6m rangefinder tower – *14 Shiki* (type 14)
2 Low angle director tower – *94 Shiki Hoiban Shageki Sōchi*
3 Upper wiring room *22 Go* radar room after January 1944
4 Officers' standby room – radar ordnance room after August 1943
5 *Sokuteki* room with *92 Shiki Sokutekiban* – target course and speed computer
6 Information room (former chart room)
7 Transom firing station (main armament)
8 Navigation room with compasses and 18cm and 12cm binoculars – compass platform
9 Commanding officer's standby room
10 Signal flag lockers
11 Tactical command centre – *Sakusen Shitsu*
12 Lower wiring room
13 Conning tower protected from all sides by 16mm Ducol steel
14 No 3 radio room
15 Fore radio room – *Denshin* and communication command centre
16 Signal platform
17 Torpedo fire control position
18 Funnel No 1
19 Funnel No 2
20 Funnel No 3
21 Boiler room ventilation supply
22 Workshop – machine-shop
23 Casting house (forge)
24 Machine gun fire-control tower – *95 Shiki Kiju Shageki Sōchi*
25 Reserve water tank
26 No 1 boiler room
27 No 2 boiler room
28 No 3 boiler room
29 No 4 and No 5 boiler room
30 No 6 and No 7 boiler room
31 No 8 and No 9 boiler room
32 Auxiliary low angle director tower – *94 Shiki Hoiban Shōjun Sōchi*
33 Auxiliary fire-control room
34 Aviation stores
35 Aviation department
36 Water supply tank
37 Forward engine rooms – No 1 and No 2
38 Rear engine rooms – No 3 and No 4
39 Main engines control room
40 20.3cm powder supply room
41 No 1 aviation store
42 No 1 crew quarters
43 Crane engine room
44 Rear radio room
45 250kW electric generator
46 Paymaster's store and kitchen office
47 Lubricant stores
48 Lower part of radio room
49 Communications generator
50 No 4 crew quarters

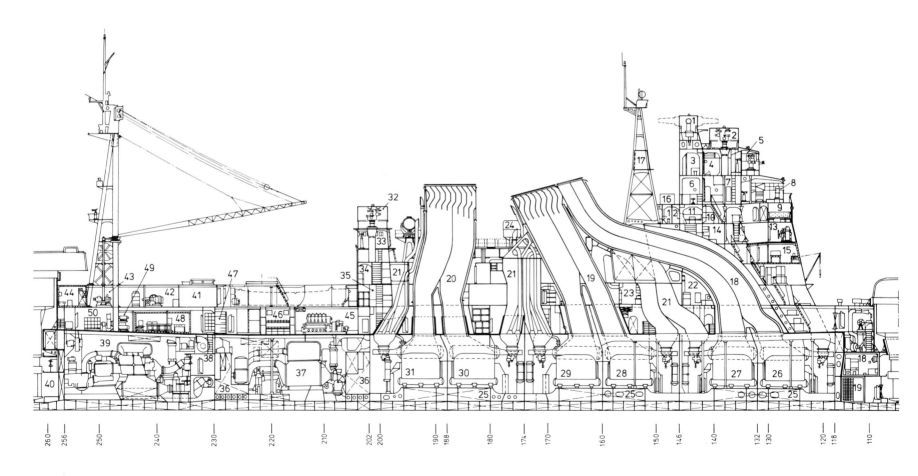

A6/5

A7	TRANSVERSE SECTIONS	21	Auxiliary main armament fire-control room with director tower – *14 Shiki*	39	Living quarters	59	Forced draught fans – two per boiler	

A7   TRANSVERSE SECTIONS
A7/1   Transverse sections 1932
(scale 1/400)

1   Miscellaneous stores
2   Steering rudder room
3   Store
4   No 8 crew quarters
5   Rudder engine room
6   Refrigerated room
7   Crew quarters
8   No 12 crew quarters
9   Oil fuel tank
10 Watertight compartment
11 Crew quarters
12 Generator room
13 No 4 turret shell magazine
14 Shell handling room with shell bogies
15 Shaft tunnel
16 No 4 turret powder handling room
17 Aircraft bomb store
18 Radio room
19 Engine room
20 Main engines control room

21 Auxiliary main armament fire-control room with director tower – *14 Shiki*
22 Radio room
23 Seaplane hangar
24 Torpedo room
25 Workshop
26 Passage
27 250kW generator
28 Electrical wire passage
29 Condenser
30 Low pressure turbine
31 110cm searchlight 'SU' Shiki protected by blast screen
32 Lookout position in searchligh tower
33 Lower part of tower – store
34 12cm HA gun in B$_2$ model mount
35 Torpedo room with rapid reload system and torpedo carrying rails
36 Funnel uptakes and ventilation cowls of boiler rooms
37 Petty officers' quarters
38 Passage

39 Living quarters
40 Store
41 Feed water tanks
42 No 9 boiler room
43 No 8 boiler room
44 Main armament director tower – *14 Shiki*
45 Officers' standby room
46 *Sokuteki* store and standby room
47 No 1 headquarters store – *Shireibu*
48 Searchlight control position
49 Tactical command centre – *Sakusen Shitsu*
50 Combat room communication
51 Aircraft store
52 Main store navigation
53 Funnel No 1 – uptakes from No 1 and No 2 boiler rooms
54 Passage
55 Torpedo room
56 Workshop
57 Living quarters for aircraft personnel
58 WC and washroom

59 Forced draught fans – two per boiler
60 No 2 boiler room
61 Paymaster's office
62 Officers' mess
63 Officer's cabin
64 Passage
65 20.3cm shell magazine
66 Shell handling room with sheel bogies (20.3cm)
67 Auxiliaries
68 20.3cm powder handling room
69 20.3cm powder magazine with powder tanks (canisters)
70 Capstan machinery room
71 Second officer's office
72 Warrant officers' food storage
73 Sonar compartment
74 Canned food store
75 Food store – soya sauce
76 Store

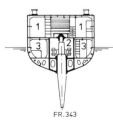

FR.343

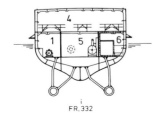

FR.332

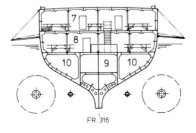

FR.316

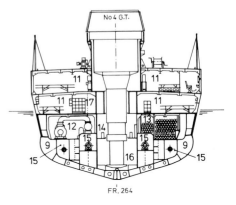

FR.264

A7/1

A General arrangement

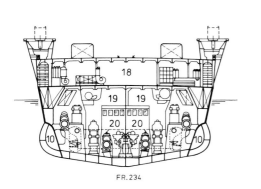

FR.234

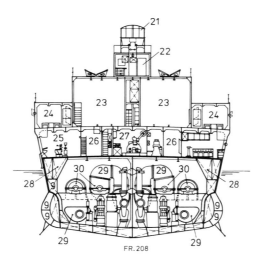

FR.208

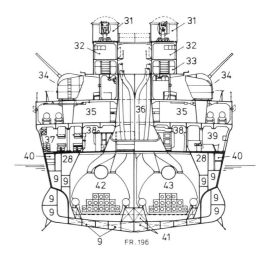

FR.196

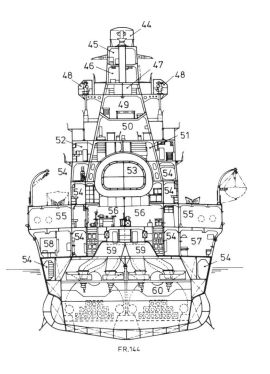

FR.144

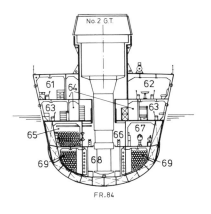

No.2 G.T.

FR.84

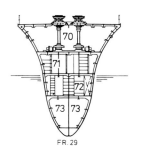

FR.29

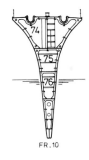

FR.10

61

A General arrangement

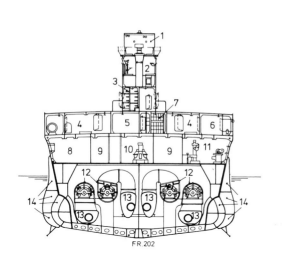
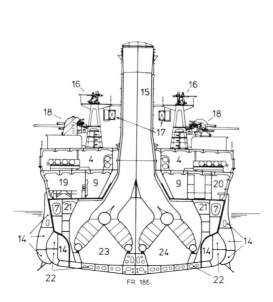
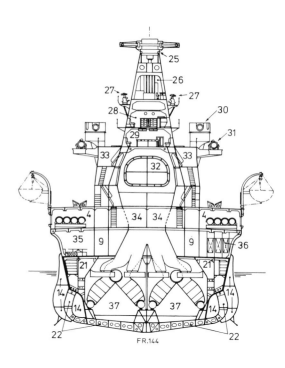

A7/2

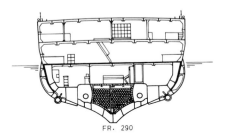

FR. 290

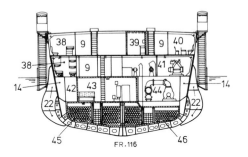

FR. 116

A General arrangement

A7/3   Hull section, 1932 (scale 1/200)

A7/4   Hull section, 1939 (scale 1/200)
(Thickness of plates and armour in millimetres)
WTC   Watertight compartment
OF   Oil fuel tank
W   Reserve feed water tank
R   Additional protection of steel pipes

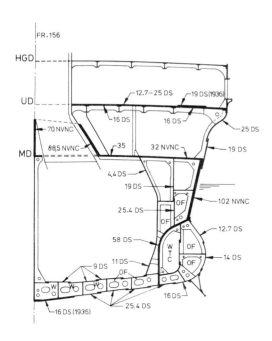

A7/3

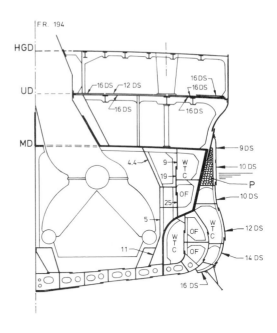

A7/4

A8	COMPARTMENTS BETWEEN DOUBLE BOTTOM AND STORE DECK WITH POWDER MAGAZINES	WTC	Watertight compartment	8	No 2 HA gun (12cm and 12.7cm) ammunition magazine with hoist, protected by 50mm–102mm NVNC steel	LO Lubricant oil tank

A8 COMPARTMENTS BETWEEN DOUBLE BOTTOM AND STORE DECK WITH POWDER MAGAZINES

WTC Watertight compartment
OFT Oil fuel tank

A8/2 Bow section (scale 1/400)
1 No 1 turret powder handling room
2 No 2 turret powder handling room
3 No 3 turret powder handling room
4 20.3cm powder magazine with canisters for cordite charges
5 Flash-tight hoist – two per turret
6 Machine-gun ammunition with hoist
7 No 1 magazine for HA gun ammunition (12cm, 12.7cm gun after August 1942) protected by 50mm–102mm NVNC steel, with hoist

A8/1 Stern section (scale 1/400)
1 No. 4 turret powder handling room
2 No 5 turret powder handling room
3 No 4 turret powder magazine with canisters for cordite charges
4 No 5 turret powder magazine with canisters
5 Flash-tight hoist drum – two per turret
6 Shaft tunnel

8 No 2 HA gun (12cm and 12.7cm) ammunition magazine with hoist, protected by 50mm–102mm NVNC steel

A8/3 Location of WTC, OFT, and other tanks in 1944 (no scale)
1 Compartments of double bottom
2 Compartments between double bottom and store deck
3 Compartments between store deck and lower deck

WTC Watertight compartment
OFT Oil fuel tank
ROFT Reserve oil fuel tank
FW Feed water tank (in engine rooms)

LO Lubricant oil tank
RFW Reserve feed water tank
SWT Spill-over water tank
WTC 3 to WTC 24 Watertight compartment in inner part of original bulges provided with quick flooding and drainage equipment (about 500 tons capacity)
Light oil – for aircraft

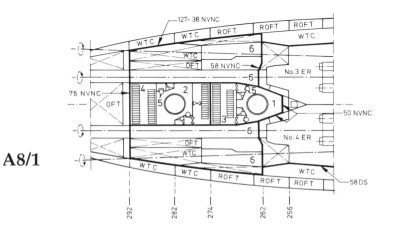

A8/1

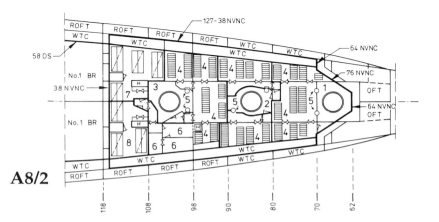

A8/2

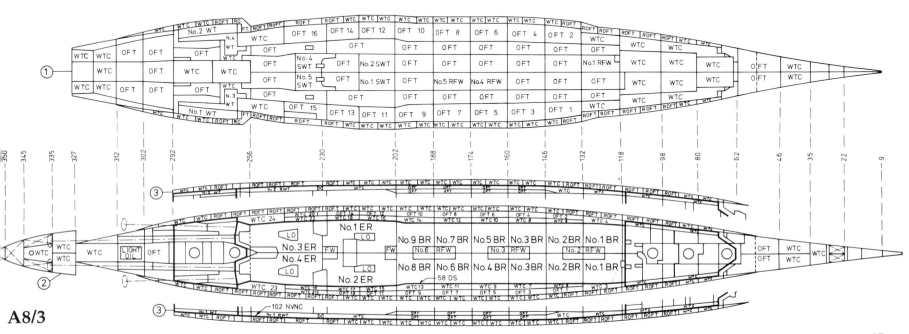

A8/3

B Lines and body plans

B1   LINES
B1/1   Sheer elevation
B1/2   Waterline plan
HGD   High angle gun deck
UF   Upper deck
FP   Forward perpendicular
AP   Aft perpendicular

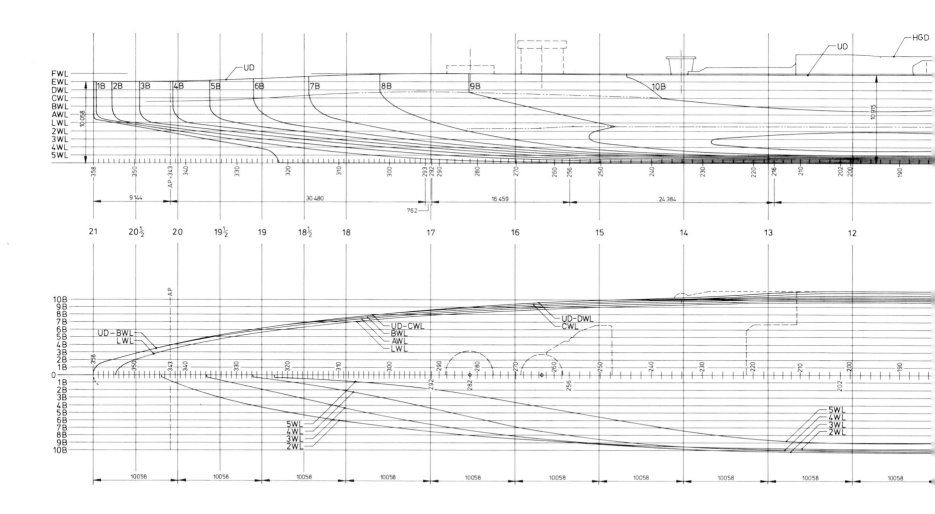

Distance between frames FP–358 (frame spaces) – official data

Frame	Distance in ft in	Parts
FP–0–1	1 7½	2
1–58	2 0	57
58–118	3 0	30
118–124	4 0	3
124–126	3 8¾	1
126–138	3 9	6
138–140	3 8¾	1
140–152	4 0	6
152–154	3 8¾	1
154–166	3 9	6
166–168	3 8¾	1
168–180	4 0	6

Frame	Distance in ft in	Parts
180–182	3 8¾	1
182–194	3 9	6
194–196	3 8¾	1
196–208	4 0	6
208–216	3 6	4
216–256	4 0	20
256–292	3 0	18
292–293	2 6	1
293–358	2 0	65

NOTE: FP–58 and 292–358 single numeration, 58–292 double numeration.
Distance between square stations
1–21 = 10058.4mm

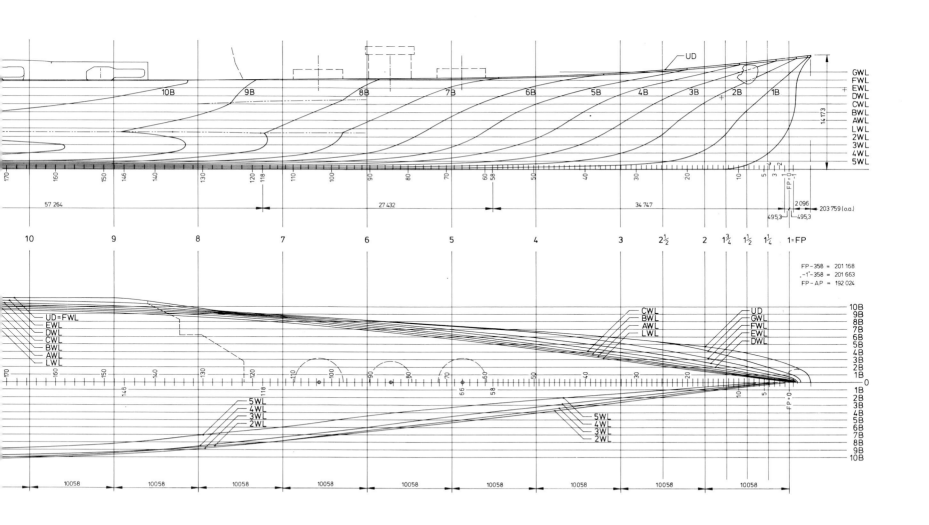

FP–358 = 201 168
–1'–358 = 201 663
FP–AP = 192 024

67

B Lines and body plans

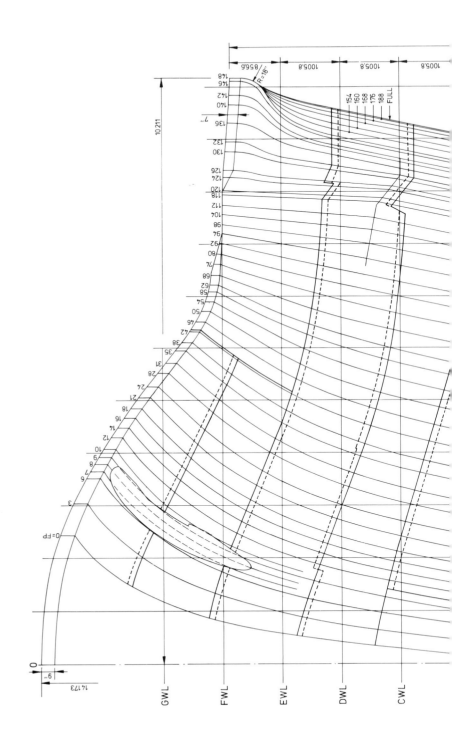

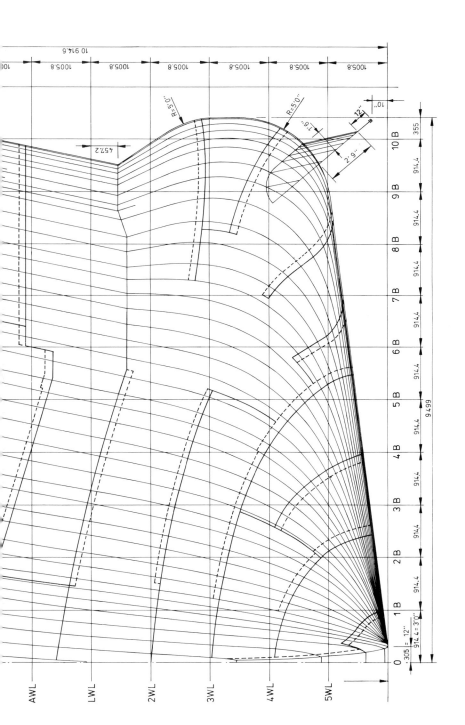

B2/1

69

B Lines and body plans

B2/2   *Body plan in 1932. Aft part of hull with construction frames and shell plating (scale 1/64)*

DR   Deadrise

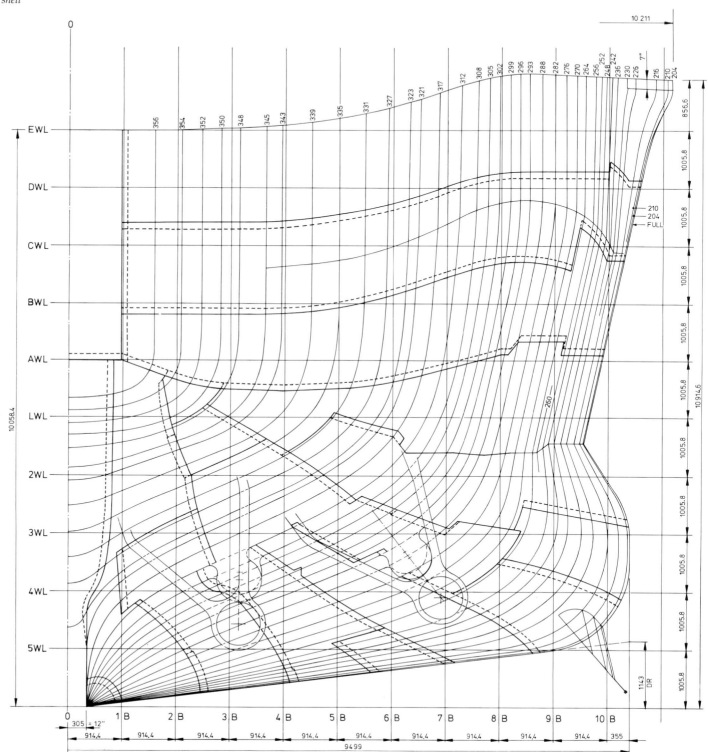

B2/2

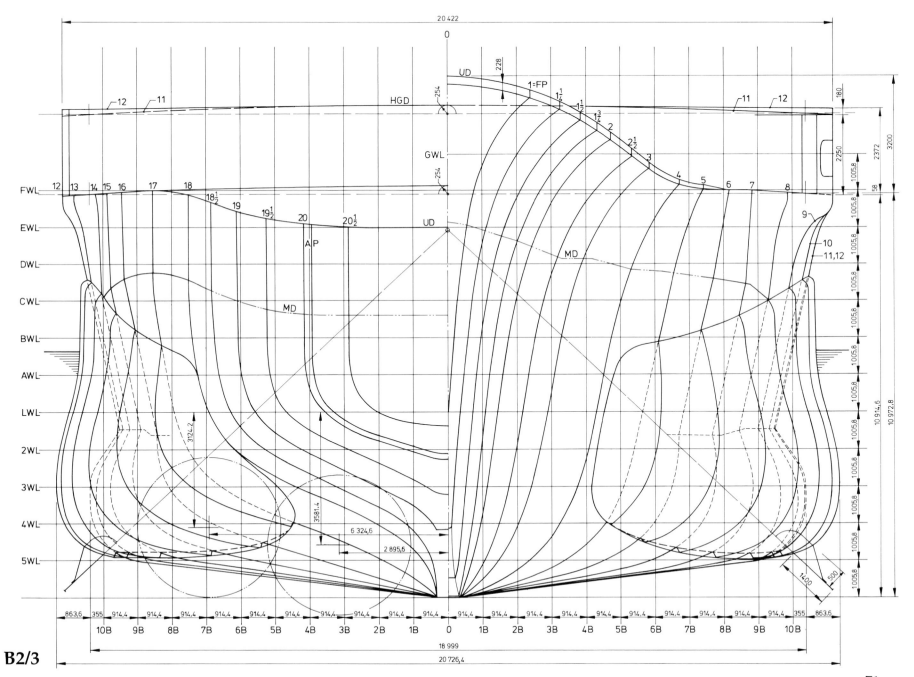

B2/3   *Body plan after 1939 refit. Original*
        bulges indicated by broken line (scale
        1/100)
FP   Fore perpendicular
1–20 – square stations, distance 10,058mm.
UD   Upper deck
HGD   High angle gun deck

B2/3

C Superstructure

C1   TOWER BRIDGE STRUCTURE AS
       COMPLETED, AUGUST 1932
C1/1   Elevation (scale 1/125)

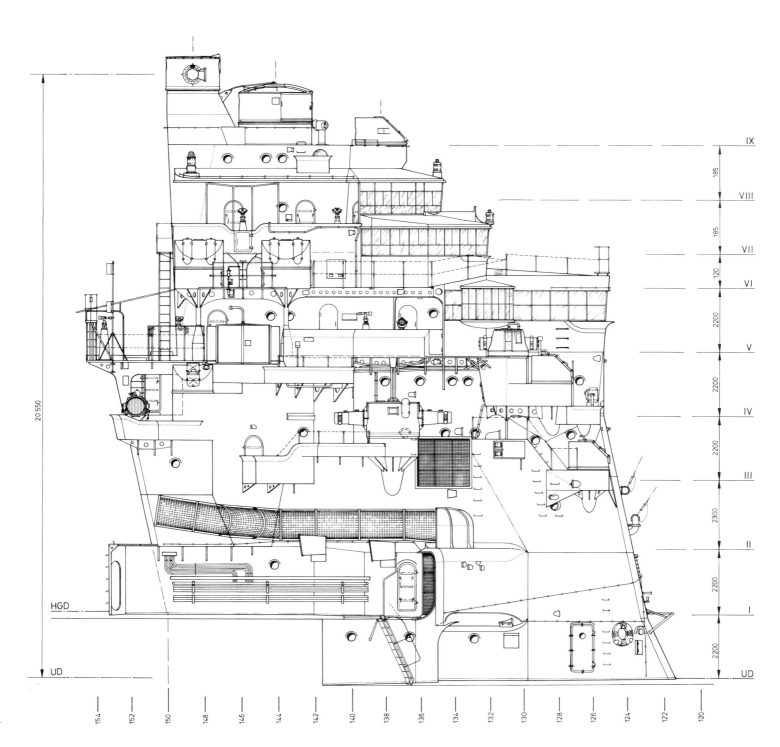

C1/1

C1/2   *Front elevation (scale 1/125)*
UD   Upper deck
I   HGD (high angle deck)
With miscellaneous stores, gunnery and torpedo
departments, crew rooms, ventilators.
II   Lower bridge deck
Note ventilator intake (frame 134) with auxiliary
air duct made from steel shapes and wire net as
support for canvas cover. Air duct was used only
in short time after commissioning and intake was
removed in 1933–34.
III   Middle bridge deck with protected
            wheelhouse
Frame 126: protected lookout position equipped
with binoculars
Frame 138: 3.5m rangefinder – *14 Shiki*
Frame 150: 60cm signal lamp.
IV   Upper bridge deck
Frame 128 and 148: protected (anti-blast) lookout
positions
V   Compass platform
Frame 130: 1.5m navigation rangefinder – *14 Shiki*
Frame 146: *91 Shiki* high angle fire director –
Kōsha Sōchi aft signal platform with signalling
position and turn signalling device (*Issei Kaito*)
VI   Fire command platform
Frames 144 and 148: searchlight control towers
Frame 146: signal lamps *Saidō*
VII   *Sokuteki* room
For calculation of target course and speed
VIII   Main gun command
            communication platform
Frame 148–150: 2kW day signal lamp (on both
sides)
IX   Main gun firing platform
Frame 138: telescope tower
Frame 144: main armament director tower – *14
Shiki*
Frame 148: 4.5m rangefinder tower – *14 Shiki*

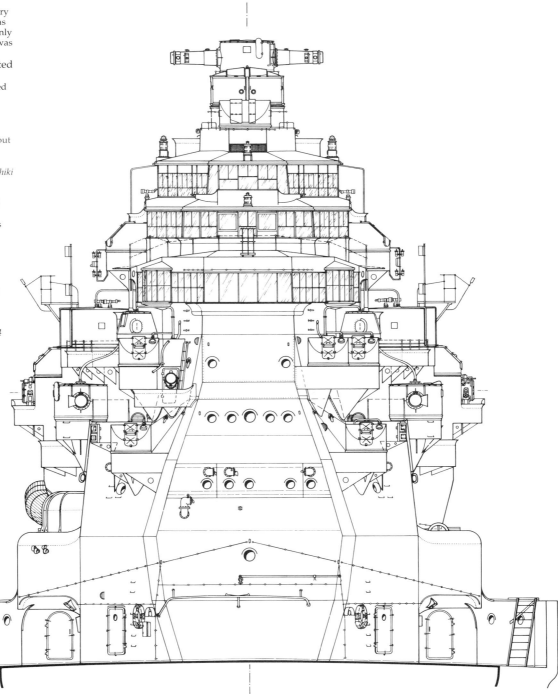

C1/2

C Superstructure

C2   TOWER BRIDGE STRUCTURE AS
COMPLETED, AUGUST 1932

C2/1   *Rear elevation (scale 1/125)*

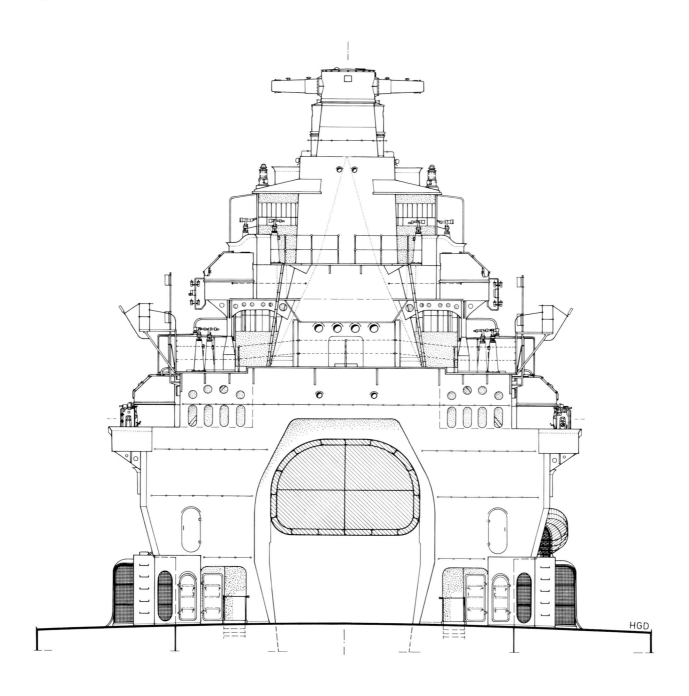

C2/1

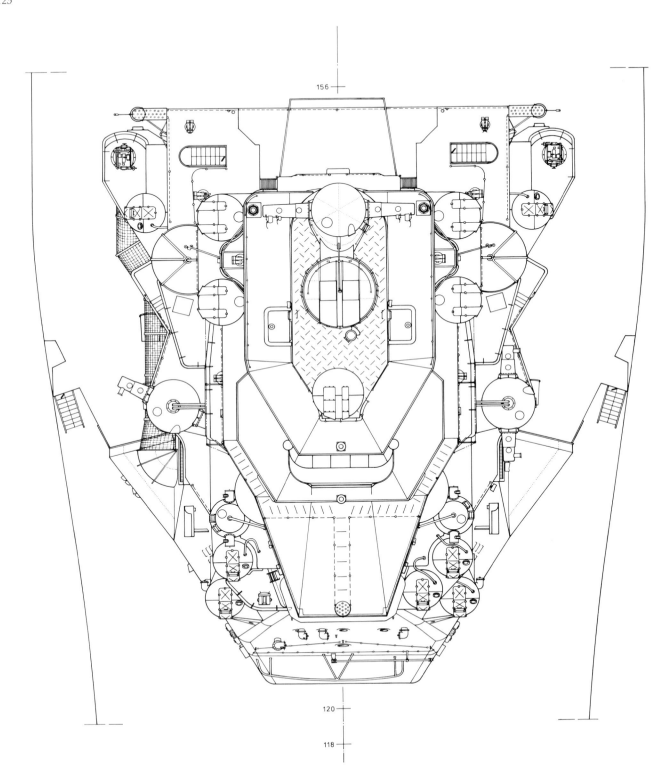

C2/2

C Superstructure

C3 DECKS OF TOWER BRIDGE
STRUCTURE, 1932–38

C3/1 *Deck level VII* - Sokuteki *platform*
(scale 1/125)

1 Computer for target course and
speed – *92 Shiki Sokutekiban*
2 Communication installation for the
Sokutekiban
3 *Sokuteki* store and standby room
4 Upper electrical circuit room
5 Standby room
6 Optical ordnance store
7 Binoculars' stand
8 Binocular – lookout position (1934–
38)
9 Bench
10 Hatch
11 Towing light
12 Increased glazed area in 1936

C3/2 *Deck level VI – fire control platform*
(scale 1/125)

1 Open fire-control position with
optical equipment
2 Fire-control room
3 No 1 communication store
4 Fire control instruments store
5 No 1 headquarters store – *Shireibu*
6 Navigation store
7 Torpedo director
8 Searchlight position – tower shield
removed in 1936
9 Signal lamps – *Saido*
10 Conning position
11 Canvas support

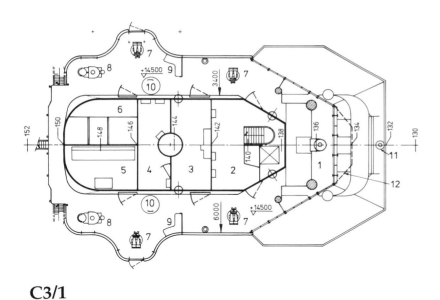

C3/1

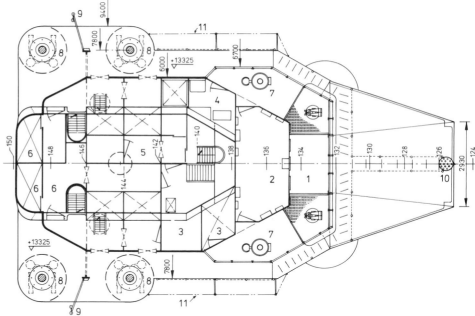

C3/2

C3/3　*Deck level V – compass bridge*
　　　(scale 1/125)
1　　Bridge with compasses and
　　　binoculars (note wood-grating on
　　　deck)
2　　No 1 emergency control room
3　　Passage
4　　Tactical command centre
5　　Chart room
6　　Signalling platform
7　　High angle fire director – *91 Shiki
　　　Kōsha Sōchi*
8　　1.5m navigation rangefinder – *14
　　　Shiki*
9　　Protected lookout position
10　　Signal lamp
11　　Deck lamp fitted in 1936
12　　Deck lamp platform fitted in 1936
　　　(broken line)
13　　Turn signalling device
14　　Signalling position
15　　Hatch

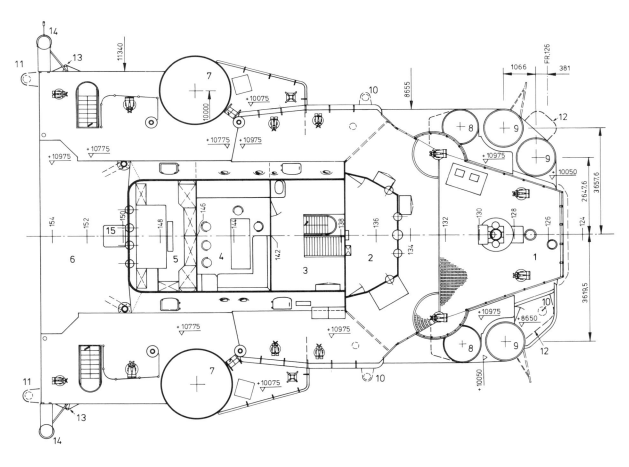

C3/3

C Superstructure

C3/4   *Deck level IV – upper bridge deck and*
        view on lower part of structure
        (scale 1/125)
1   Captain's standby room
2   Flag officer's standby room
3   No 2 Communication battery room
4   Staff officers' standby room
5   No 2 telephone room – *Denwa*
        Shitsu
6   Passage
7   Heads
8   Passage and store
9   Communication control room
10   Navigation room and standby
        room
11   HA gunnery control room and
        communication room
12   60cm signal lamp position
13   Protected (anti-blast) lookout
        position
14   3.5m rangefinder – *14 Shiki*
S   Sofa

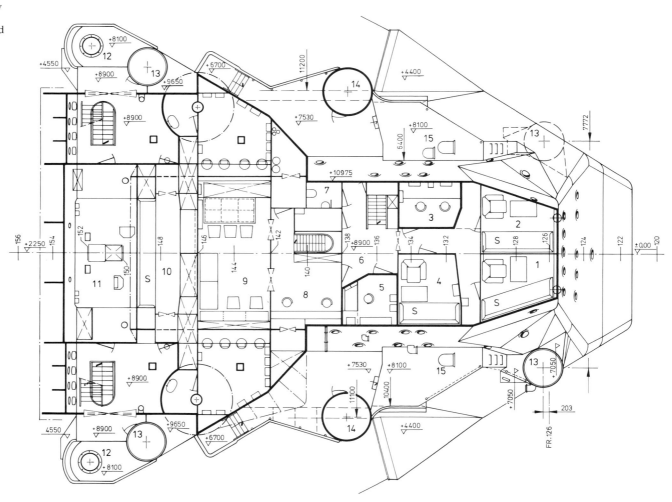

C3/4

C3/5   *Rear starboard fragment of tower –*
        level I = HGD (scale 1/125)
C3/6   *Rear starboard fragment of tower –*
        level II = lower bridge deck
        (scale 1/125)
C3/7   *Rear starboard fragment of tower –*
        plan of the ventilation (scale 1/125)
Cowl fitted below the 60cm signalling
searchlights' platform and on rear wall in 1933–
34. Geometrical structure form of the bridge
tower walls on drawing without small outer
structures (grey colour) level II to V, 1/62.5 scale.
C3/8   *Starboard view (scale 1/125)*
C3/9   *Front view (scale 1/125)*

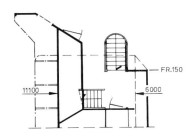

C3/5

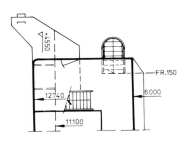

C3/6

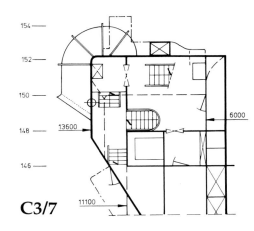

C3/7

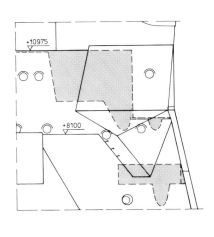

C3/8

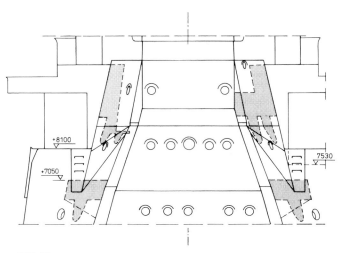

C3/9

C Superstructure

C4   TOWER BRIDGE STRUCTURE,
         JULY 1937
C4/1   *Elevation (scale 1/125)*

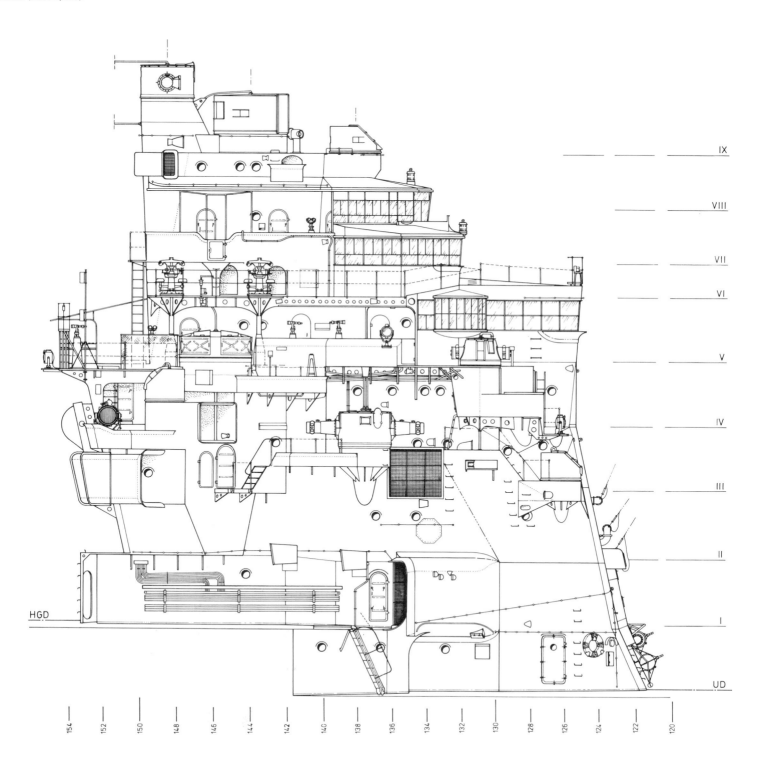

C4/1

Front elevation (scale 1/125)

Main changes

UD: Two paravanes and antenna wiring conduit on front face.

II: Intake removed at frame 134

III: Modernised gangway leading to the 3.5m rangefinder

IV: Small new platforms for deck lights; removal of the protected lookout position, and addition of new type shield to rear lookout position

V: *91 Shiki* director – *Kōsha Sōchi* with new type shield; two deck lights added at rear of signalling platform

VI: Shield protection removed from searchlight positions

VIII: Fore part of *Sokutekiban* room enlarged; 2kW daytime signal lanterns removed; new ventilation intakes added

IX: Shield of main armament director tower altered; voice tubes from 4.5m rangefinder to foremast stands

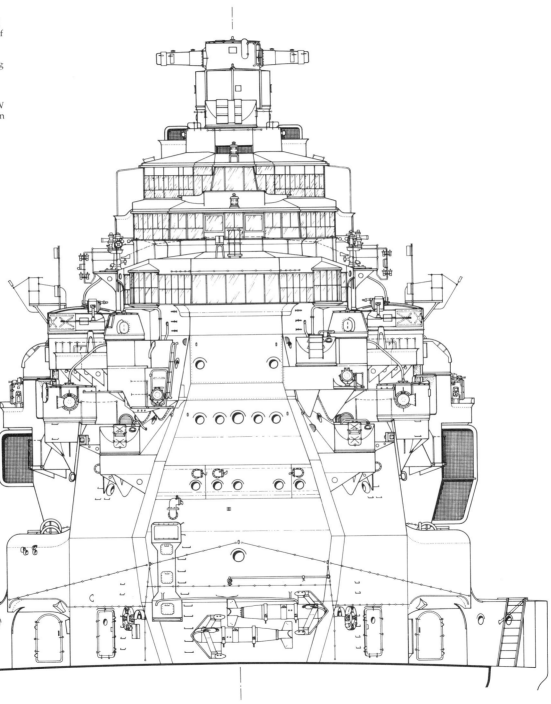

C4/2

C Superstructure

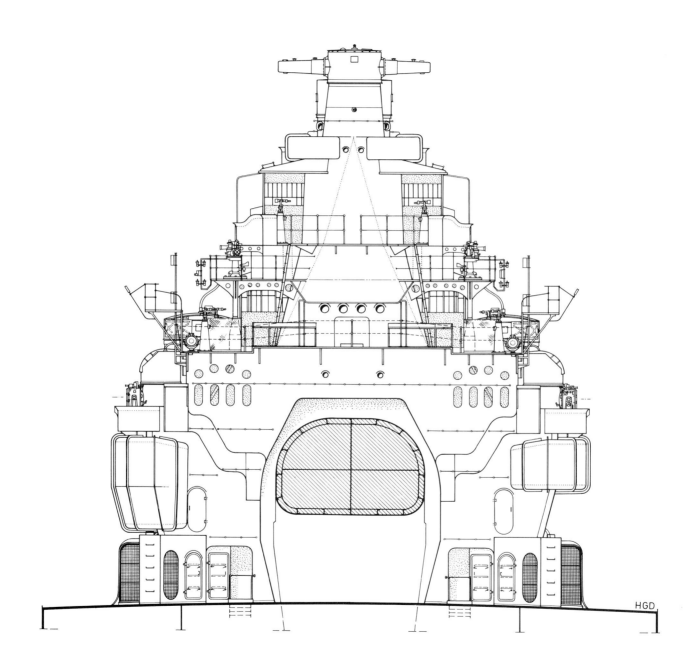

C5/1

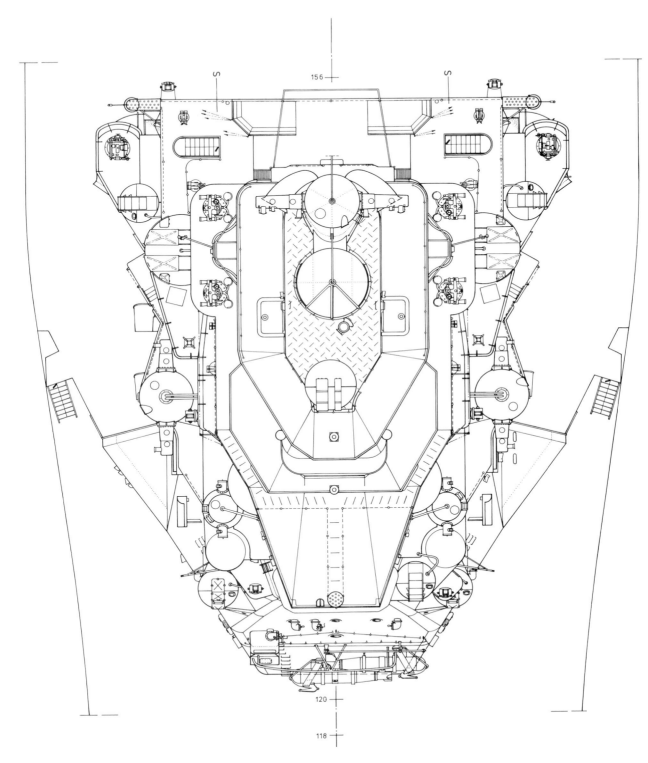

C5/2

C5̄/3   Port elevation (scale 1/125)

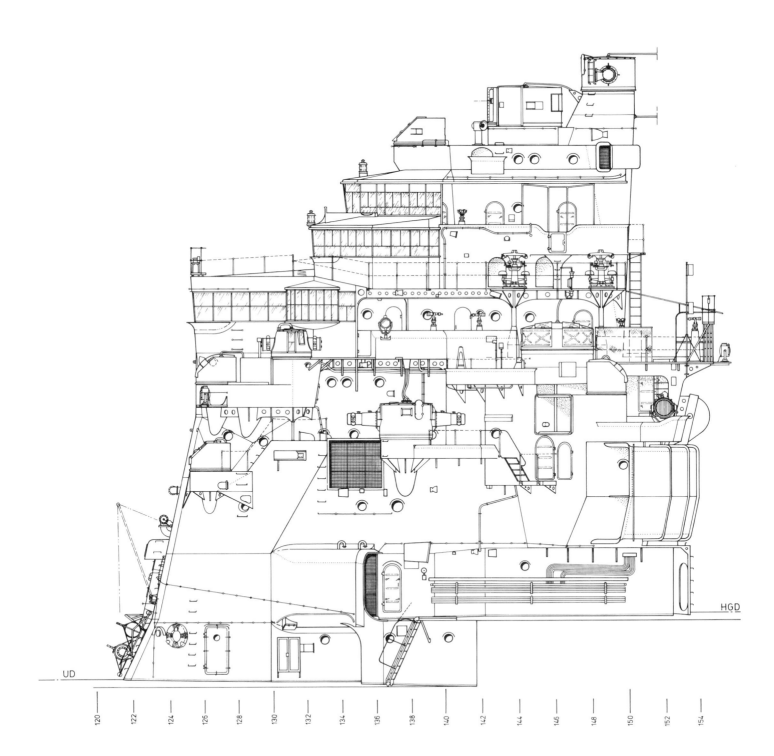

UD

HGD

C5/3

120 122 124 126 128 130 132 134 136 138 140 142 144 146 148 150 152 154

C5/4   *Detail of bridge drop windows (no scale)*

C5/5   *Typical steel welded joints, on fore surface of tower bridge (no scale)*

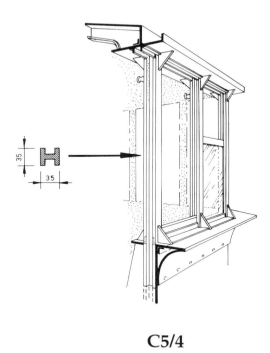

C5/4

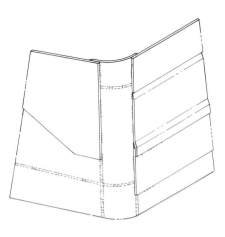

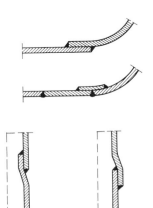

C5/5

C Superstructure

C6 TOWER BRIDGE STRUCTURE
AFTER RECONSTRUCTION,
AUGUST 1939

C6/1 Port elevation (scale 1/125)
IV Upper bridge deck
Frame 130: 13mm MG *93 Shiki* (twin machine-gun)
Frame 134: lower direction lookout position in wind deflector shield
Frame 140: HA director type 91 (*91 Shiki*) *Kōsha Sōchi*
Frame 148: 60cm signal lamp
Frame 150: 4.5m HA rangefinder (it was located on hangar superstructure before reconstruction) *91 Shiki*
V Compass platform
Frame 126: 1.5m navigation rangefinder *14 Shiki* – on sides of navigation room
Frames 132–138: torpedo firing equipment
VI *Sokutekiban* (for calculation of the target course and speed) platform
Frames 140–146: platform with *94 Shiki* searchlight control equipment
VII Main armament control platform
Frame 138: low angle director tower – *94 Shiki Hoiban Shageki Sōchi*
Frame 140: 6m rangefinder tower – *14 Shiki* – from No 1 turret
C6/2 Compass platform on deck V – view on small platform before navigation room (on drawing view without 1.5m rangefinder) (scale 1/125)

C6/2

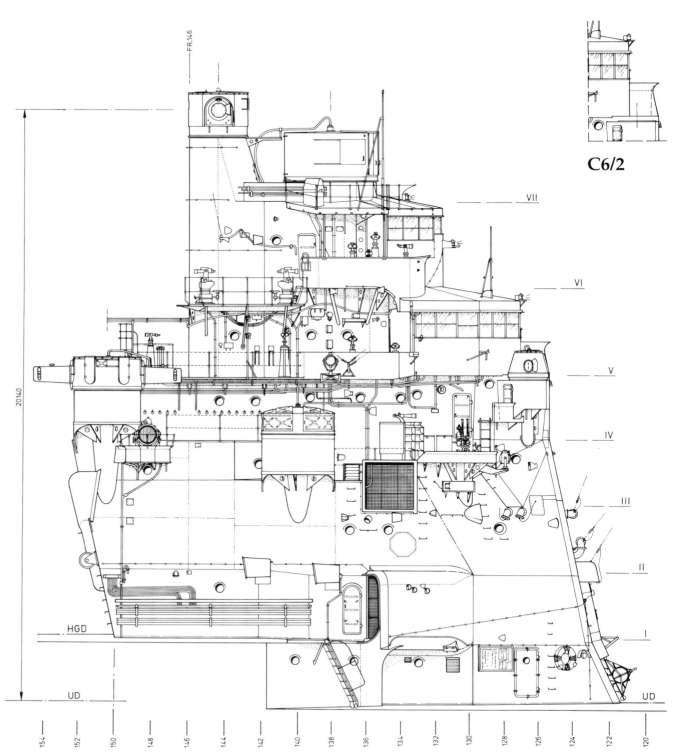

C6/1

C6/3 *Rear part of deck IV and V (signal platform) on drawing without 4.5m HA rangefinder (scale 1/125)*
1 Twin voice pipe from 4.5m HA rangefinder
2 Voice pipes
3 Signalling position with voice pipe
4 Voice pipes and electrical cables from foremast stands
5 8cm binocular
6 Fore funnel
C6/4 *Front elevation (scale 1/125)*
C6/5 *Front view on starboard 60cm searchlight platform (scale 1/125)*

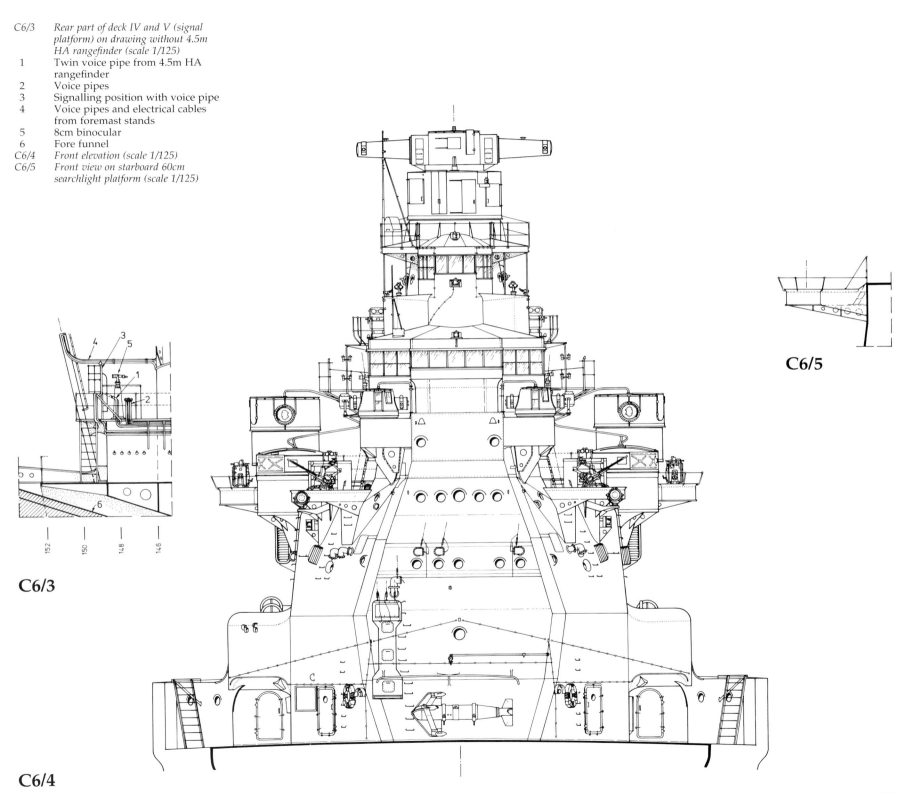

C6/5

C6/3

C6/4

C Superstructure

C6/6   Rear elevation (scale 1/125)

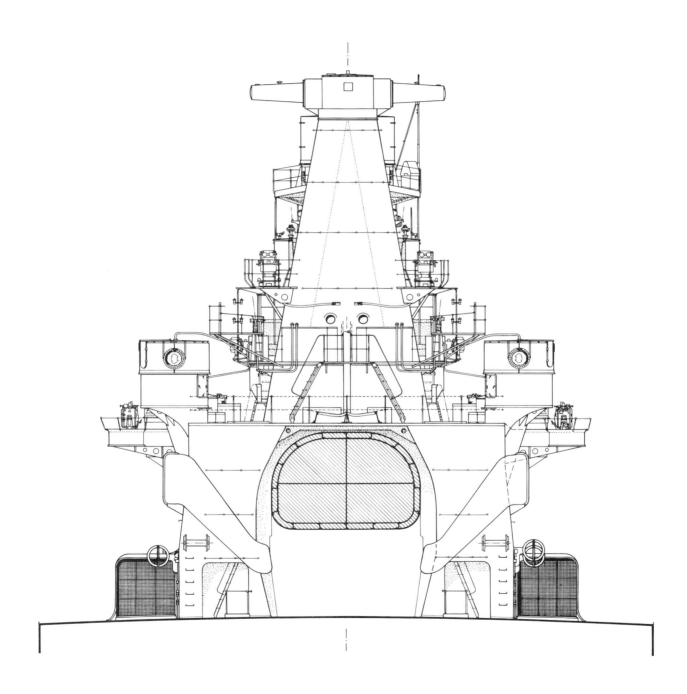

C6/6

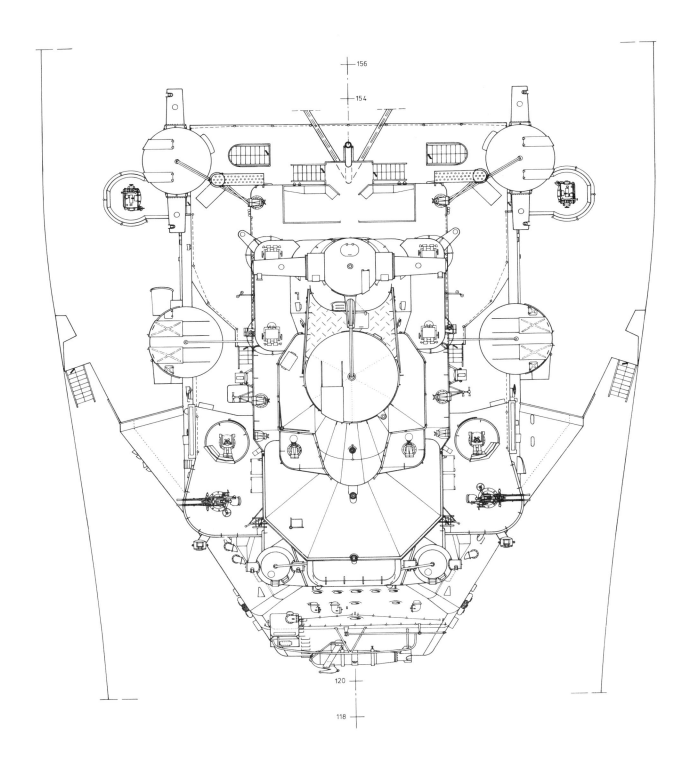

C6/7

C Superstructure

C7   TOWER BRIDGE STRUCTURE,
        SEPTEMBER 1944

C7/1   *Elevation (scale 1/125)*

III   Middle bridge deck
Frames 142–146: stand-by room for crew of
machine-gun and HA director

IV   Upper bridge deck, autumn 1941
13mm MG replaced with twin 25mm *96 Shiki* MG
on enlarged platform

V   Compass platform
Frame 144: message transmitter – *shoshingi*

VI   Frames 126–130
Anti aircraft platform with lookout positions
equipped with binoculars and *93 Shiki* goniometer
antenna in fore part; new lookout positions on
rear section.

VII   Main armament control platform
Frame 146: *22 Go* radar horn antennae fitted in
January 1944

C7/1

C7/2   *Internal profile of bridge's upper part (scale 1/125)*

1   Anti-aircraft platform. Note wood-grating on the deck
2   Navigation room with compasses and 12–18cm binoculars
3   *Sokuteki* room with *92 Shiki Sokutekiban*
4   Wind baffle
5   Towing light
6   Low angle director tower – *94 Shiki Hoiban Shageki Sōchi*
7   Main armament transmitting station

C7/3   *Front elevation (scale 1/125)*

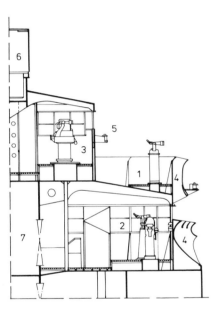

C7/2

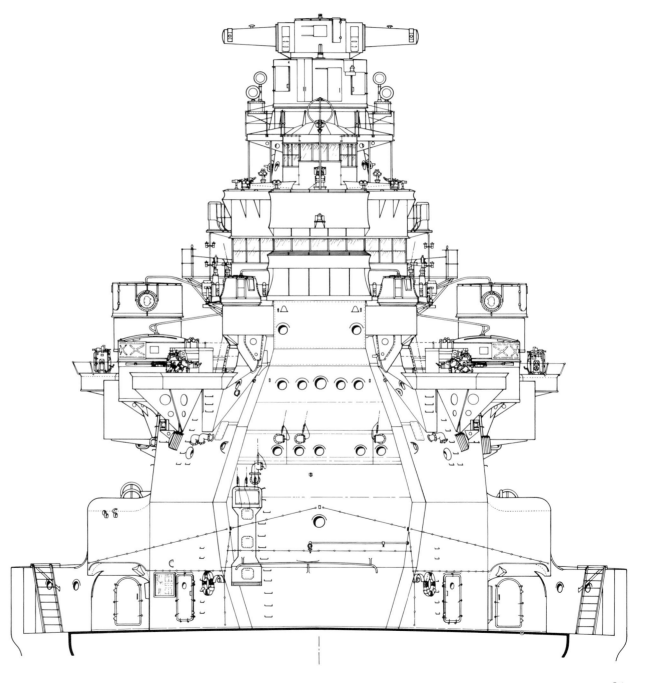

C7/3

C7/4   Rear elevation

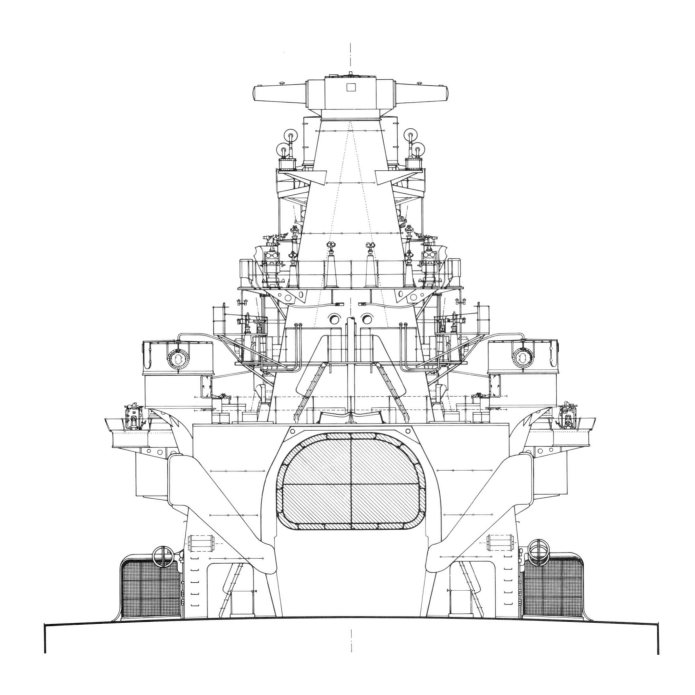

C7/4

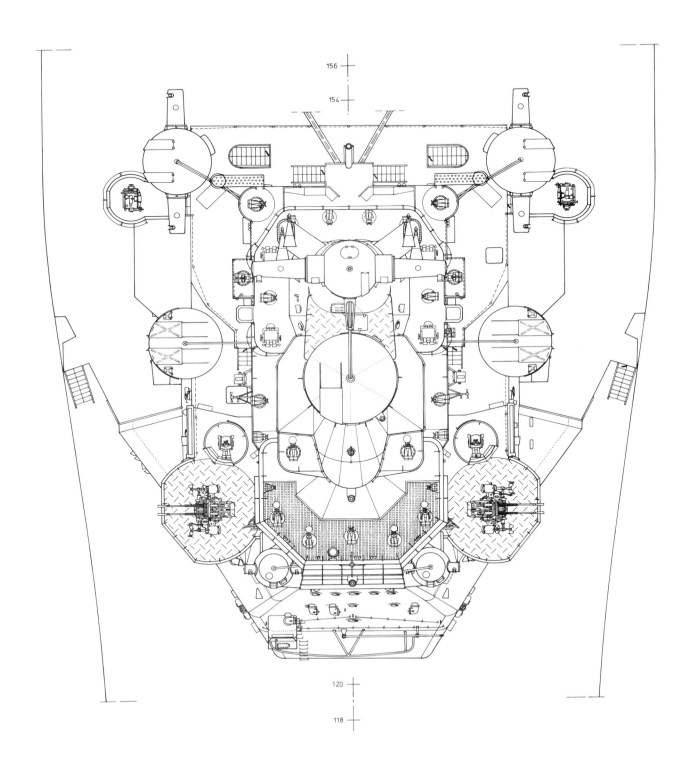

C7/5

C Superstructure

C8 DECKS OF TOWER BRIDGE
STRUCTURE 1939–45

C8/1 *Deck VI – Sokuteki and lookout
platforms, August 1939 (scale 1/125)*

1 *Sokuteki* room with *92 shiki
Sokutekiban* – note wood grating on
deck

2 Store. Radar ordnance room after
1943

3 Upper wiring room (*Haisen*). 22 *Gō*
radar room after January 1944

4 Radio antenna
5 Towing light
6 Upper direction lookout position
7 *93 Shiki* torpedo *Sokutekiban*
8 12cm binocular
9 *94 Shiki* searchlight control
installation
10 Signal lamp – *Saido*

C8/2 *Deck VI – Sokuteki and lookout
platforms – July 1944 (scale 1.125)*

1 Anti-aircraft (air defence)
command platform with 6–12cm
binoculars

2 *93 Shiki* goniometer antenna
3 Wind baffle
4 12cm binocular for AA gunnery
officer
5 Radio equipment
6 Aft air defence platform with 8–
12cm binoculars
Remaining equipment as on
former drawing

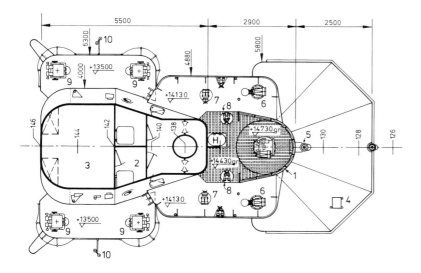

C8/1

C8/2

1   Small open platform in front of
     navigation room
2   Navigation room – compass bridge
     – with compasses and binoculars
3   Store
4   Main armament transmitting
     station – *Denreisho*
5   Chartroom, later information room
6   1.5m navigation rangefinder – *14*
     Shiki
7   18cm binoculars
8   Torpedo *Hoiban – 93 Shiki*
9   Fire torpedo command board
10   12cm binocular with infra-red
     signal lamp
11   Signal lamp support
12   Signal lamps *Saido* support
13   8cm binoculars
14   Signalling position

1   Wind baffle
2   Message transmitter – *Shōshingi*
     Remaining equipment as on
     former drawing

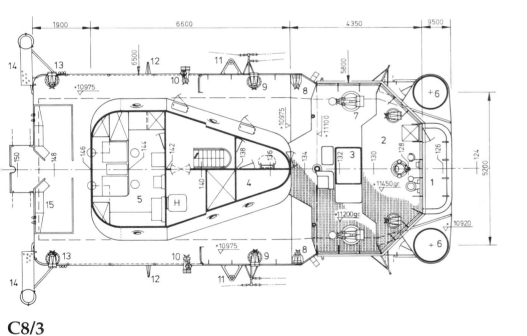

C8/3

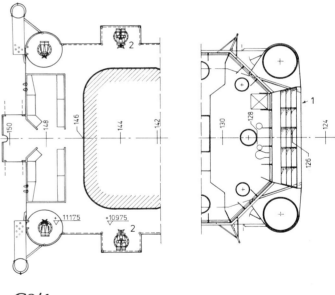

C8/4

C Superstructure

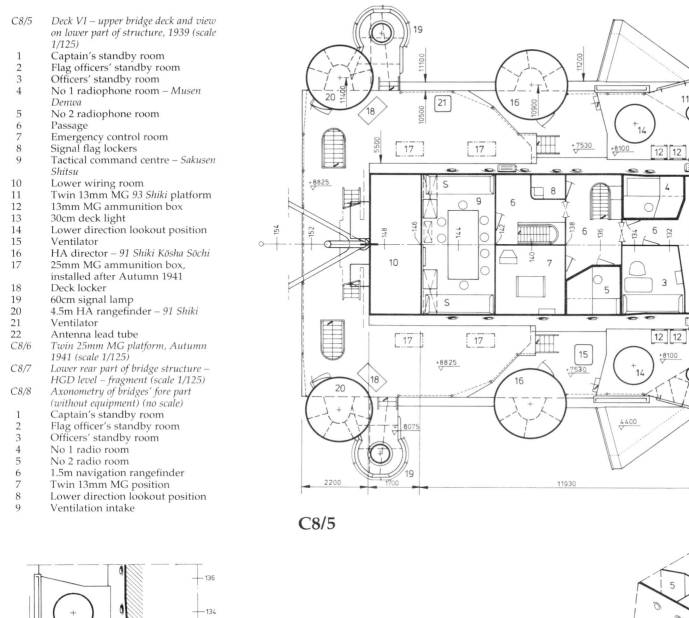

C8/5

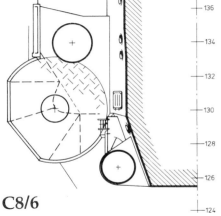

C8/6

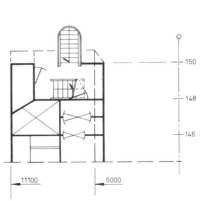

C8/7

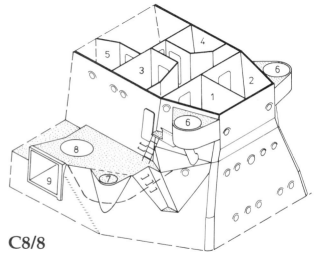

C8/8

C9   PERSPECTIVE OF BRIDGE
      STRUCTURE, AUTUMN 1932
      (no scale)
      (Drawing made from simplified
      computer simulation by Peter
      Czulak)

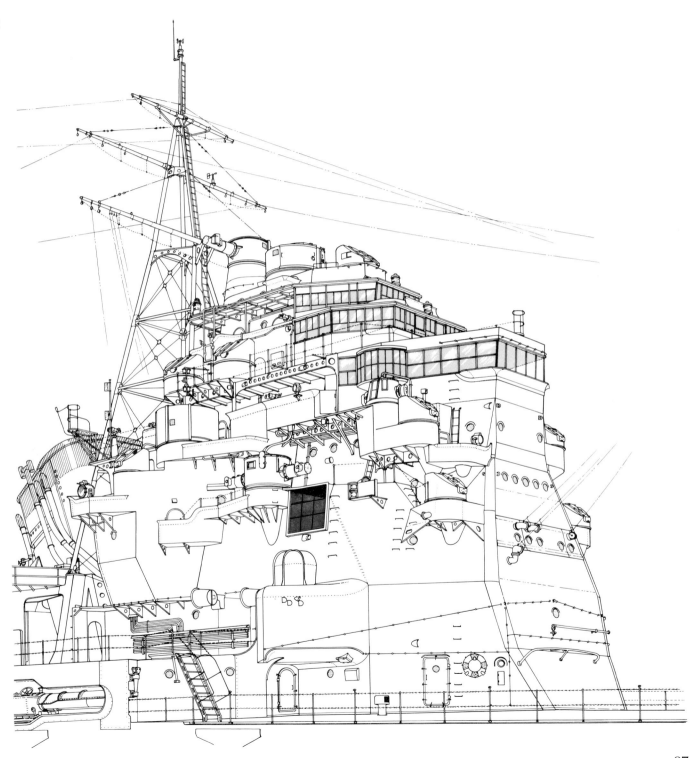

C9

C Superstructure

C10   FORWARD FUNNEL – FUNNEL
       NO 1 AND NO 2
C10/1   *Starboard profile (scale 1/100)*
C10/2   *Plan (scale 1/100)*
1   Frame for canvas cover
2   Hood
3   Lower limit to black funnel
      topping
4   Foghorn
5   Steam pipes from boiler safety
      valves (300mm)
6   Rear support
7   Boxes of fore supports
8   Air space of funnel No 2 with rain
      cover
9   Ventilation holes
10   Drain pipe
11   Lower rain cover
12   Rear of bridge structure
13   Antennae support
14   Ventilators from boiler rooms
      closed by wire netting screen –
      gauge of wire net 50 × 50mm
15   Removable hatch
16   Funnel stay band with eyes
17   Small roller crane
18   Rain gutter
C10/3   *Rear funnel's support (no scale)*

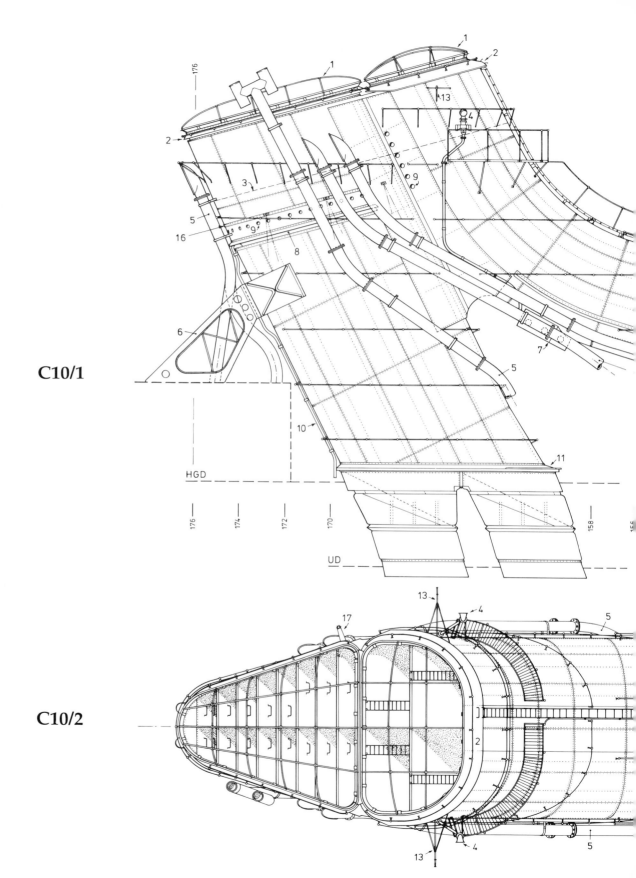

C10/1

C10/2

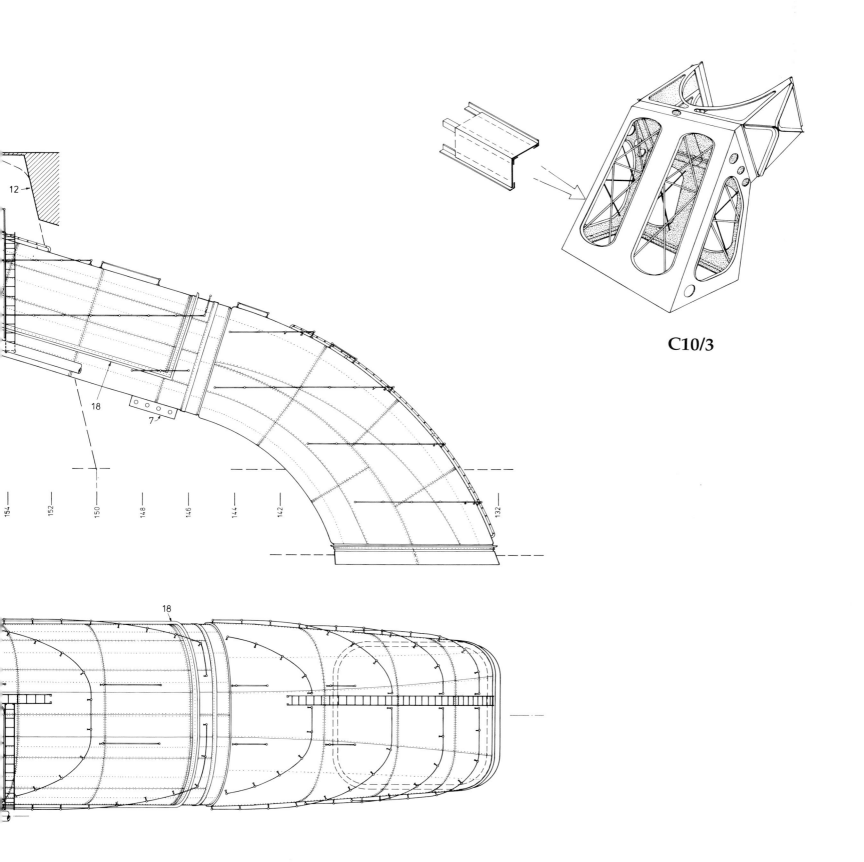

C10/3

12

18

7

154 152 150 148 146 144 142 132

18

C10/4   Port side profile (scale 1/100)

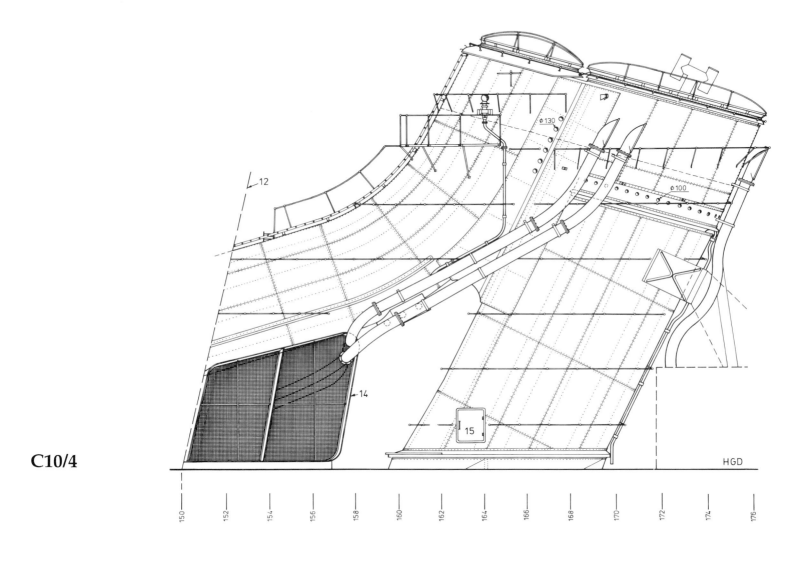

C10/4

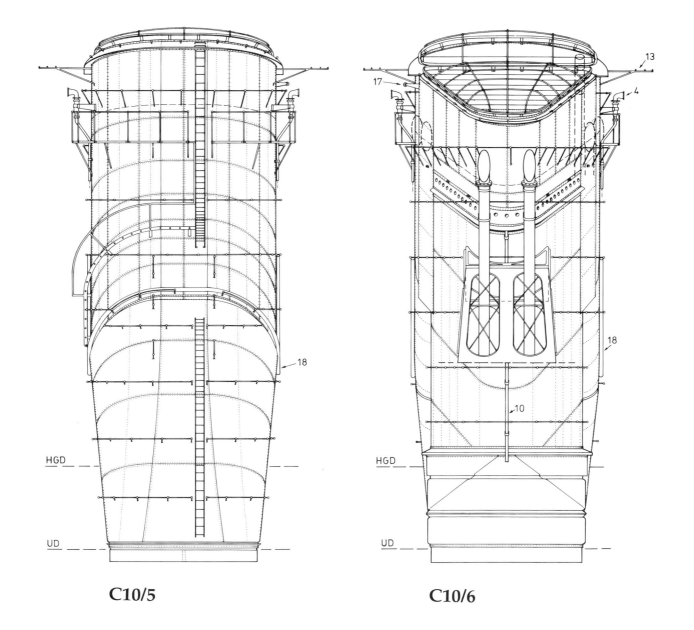

C10/5

C10/6

C Superstructure

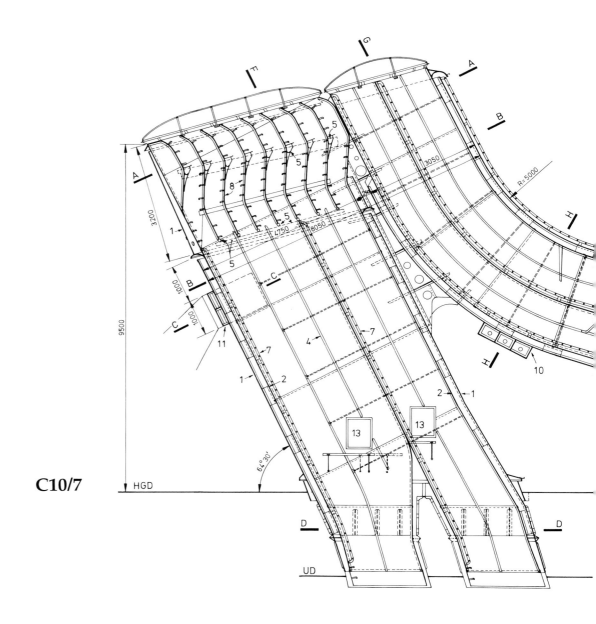

C10/7

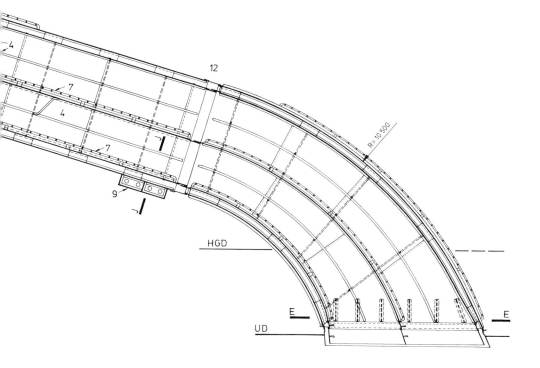

R= 10 500

12

7

4

7

9

HGD

E   E

UD

103

C Superstructure

C10/8　Transverse sections of upper part
　　　　(scale 1/100)
1　Casing
2　Uptake
3　Division plate
4　Inner framing (framework,
　　skeleton of the structure of steel
　　pipes)
5　Rain gutter
6　Baffle plates
7　Inspection ladder
8　Clamp
9　Support framing (fore)
10　Support framing (middle)
11　Support framing (rear)
12　Expansion joint
13　Removable hatch

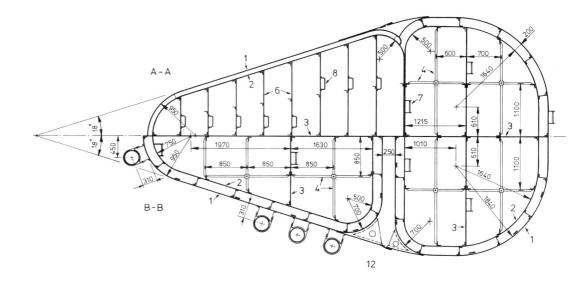

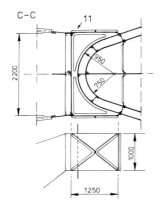

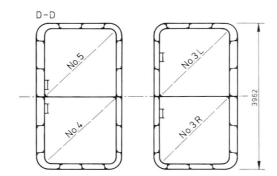

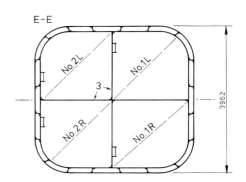

C10/8

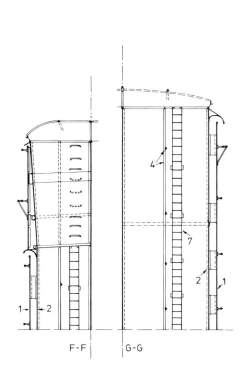

F-F

G-G

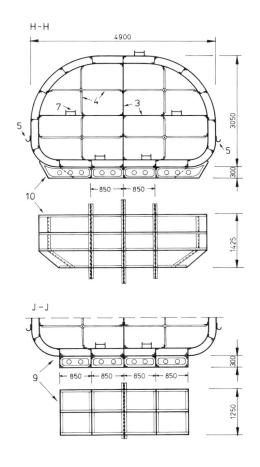

H-H

J-J

C Superstructure

C11   TYPICAL FUNNEL STEEL PLATE JOINTS

C11/1   *Riveted joint of casing – upper part of funnel (scale 1/5)*

C11/2   *Welded joint of uptake – upper part of funnel (scale 1/5)*

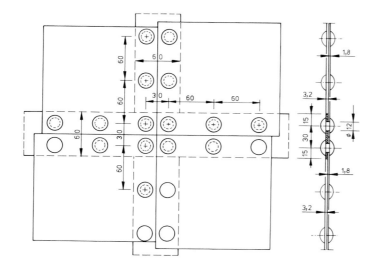

C11/1

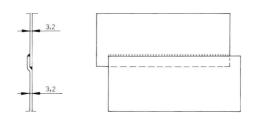

C11/2

C11/3   Screw and rivet joint of casing – lower
         part of funnel (scale 1/5)
C11/4   Welded joint of uptake – lower part of
         funnel (scale 1/5)

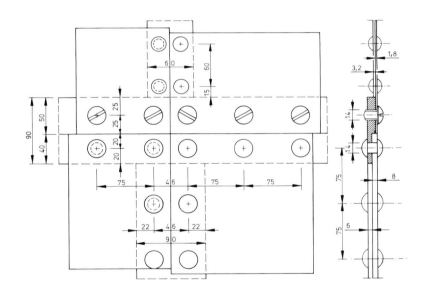

C11/3

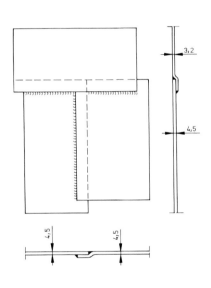

C11/4

C Superstructure

C12   AFTER FUNNEL – FUNNEL NO 3
C12/1   *Starboard profile (scale 1/100)*
C12/2   *Plan (scale 1/100)*
C12/3   *Front elevation (scale 1/100)*
C12/4   *Rear elevation (scale 1/100)*
  1   Frame for canvas cover
  2   Hood
  3   Lower limit to black funnel
        topping
  4   Smoke pipe of donkey boiler
  5   Steam pipe
  6   Air space with rain cover
  7   Ventilation holes
  8   Scupper pipe
  9   Lower rain cover
 10   Funnel stay band eyes
 11   Small roller crane
 12   Removable hatch (only on port
        side)
C12/5   *Longitudinal section (scale 1/100)*

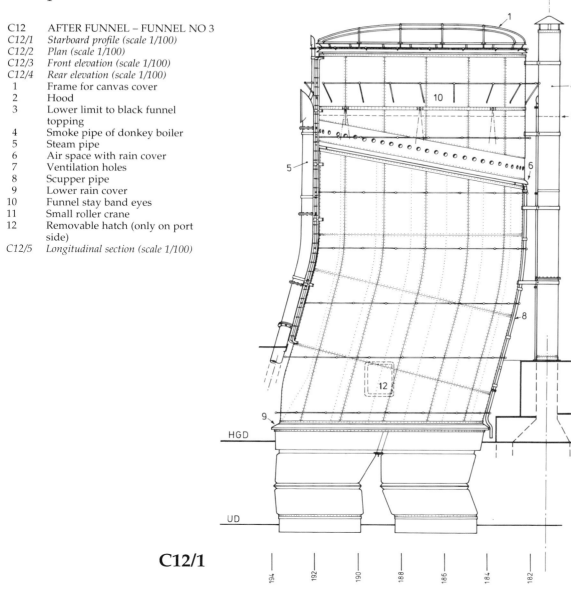

C12/1

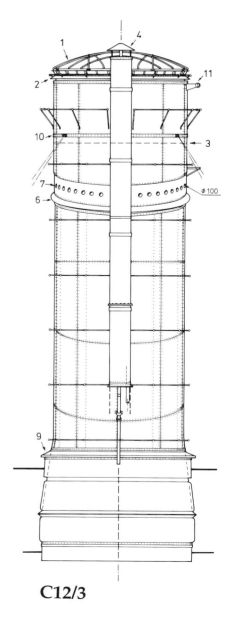

C12/3

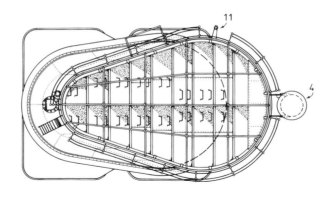

C12/2

108

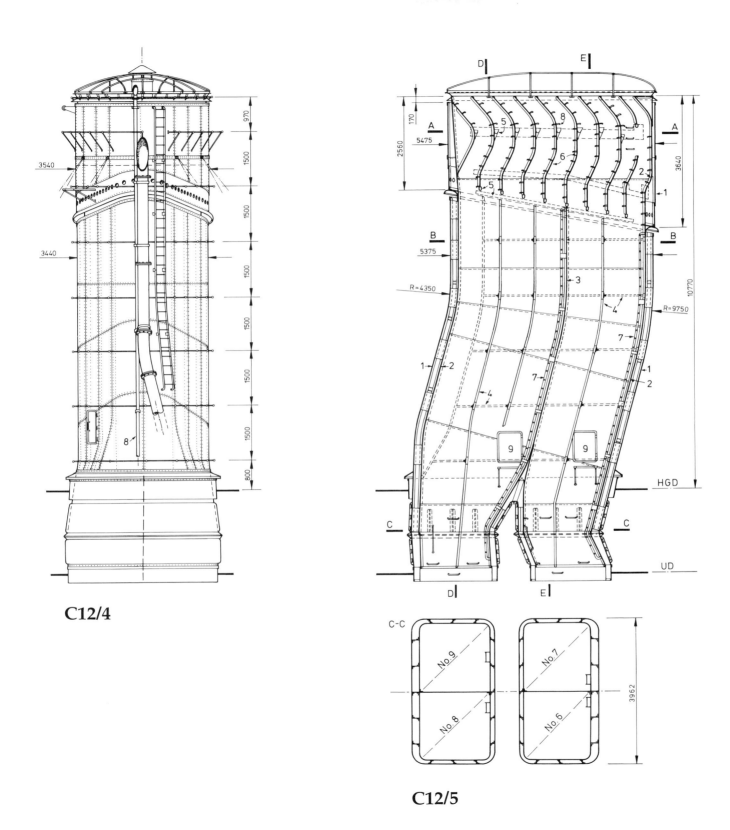

C12/4

C12/5

C Superstructure

C12/6	*Section (horizontal) (scale 1/75)*
1	Casing
2	Uptake
3	Division plate
4	Inner framing
5	Rain gutter
6	Baffle plates
7	Inspection ladder
8	Clamp
9	Removable hatch
10	Smoke pipe of donkey boiler
C12/7	*Transverse section of rear funnel (scale 1/100)*
C12/8	*View of rear funnel upper rail (no scale)*
C12/9	*View of funnel stay band with eyes (no scale)*
C12/10	*View of lower handrails (no scale)*

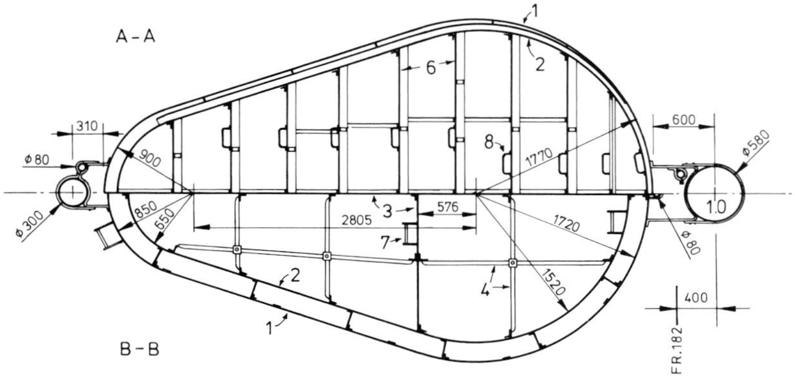

C12/6

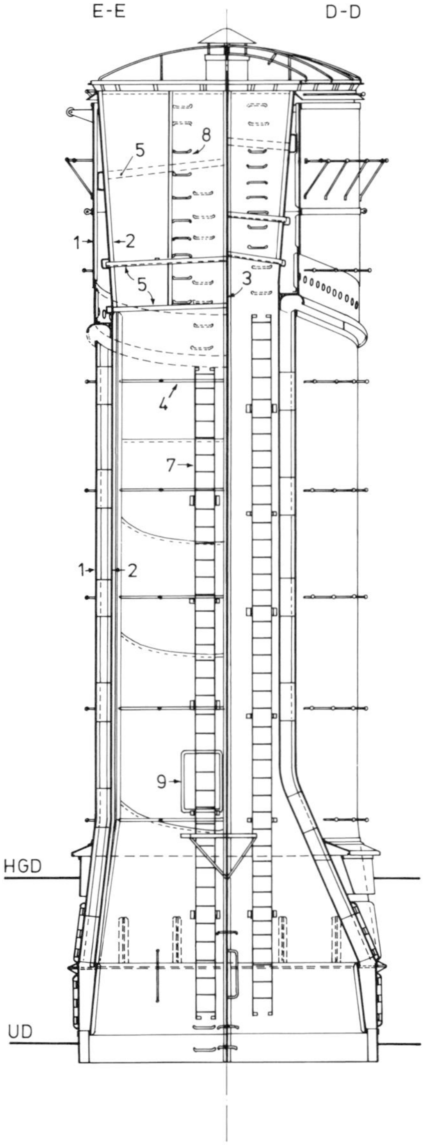

C12/7

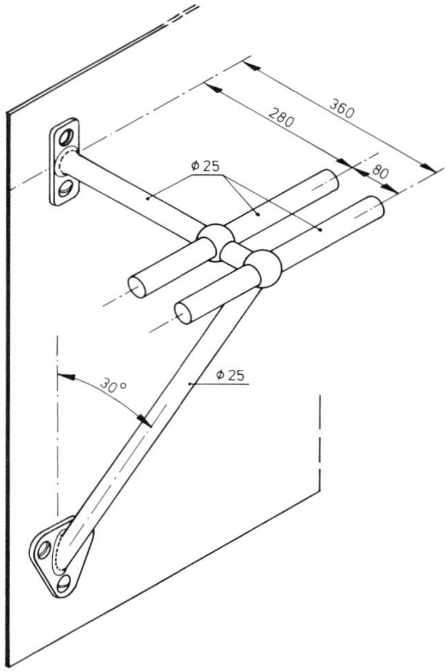

C12/8

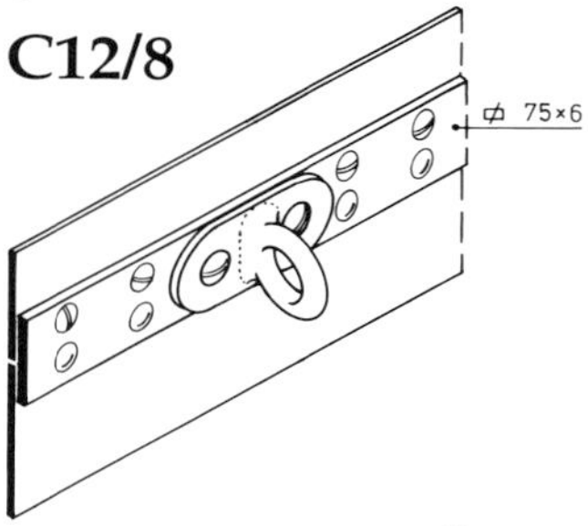

C12/9

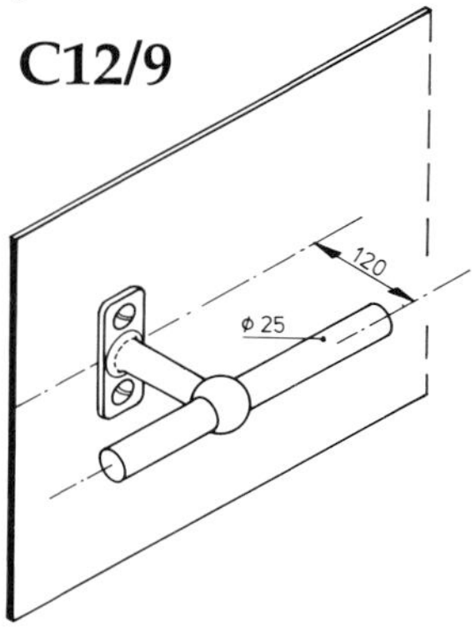

C12/10

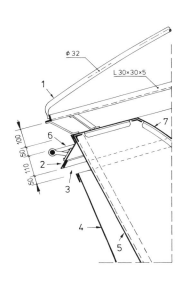

C13/1

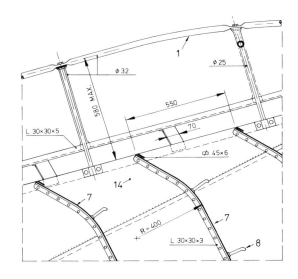

C13/2

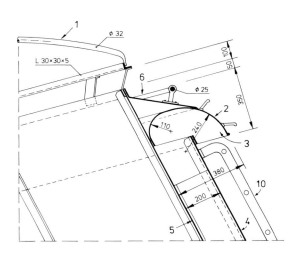

C13/3

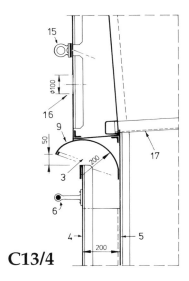

C13/4

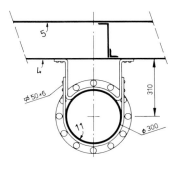

C13/5

C Superstructure

C14 DETAILS OF AFTER FUNNEL
(see key below)
C14/1 *Detail of air space (scale 1/20)*
C14/2 *Section of upper fore part (scale 1/20)*
C14/3 *Section of lower fore part (scale 1/20)*
C14/4 *Section of aft part (scale 1/20)*
1 Frame
2 Hood
3 Air space
4 Casing
5 Uptake
6 Handrail
7 Baffle plates
8 Clamp
9 Air space cover
10 Ladder
11 Steam pipe with support
12 Smoke pipe of donkey boiler
(removed in 1938–39
reconstruction)
13 Drain pipe (scupper pipe)
14 Division plate
15 Funnel stay band with eyes
16 Ventilation holes
17 Rain gutter
C14/5 *Detail of baffle plate for furnace gas
(smoke brace) (scale 1/5)*

C15 DETAIL OF DIVISION PLATES
(no scale)
1 Division plates
2 Baffle plates
3 Inner framing made of steel angle
bars and pipes

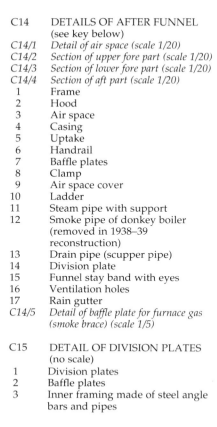
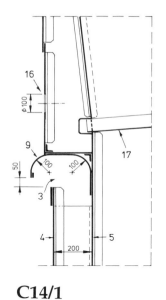

C14/1

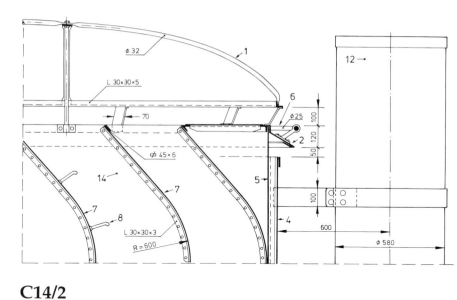

C14/2

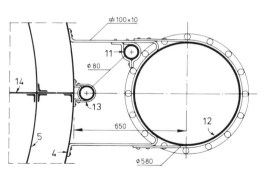

C14/3

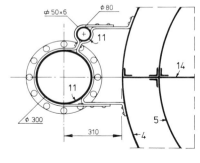

C14/4

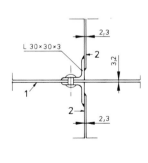

C14/5

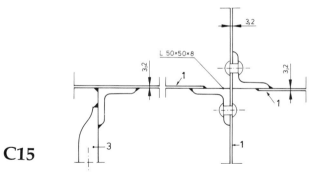

C15

112

C16   HANGAR SUPERSTRUCTURE,
        AUGUST 1932

C16/1   *Plan (scale 1/150)*

C16/2   *Starboard elevation without 4.5m*
        rangefinder (scale 1/150)

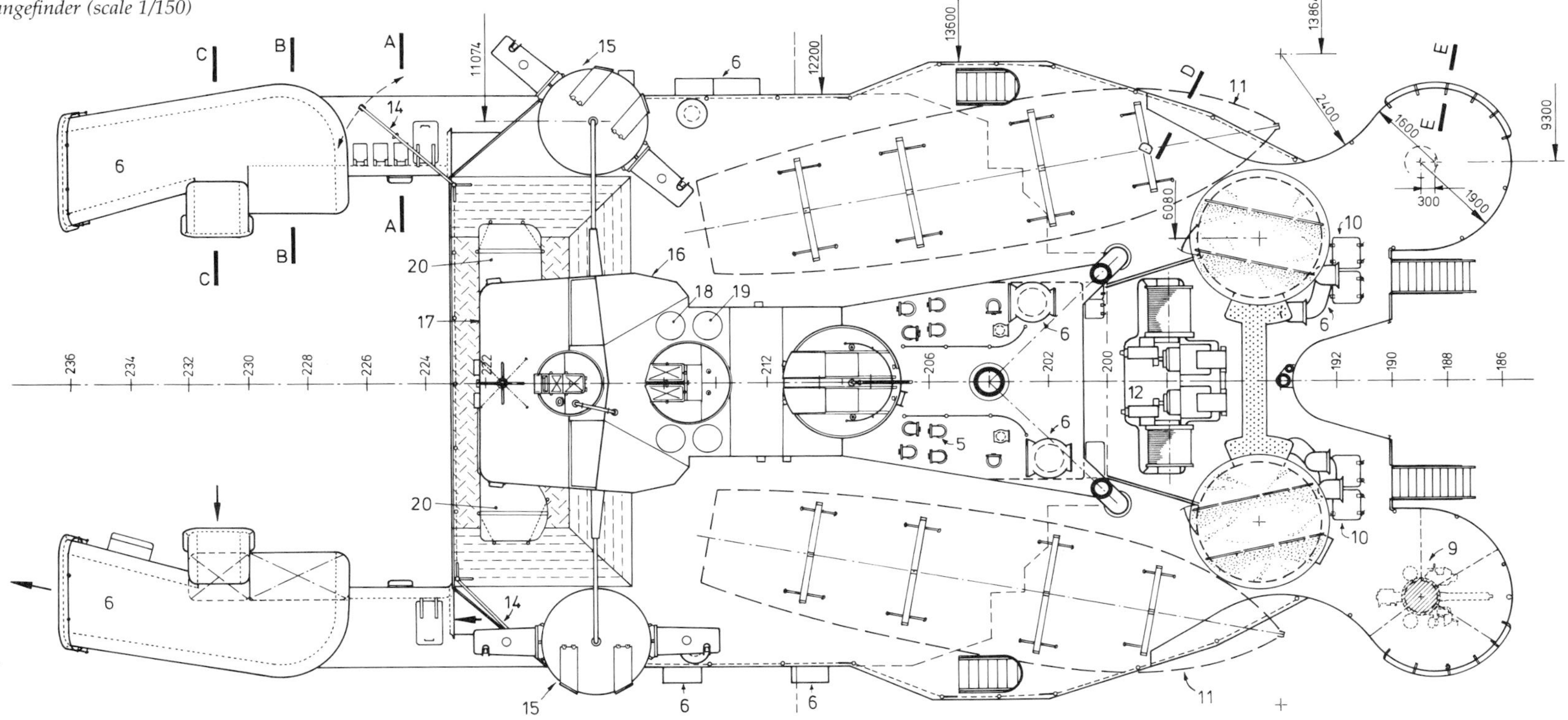

C16/1

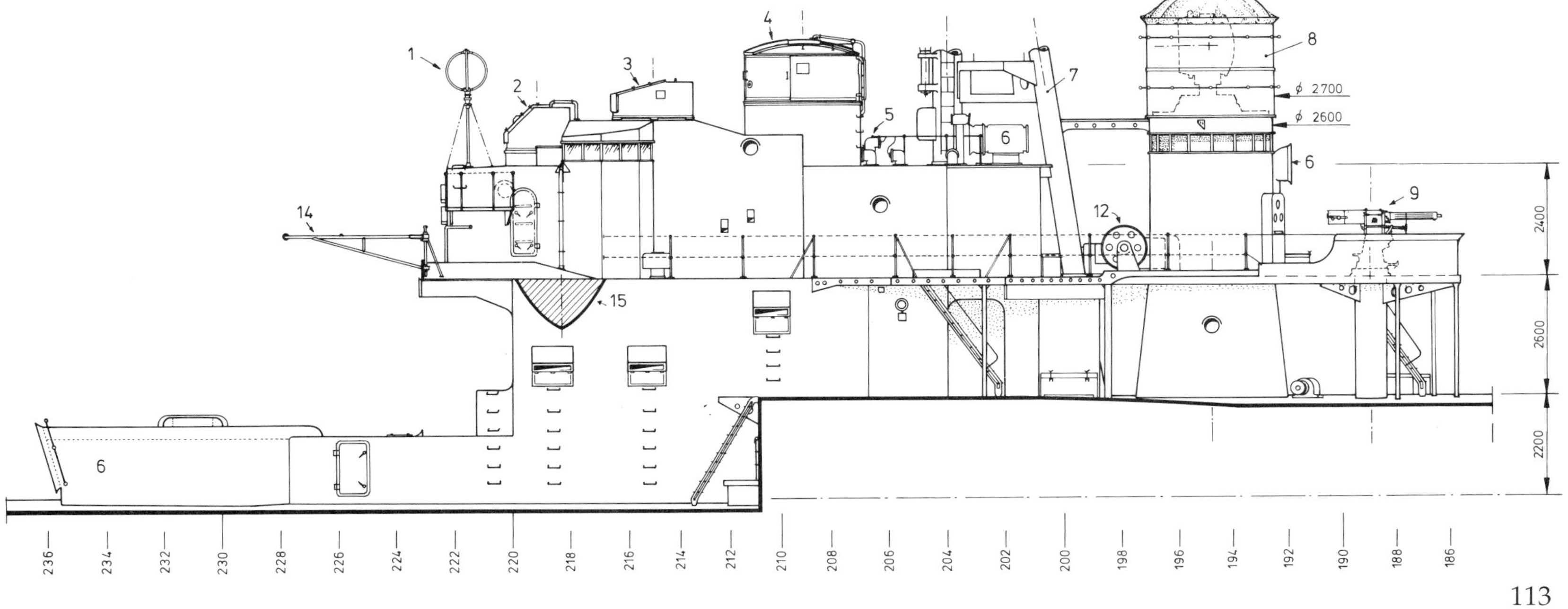

C16/2

C Superstructure

1   Goniometer antenna
2   Protected lookout position
3   Searchlight control position
4   Auxiliary main armament director tower – *14 Shiki*
5   Antenna lead connecting tube
6   Ventilators
7   Mainmast
8   Searchlight tower with 'SU' *Shiki* 110cm searchlight protected by

blast screen and canvas roof. In middle section lookout position, in lower section store.
9   40mm 62cal 'HI' *Shiki Kiju* (Vickers type 2pdr Mk VIII) machine-gun
10   40mm MG ammunition box
11   12m motor launch stand
12   Crane winch
13   Hangar for two seaplane, closed

by canvas cover
14   Auxiliary small crane
15   4.5m HA rangefinder – *14 Shiki*
16   Torpedo director tower (note scuttle on port side)
17   Rear fire control room
18   Peep hole (covered
19   Exhaust hole (covered)
20   Portable 1.5m rangefinder

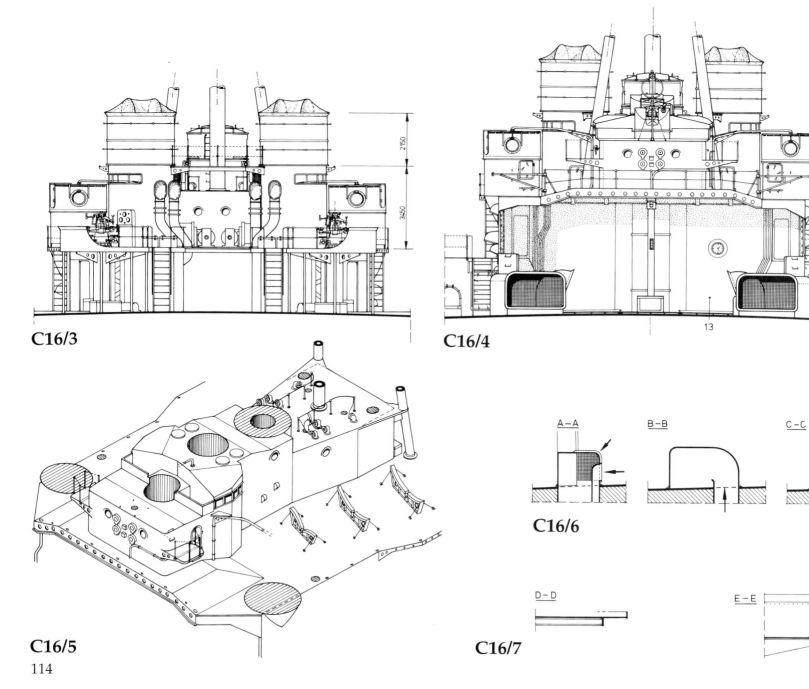

C16/3

C16/4

C16/5

C16/6

C16/7

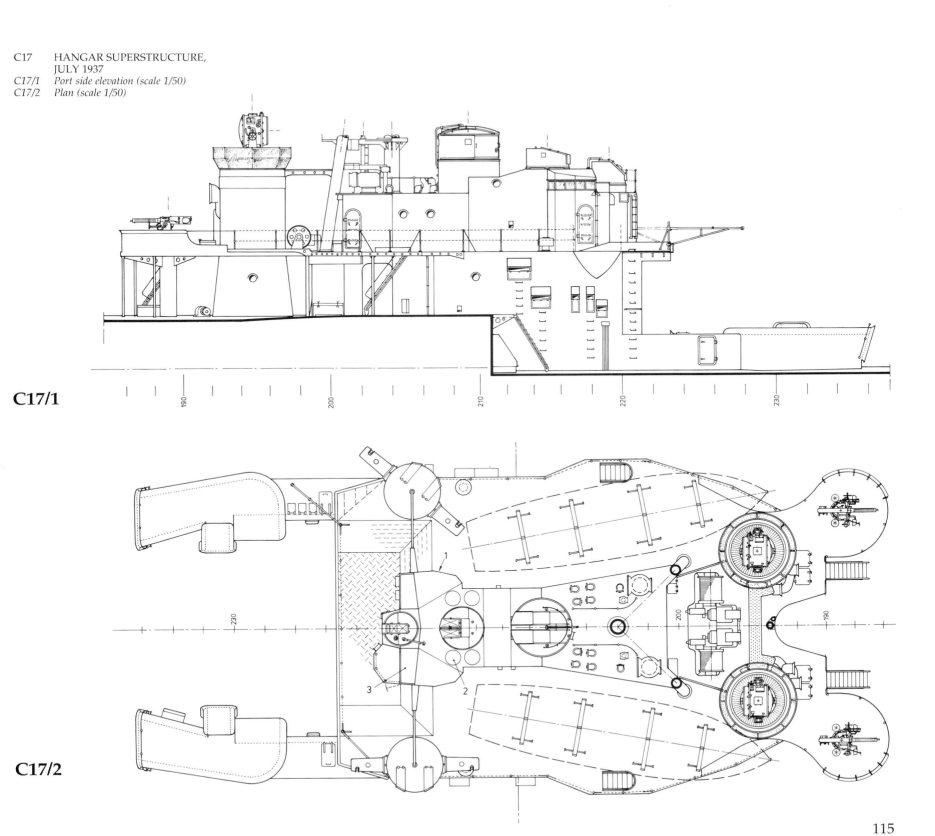

C17   HANGAR SUPERSTRUCTURE,
         JULY 1937
C17/1   *Port side elevation (scale 1/50)*
C17/2   *Plan (scale 1/50)*

C17/1

C17/2

C Superstructure

C17/3 *Rear view as seen from stern*
(scale 1/50)
1   Secondary battery (HA guns)
        communication room
2   Hatch
3   Aircraft store

Reconstruction
–   Rear part of hangar – frame 220–
        222
–   Shortering of upper part of hangar
        – frame 220
–   Removal of blast protection from
        searchlight towers, fitting new
        110cm *92 Shiki* searchlights, closed
        and suppression of lookout
        positions
–   Addition of shields on torpedo
        auxiliary doors (both sides of
        hangar)

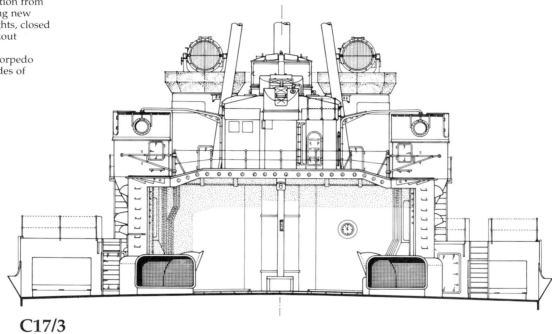

C17/3

D Rig

D1   FOREMAST, 1932–36
D1/1   *View from forward (scale 1/150)*
D1/2   *Top mast 1935–36 (scale 1/150)*
D1/3   *Profile view (scale 1/150)*

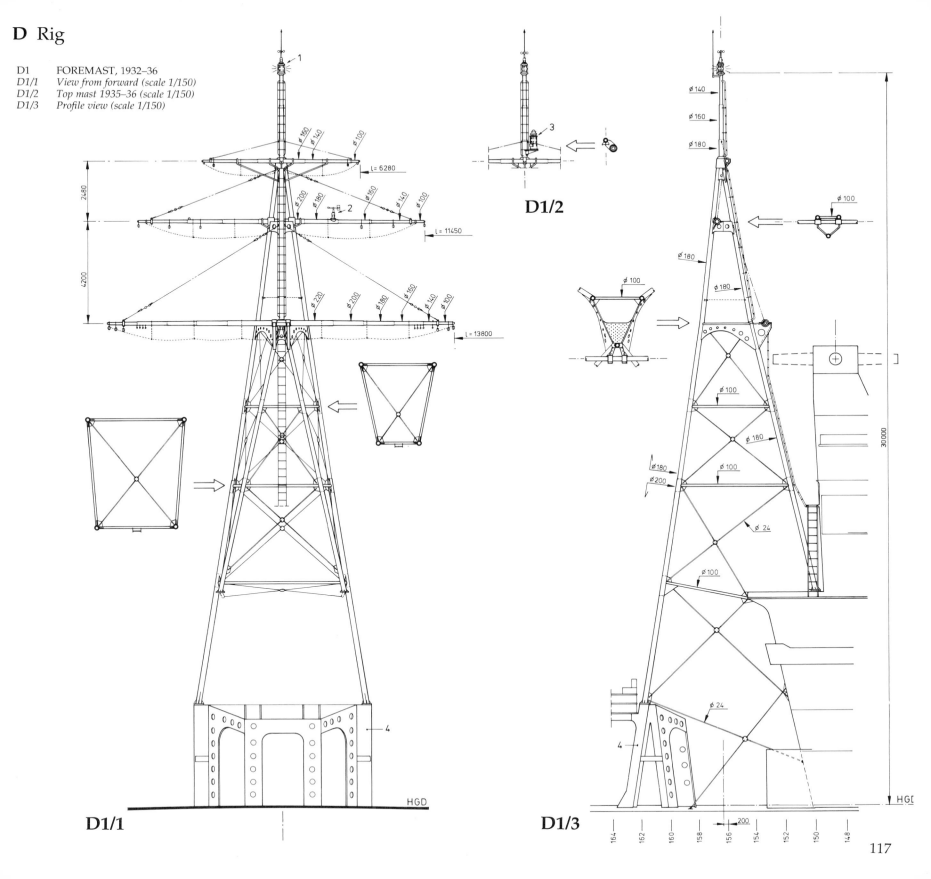

D1/2

D1/1

D1/3

117

D Rig

D1/4 Plan (scale 1/150)
1 Masthead light with wind strength indicator
2 Wind direction indicator
3 2kW daylight signal lamp – former position on roof under main 4.5m rangefinder – both sides (second lamp fitted on mainmast)
4 Support of mast and fore funnel
D1/5 Details of mast truss joint (no scale)
1 Mast leg
2 Joining sleeve
3 Horizontal construction pipe
4 Plate
5 Ring
6 Stay

D2 FOREMAST AFTER REFIT, JULY 1937
D2/1 View from forward with plans of platforms (scale 1/150)

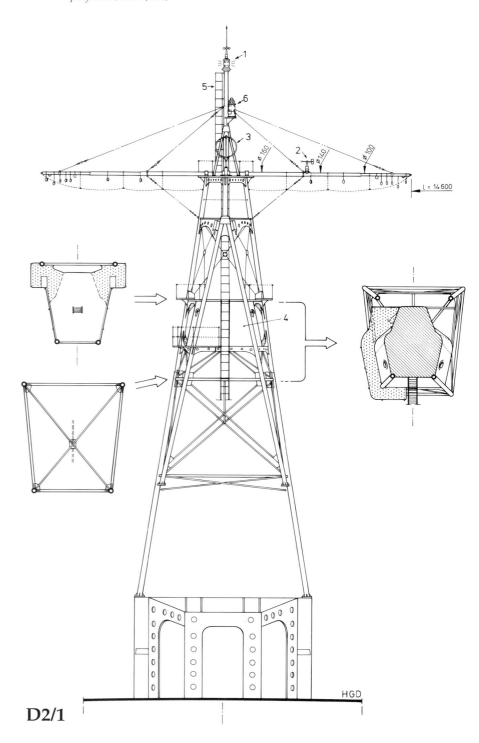

D1/4

D1/5

D2/1

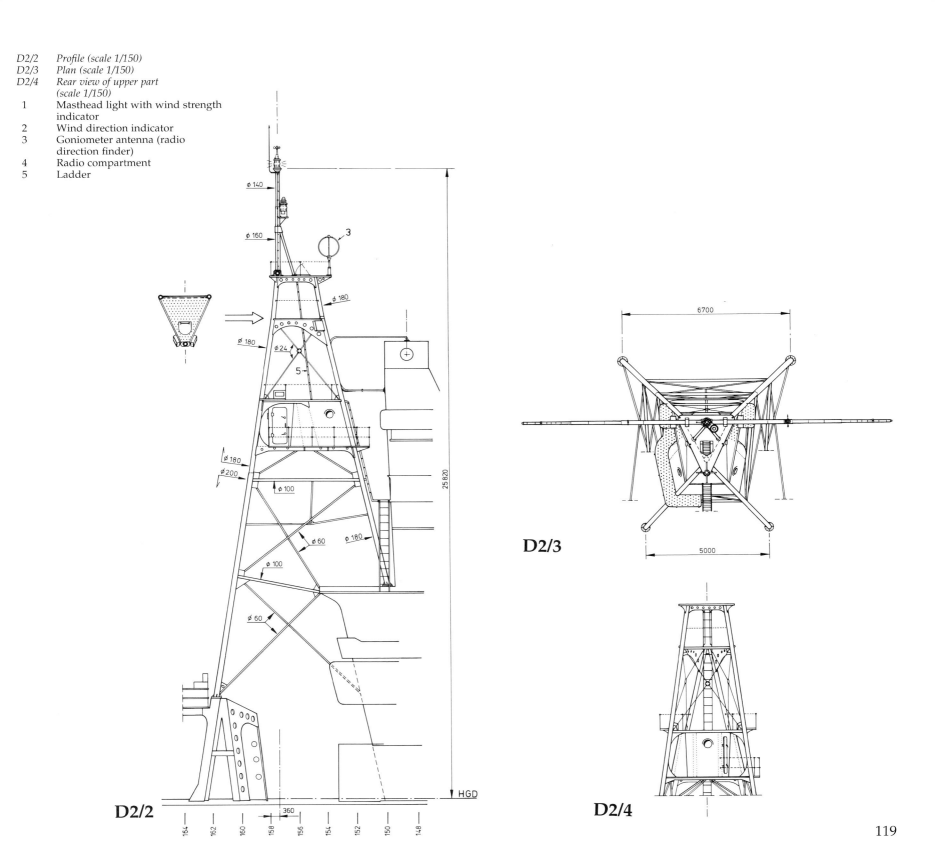

D2/2   Profile (scale 1/150)
D2/3   Plan (scale 1/150)
D2/4   Rear view of upper part
        (scale 1/150)
1   Masthead light with wind strength
        indicator
2   Wind direction indicator
3   Goniometer antenna (radio
        direction finder)
4   Radio compartment
5   Ladder

D2/2

D2/3

D2/4

119

D Rig

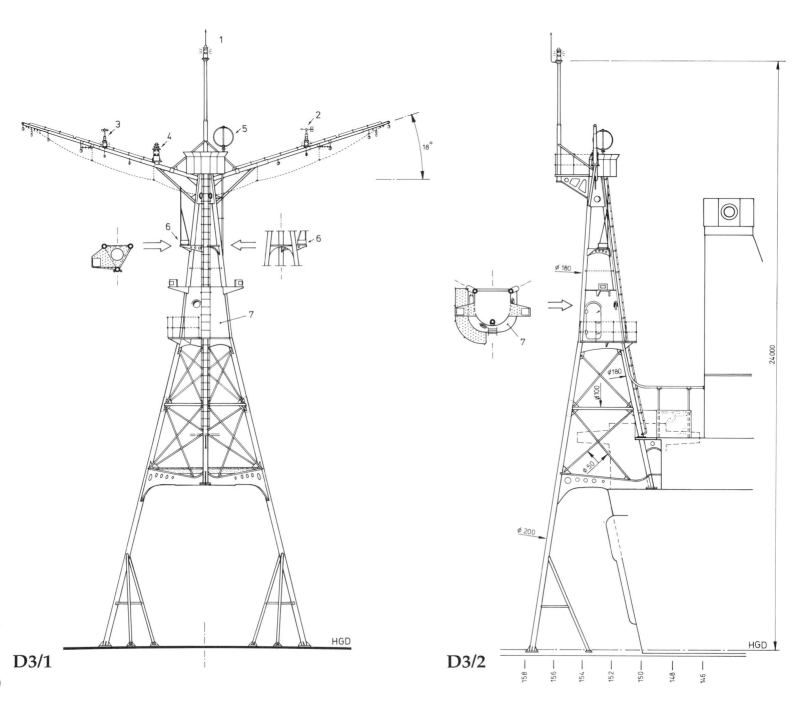

D3/1

D3/2

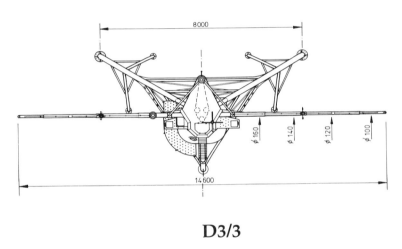

D3/3

D Rig

D4   FOREMAST, SEPTEMBER 1944
D4/1   *Fore view (scale 1/150)*
D4/2   *Profile (scale 1/150)*
D4/3   *Plan (scale 1/150)*
1   Type *21 Gō* radar antenna
2   Type *13 Gō* radar antenna
3   Radio equipment
4   *21 Gō* and *13 Gō* types radar rooms
5   Auxiliary compartment

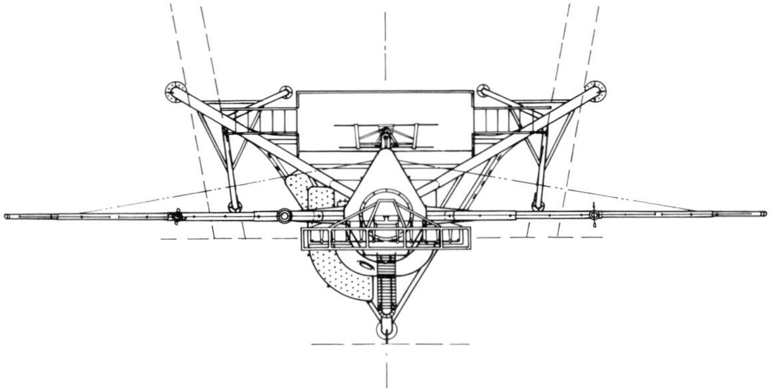

D4/3

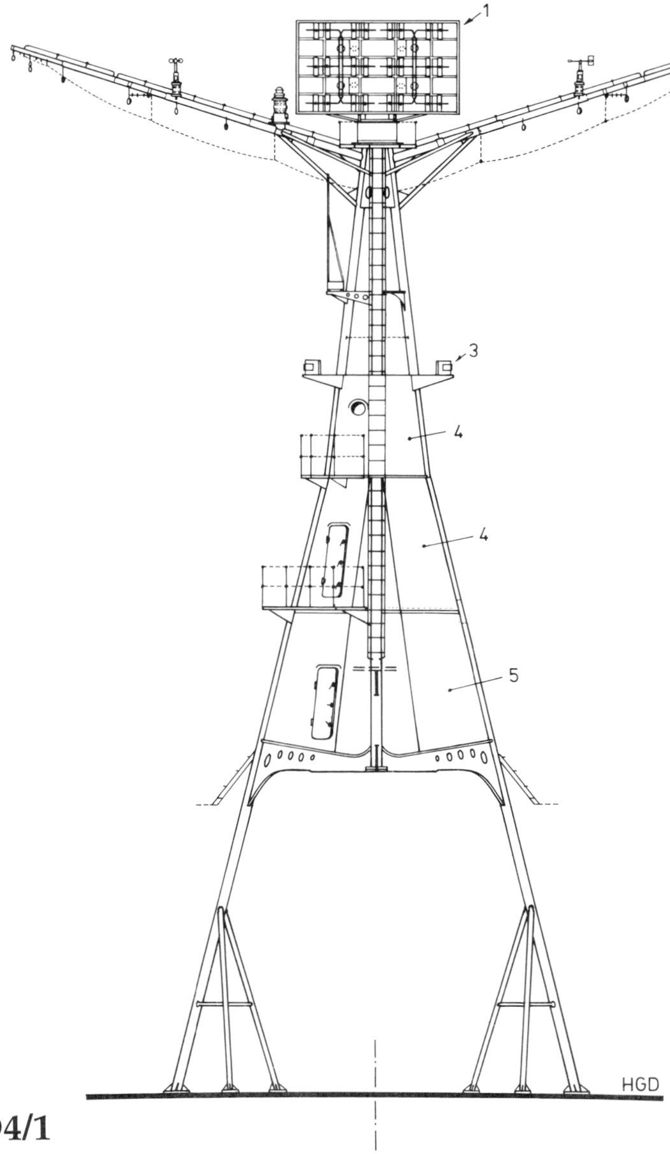

D4/1

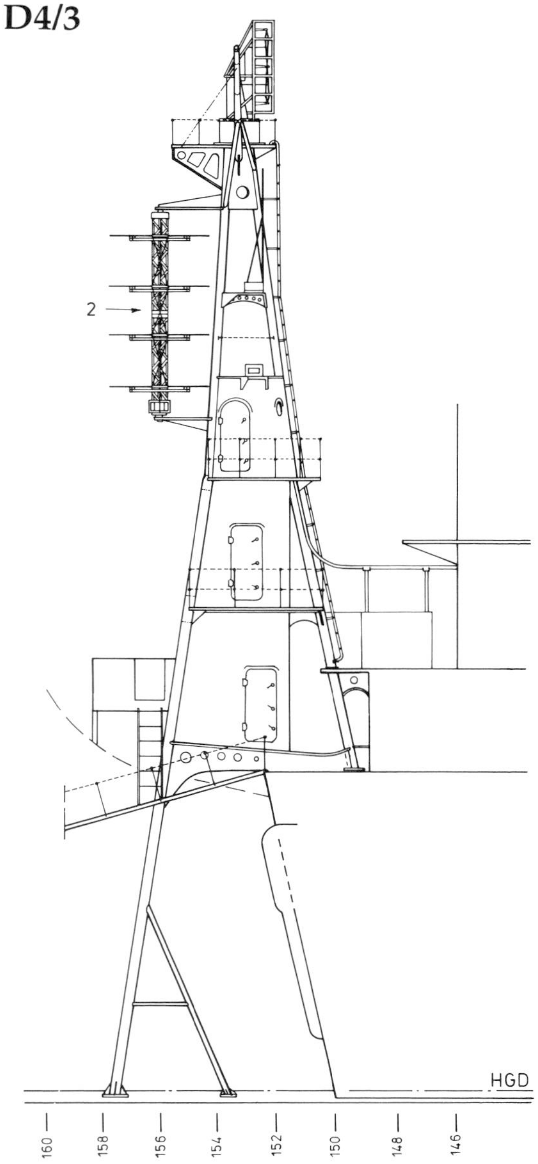

D4/2

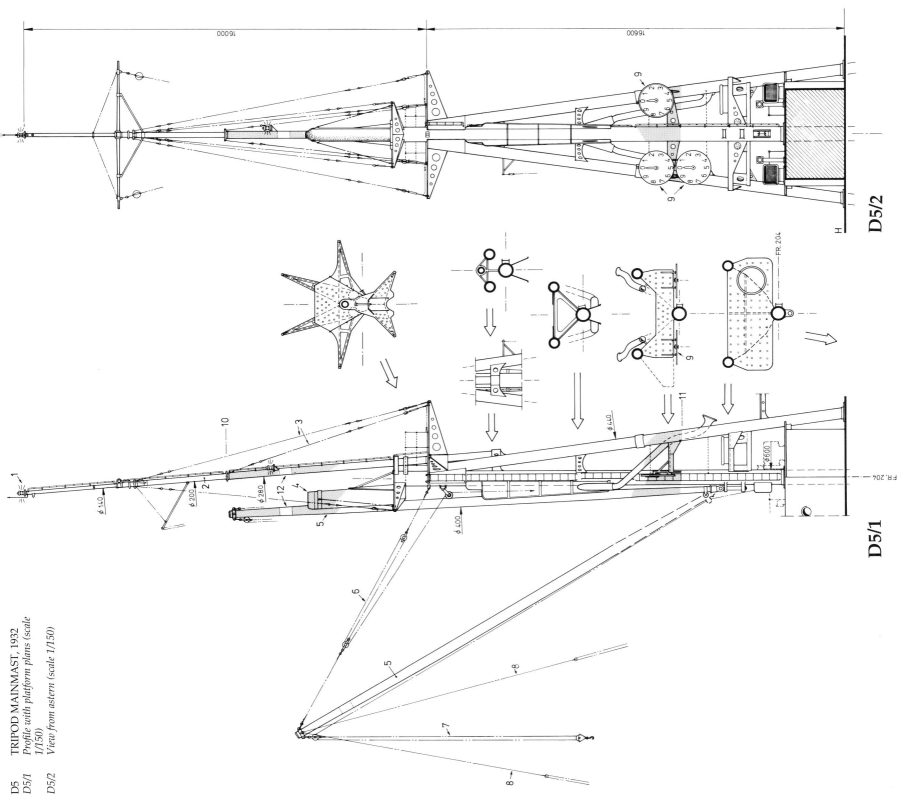

D5/2

D5/1

D5 TRIPOD MAINMAST, 1932
D5/1 Profile with platform plans (scale 1/150)
D5/2 View from astern (scale 1/150)

16000

16600

φ 140

φ 200

φ 280

φ 400

φ 440

φ 600

FR. 204

123

D Rig

D5/3	*Partial view from forward (scale 1/150)*
D5/4	*Plan (scale 1/150)*
D5/5	*View on lower platform (no scale)*
D5/6	*Support of signalling dial plate (no scale)*
D5/7	*Signalling dial plate (scale 1/75)*
D5/8	*Section at head of mainmast (scale 1/40)*
1	Masthead light
2	Main topmast
3	Topmast stay
4	Crutch to hold derrick into mast
5	20m derrick
6	Topping lift
7	Purchase wire
8	Vargs
9	Signalling dial plate – black with white numbers and pointer (starboard dial with white circuit).
10	Upper limit of black marking
11	Lower limit of black marking
12	White stripes
H	Deck of hangar superstructure

D5/3

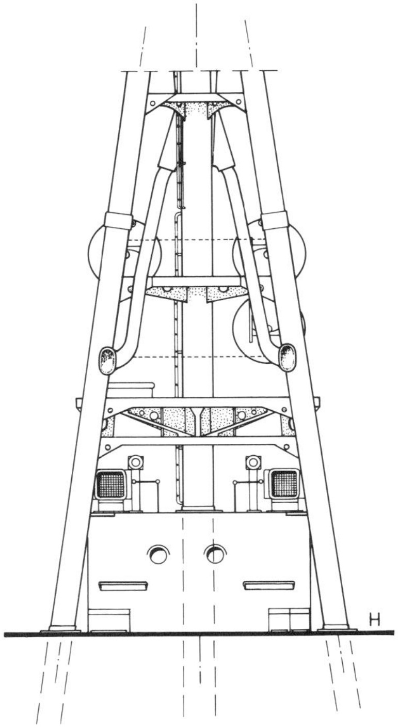

D5/5

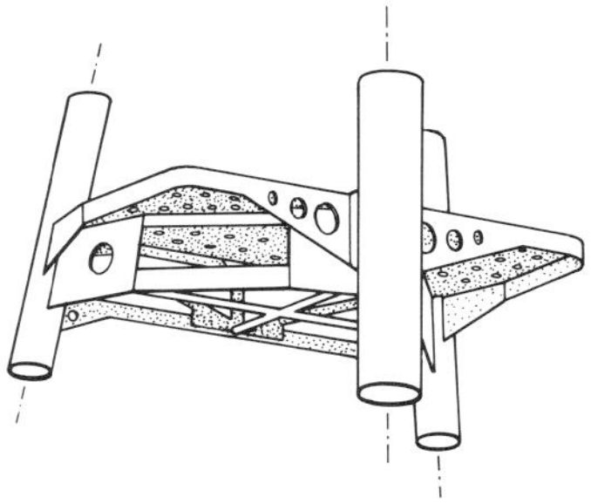

D5/6

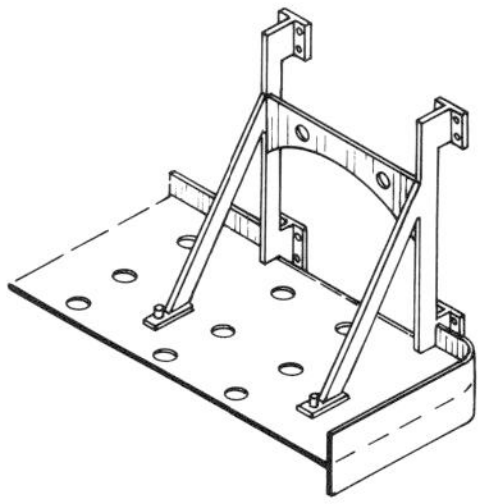

D5/4

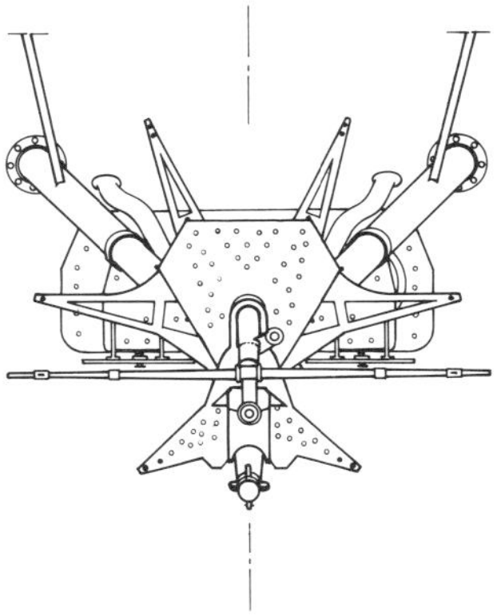

D5/7

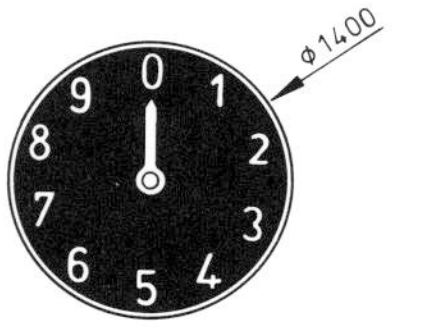

D5/8

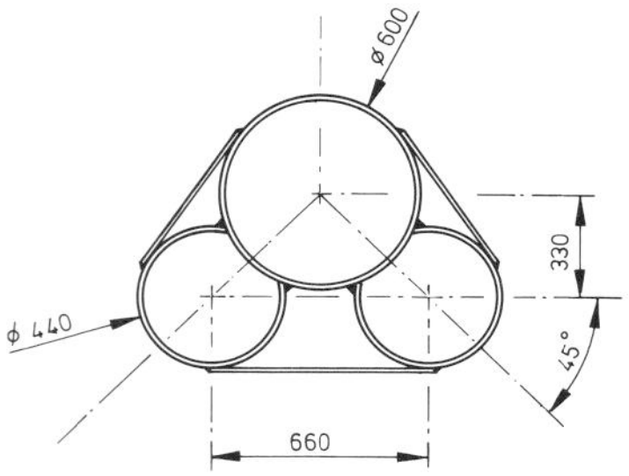

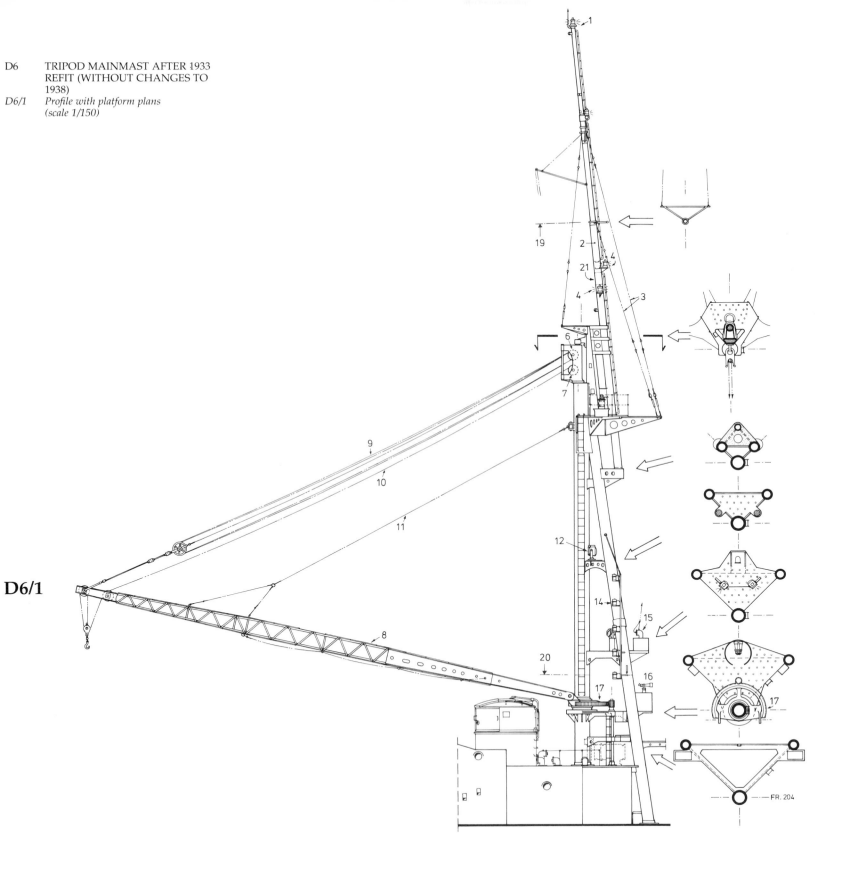

D6   TRIPOD MAINMAST AFTER 1933
        REFIT (WITHOUT CHANGES TO
        1938)

D6/1   *Profile with platform plans*
        (scale 1/150)

D6/1

FR. 204

D Rig

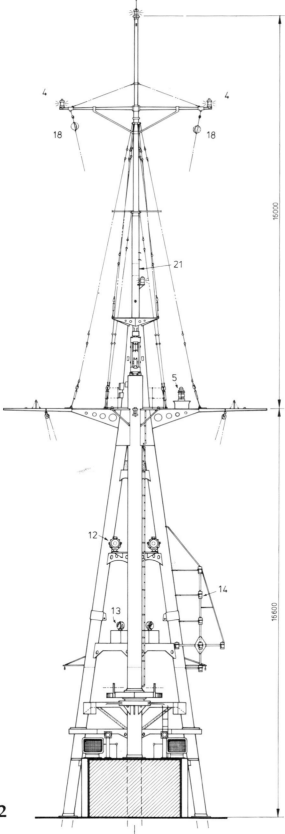

D6/2

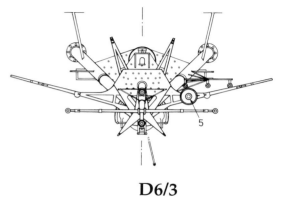

D6/3

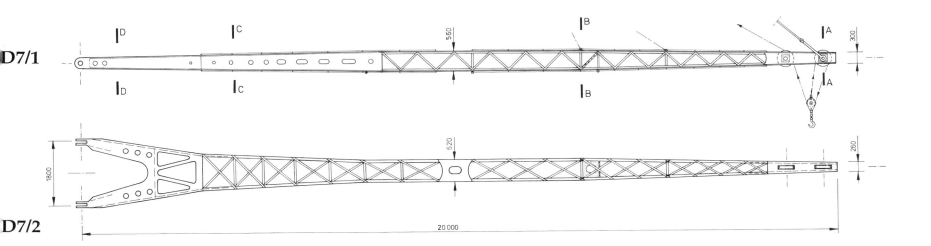

D7/1

D7/2

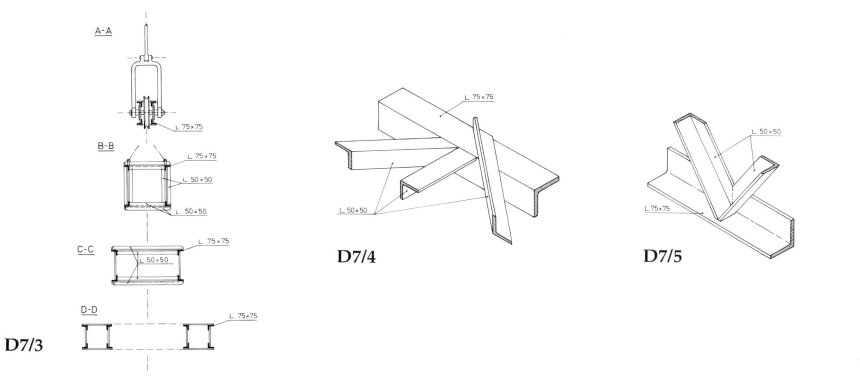

A-A

L 75×75

B-B

L 75×75

L 50×50

L 50×50

C-C

L 75×75

L 50×50

D-D

L 75×75

D7/3

L 75×75

L 50×50

D7/4

L 50×50

L 75×75

D7/5

D Rig

D8   TRIPOD MAINMAST AFTER
RECONSTRUCTION, AUGUST
1939

D8/1   *Profile (scale 1/150)*

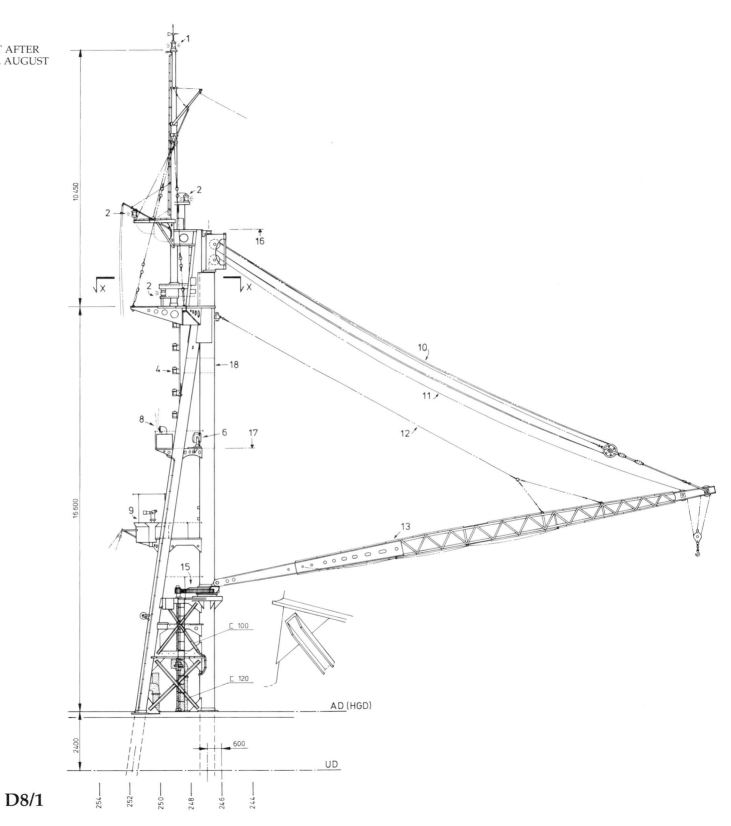

D8/1

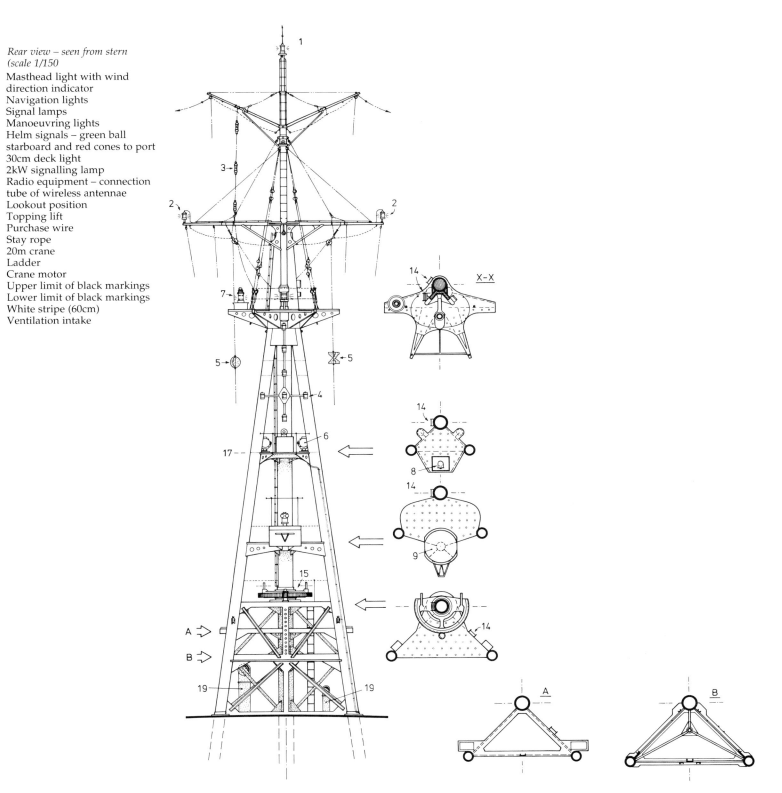

D8/2

D Rig

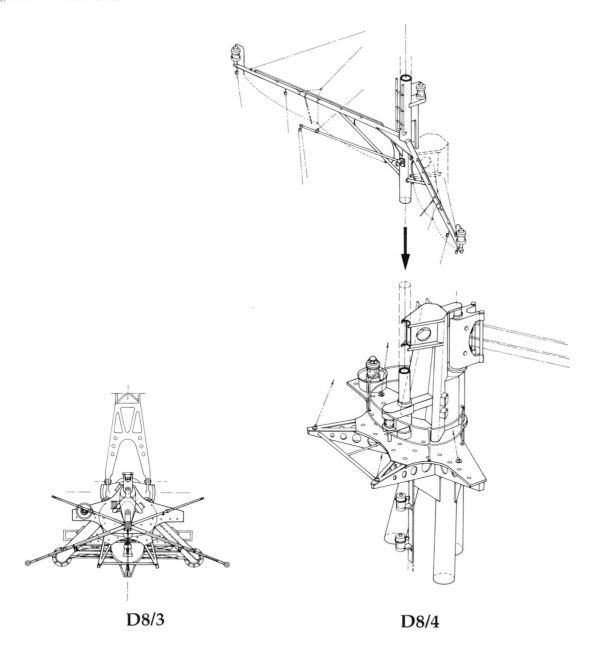

R.

G.

R.

G. W. G.

R.

D8/5

D8/3

D8/4

E Armament

E1   NO 1 20.3cm 50cal *3 NENDO
SHIKI TURRET, MODEL 'E'
MOUNT, 1932
E1/1   *Profile view (scale 1/75)*
E1/2   *Plan (scale 1/75)*

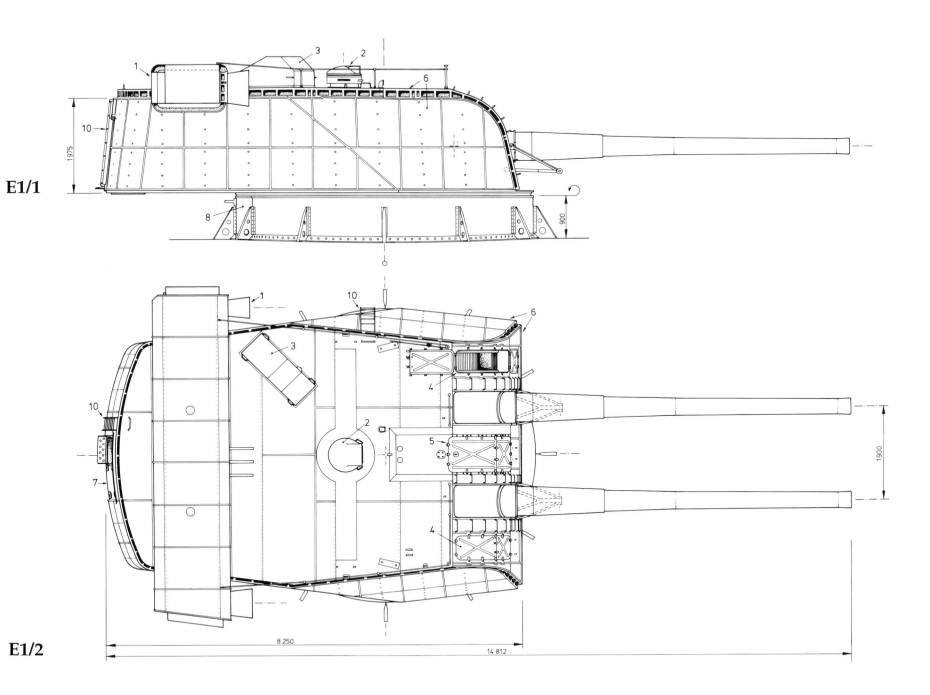

E1/1

E1/2

E Armament

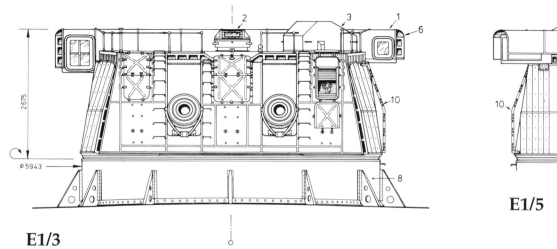

E1/3

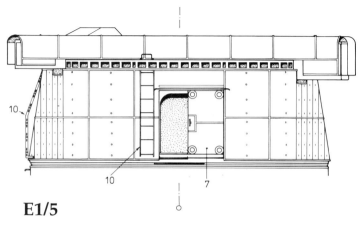

E1/5

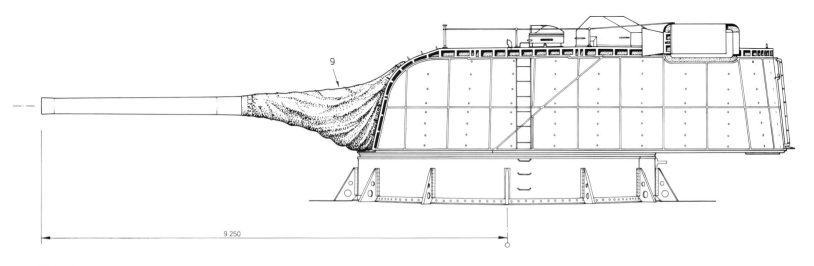

E1/4

E2   NO 2 20.3cm TURRET – AFTER
      RECONSTRUCTION, AUGUST
      1939 – WITH TRIPOD AERIAL
      MAST

E2/1   Profile view (scale 1/75)

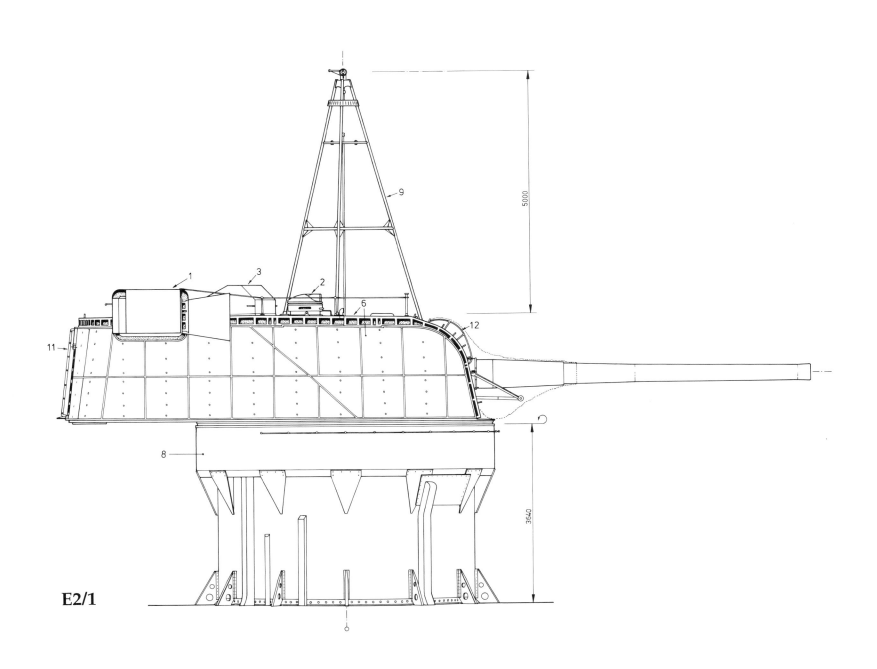

E2/1

E Armament

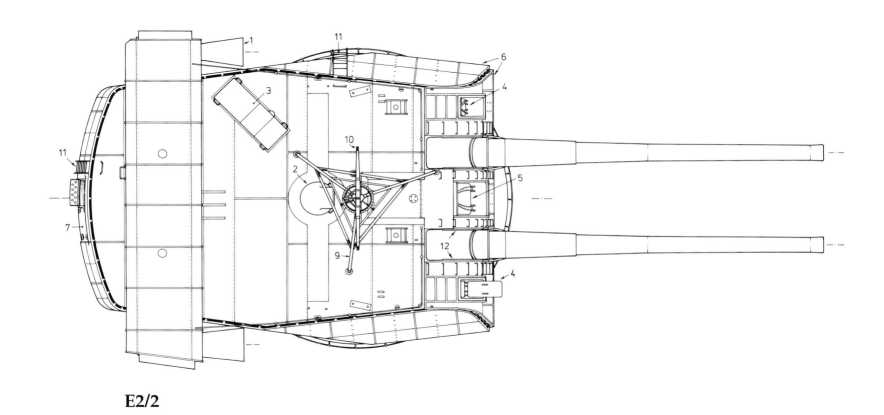

E2/2

E2/3   Front elevation (sale 1/75)
E2/4   Rear elevation (scale 1/75)
E2/5   Canvas blast cover, new type
Shorter than in previous version and reinforced
by flexible cord network

E2/6   Side of turret rangefinder with
        enlarged window shield – No 1 turret,
        1937–38, and No 2 turret 1937–45
        (scale 1/75)
1   6m rangefinder – 14 Shiki
2   Gun captain's periscope
3   Exercise aiming device
4   Laying porthole with new type
        window
5   Training porthole with new type
        window

6   Heat resistant steel sheet lagging
7   Sliding armoured doors
8   Barbette (with dimensions
        identical to No 4 turret)
9   Tripod aerial mast
10   Spar – non rotating in relation to
        ship's axis
11   Ladder
12   Stop (limiter) for blast bag

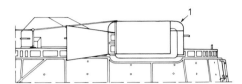

E2/6

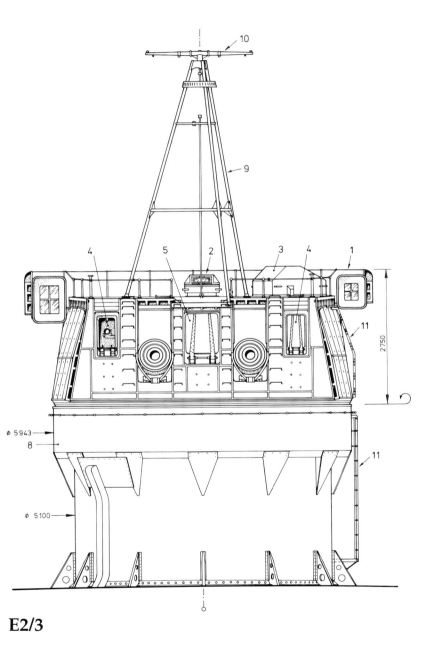

E2/3

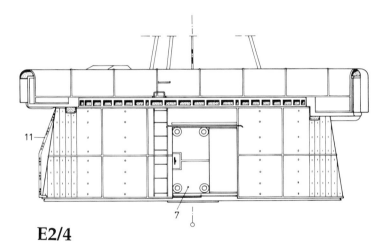

E2/4

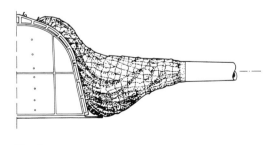

E2/5

135

E Armament

E3   REAR PART OF 20.3cm TURRETS
NO 3 AND NO 5
E3/1   *Elevation (scale 1/75)*
E3/2   *Plan (scale 1/75)*
E3/3   *Rear part of tower No 1 after*
removing casing of rangefinder and
exercise aiming device, 1943 (scale
1/75)
E3/4   *Joint of gunhouse 50mm armour*
plates and steel sheet lagging plates
(no scale)

1   50mm armour plate
2   Heat protection
3   Reinforced strip
4   Axis of turret rotation

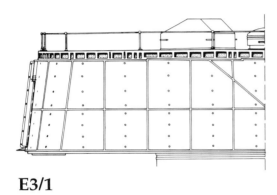

E3/1

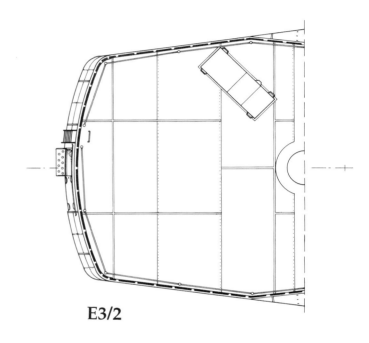

E3/2

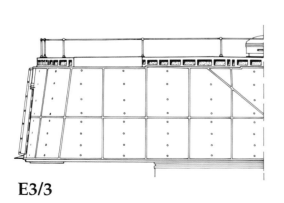

E3/3

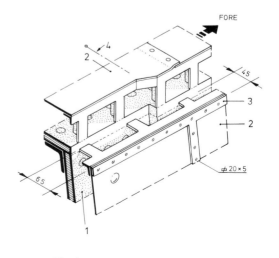

E3/4

E4   TRIPOD AERIAL MAST ON
          20.3cm TURRET NO 2, 1932–38
E4/1   *Profile (scale 1/75)*
E4/2   *Front view of upper part (scale 1/75)*
E4/3   *Plan (scale 1/75)*

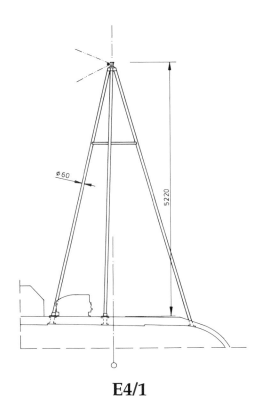

E4/2

E4/1

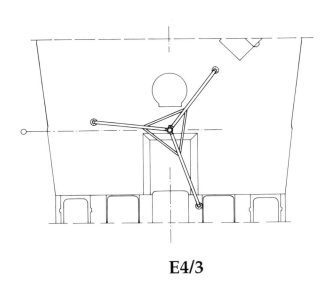

E4/3

E Armament

E5   TRIPOD AERIAL MAST ON
    20.3cm TURRET NO 4, 1932–38
E5/1   Profile (scale 1/75)
E5/2   Rear view – as seen from stern (scale 1/75)
E5/3   Plan (scale 1/75)

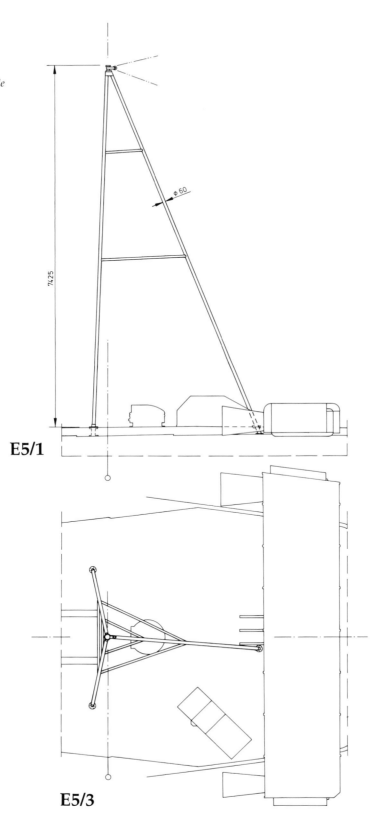

E5/1

E5/3

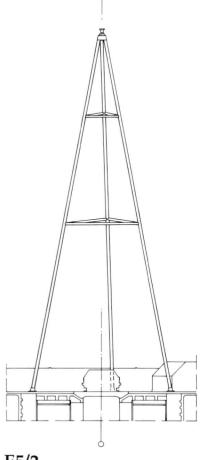

E5/2

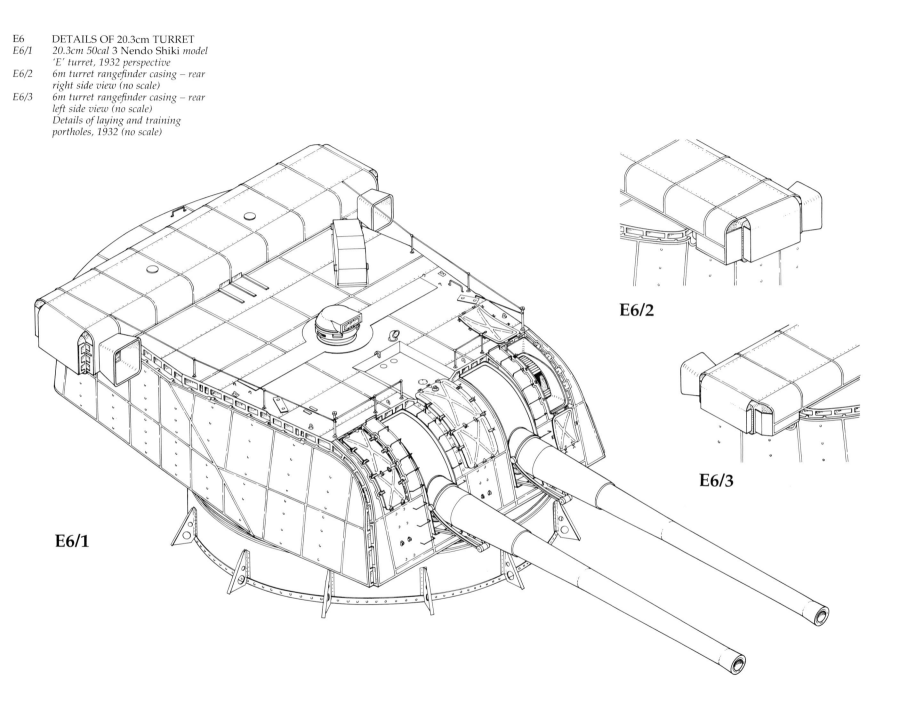

E6 DETAILS OF 20.3cm TURRET
E6/1 *20.3cm 50cal 3 Nendo Shiki* model
'E' turret, 1932 *perspective*
E6/2 *6m turret rangefinder casing – rear*
right side view (no scale)
E6/3 *6m turret rangefinder casing – rear*
left side view (no scale)
Details of laying and training
portholes, 1932 (no scale)

E6/2

E6/3

E6/1

E Armament

E6/4   Side butterfly clip (no scale)
E6/5   Butterfly clip between upper and
        lower covers (no scale)
E6/6   Upper hinge (no scale)
E6/7   Lower hinge (no scale)
E6/8   20.3cm 50cal turret, 1939–45
        (no scale)
E6/9   Casing of removed 6m rangefinder
        (fitted on top of tower bridge) as in
        1939–43 (no scale)

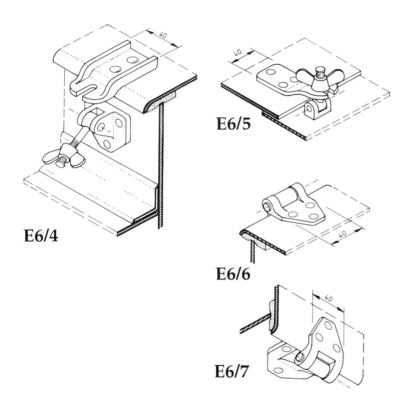

E6/4

E6/5

E6/6

E6/7

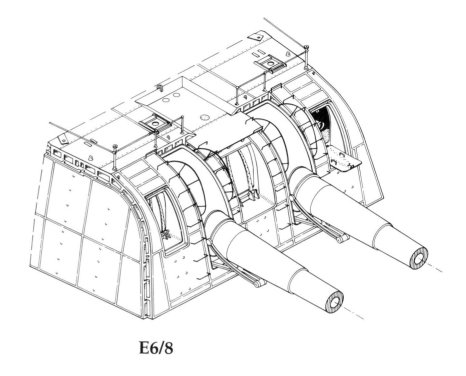

E6/8

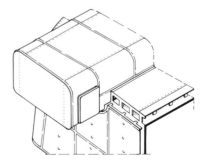

E6/9

E6/10   Turret ladder (no scale)
E6/11   Heat resistant steel sheet lagging –
        detail of upper part (no scale)
E6/12   Heat resistant steel sheet lagging –
        detail of fore part (no scale)

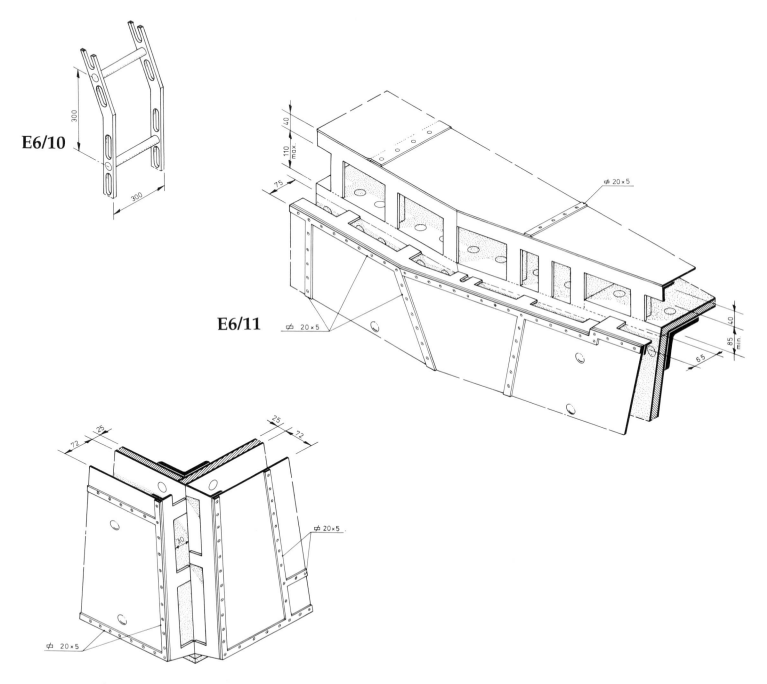

E6/10

E6/11

E6/12

141

E Armament

E7   20.3cm 50cal GUN MOUNTING
      – SECTIONS OF NO 1 TURRET
E7/1   *Internal profile (scale 1/75)*
       See page 143 for key

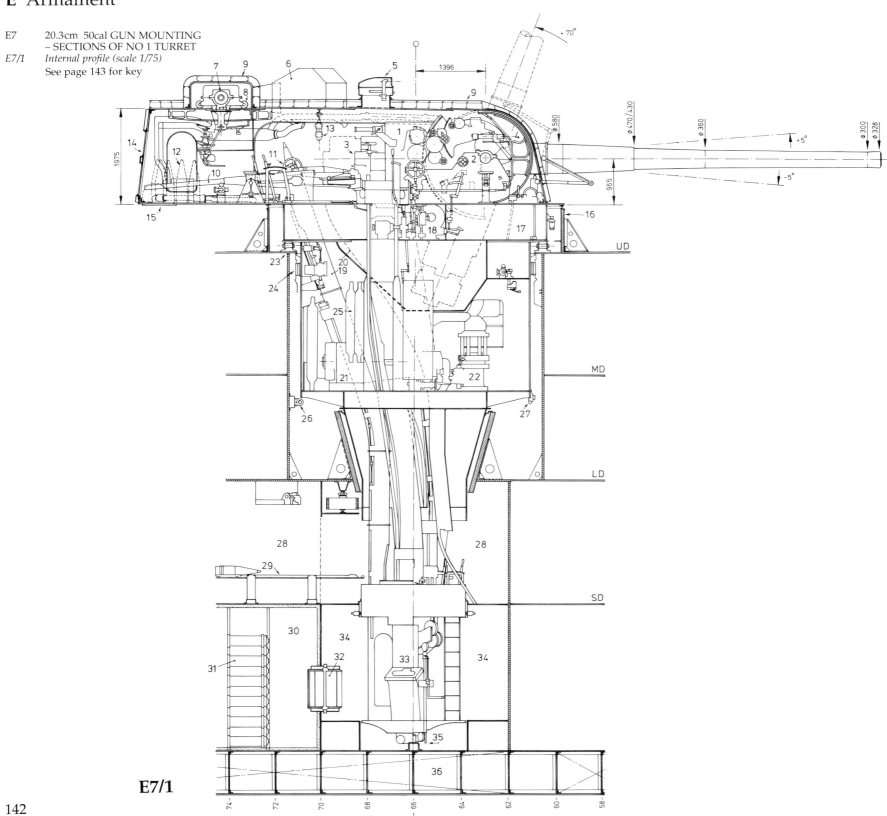

E7/1

142

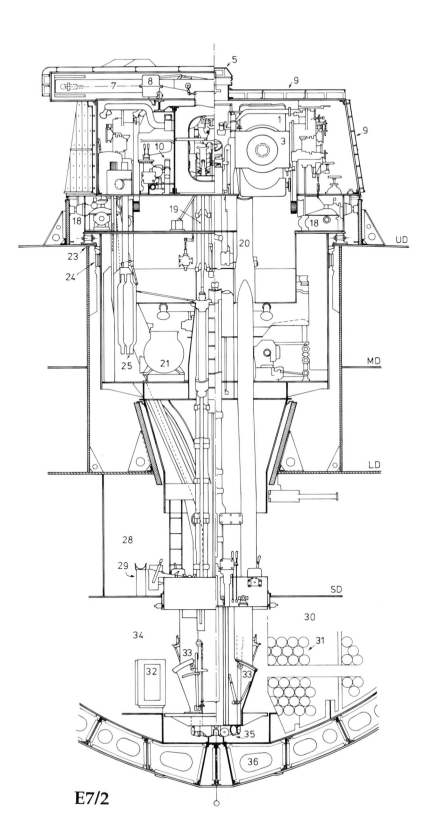

E7/2   *Rear view sections left upper part 6m rangefinder compartment, right part and lower part, central part (scale 1/75)*

1   Gun cradle, dashed line – maximum length of recoil rest positions: turret No 1 = +5°, turret No 3 = +6°, turrets No 2, No 4 and No 5 = +3°
2   Trunnion bearing
3   Breech mechanism
4   Splinter protection
5   Gun captain's periscope
6   Exercise aiming device
7   6m rangefinder
8   Rangefinder truck
9   Heat resistant shield
10   Shell rammer
11   Shell transfer mechanism
12   Auxiliary shells for ready use
13   Radial service crane
14   Armoured door (sliding)
15   Cover plate
16   Barbette
17   Turntable
18   Hydraulic training engine
19   Shell hoist
20   Cordite hoist
21   Motor for pump
22   Pump
23   Turret rollers
24   Training rack
25   Air bottles
26   Limiter of turret rotation – barbette part
27   Limiter of turret rotation – turret part
28   Shell handling room
29   Shell bogie and rail
30   Cordite magazine
31   Cordite stowage with flash-tight canisters
32   Flash-tight scuttle
33   Cordite hoist
34   Powder handling room
35   Cable lead installation
36   Double bottom

E7/2

E Armament

E7/3   20.3cm 50cal turret – plan with turret crew position circle (scale 1/120)

1   Gun captain's position
2   Turret crew commander
3   Bearing number
4   Sighting numbers
5   Gun ranging crew
6   Elevating numbers
7   Powder hoisting numbers
8   Breech workers
9   Hoist number for high angle fire
10   Shell supply numbers
11   Shell hoist numbers
12   Powder handling numbers
13   Loading (charge) numbers
A   Shell hoist for armour-piercing (AP) and high explosive HE shells
B   Shell hoist for high angle fire (AA fire)
C   Powder hoist tube
D   Powder hoist tube for high angle fire
E   Shell rammer
F   6m rangefinder
G   Rangefinder compartment
H   Trunnion bearing
I   Shell stowage for ready use

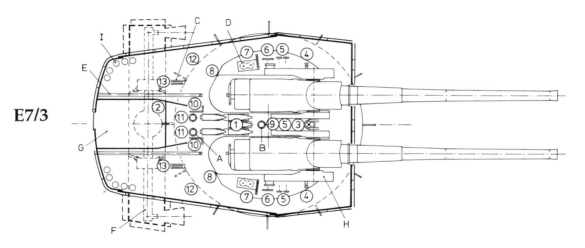

E7/3

E7/4 Scheme of barbette and turret rollers
      (thickness in mm) (scale 1/120)
1   Turret roller
2   Deck support
E7/5 Section AA, side part of barbette and
      turret (scale 1/50)
E7/6 Section BB, rear side of barbette and
      turret (scale 1/50)

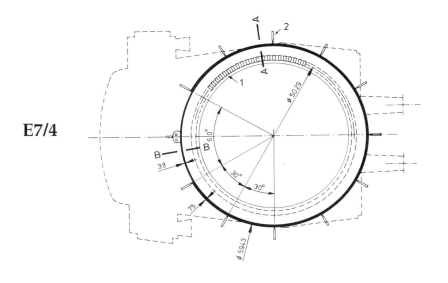

E7/4

A - A

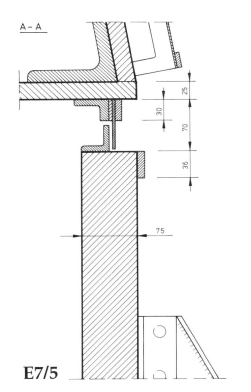

E7/5

B - B

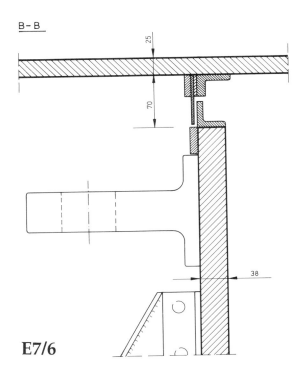

E7/6

145

E Armament

E8   20.3cm AMMUNITION

E8/1   *Type 91 'Hibô Tetsukôdan' 20.3cm AP projectile, weight 125.85kg (scale 1/10)*

E8/2   *Type 91 20.3cm AP projectile – section (scale 1/10)*

1   Hood – special wind-water shield
2   Cap
3   Body
4   Cork lining and wool wrap-around filler
5   Tri-nitro Anisol filler – 3.11kg

6   Fuse – type 13 Mk 5 short delay base fuse
7   Copper rotating bands
8   Base
9   Copper gas-check rings – copper caulking
10   Fuse adapter

E8/3   *20.3cm 3 Shiki 'Sandaikan' AA common projectile Model 3, weight 125.85kg. Number of fragments 246 (198 incendiary fragments and 48 stays) (scale 1/10)*

E8/4   *20.3cm 'Sandaikan' projectile – section (scale 1/10)*

1   Time fuse
2   Projectile head
3   Speed fuse rod
4   Projectile head set screw
5   Quick match
6   Fuse plate
7   Incendiary fragments – rubber thermite

8   Rotating attachment rivet
9   Base block
10   Ejecting charge and black powder
11   Delayed action charge
12   Fuse base
13   Copper rotating bands
14   Detonating fuse (with small delay)
15   Bursting charge (picric acid)
16   Body
17   Base
18   Copper gas-check ring

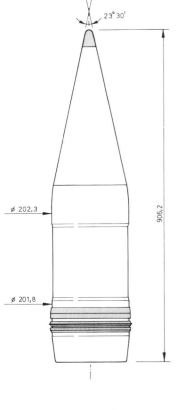

E8/1

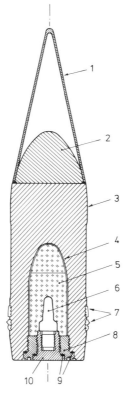

E8/2

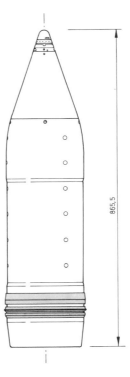

E8/3

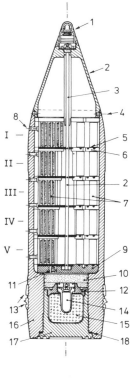

E8/4

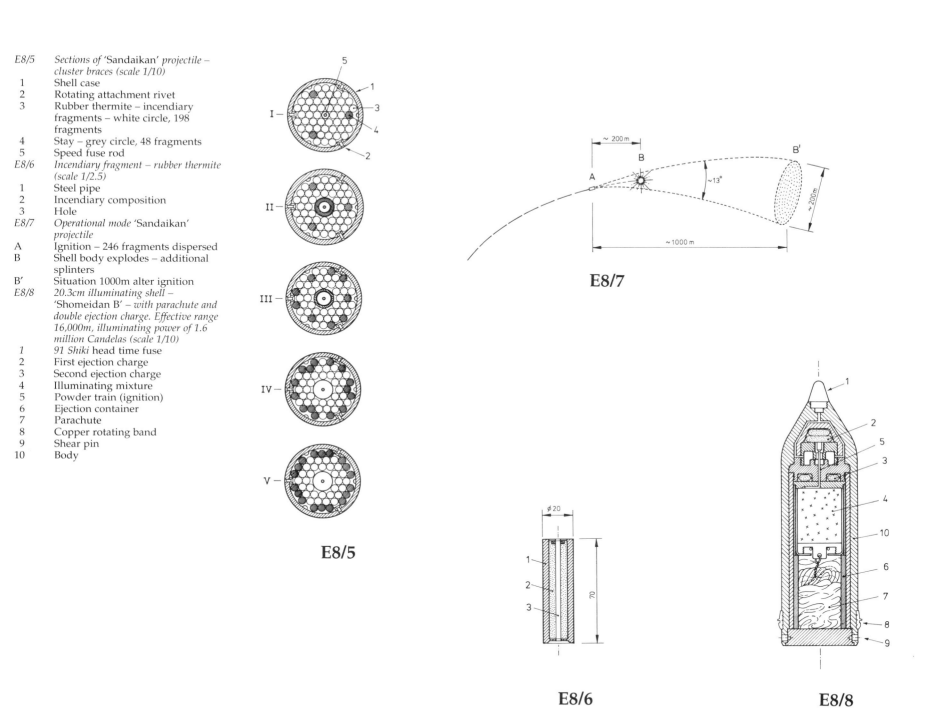

E8/5   Sections of 'Sandaikan' projectile –
        cluster braces (scale 1/10)
1   Shell case
2   Rotating attachment rivet
3   Rubber thermite – incendiary
        fragments – white circle, 198
        fragments
4   Stay – grey circle, 48 fragments
5   Speed fuse rod
E8/6   Incendiary fragment – rubber thermite
        (scale 1/2.5)
1   Steel pipe
2   Incendiary composition
3   Hole
E8/7   Operational mode 'Sandaikan'
        projectile
A   Ignition – 246 fragments dispersed
B   Shell body explodes – additional
        splinters
B'   Situation 1000m alter ignition
E8/8   20.3cm illuminating shell –
        'Shomeidan B' – with parachute and
        double ejection charge. Effective range
        16,000m, illuminating power of 1.6
        million Candelas (scale 1/10)
1   91 Shiki head time fuse
2   First ejection charge
3   Second ejection charge
4   Illuminating mixture
5   Powder train (ignition)
6   Ejection container
7   Parachute
8   Copper rotating band
9   Shear pin
10   Body

E8/5

E8/7

E8/6

E8/8

E Armament

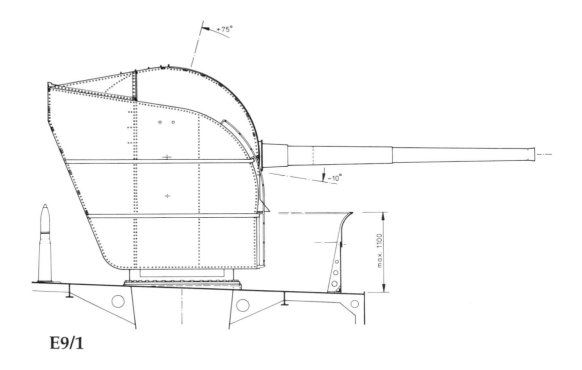

E9/1

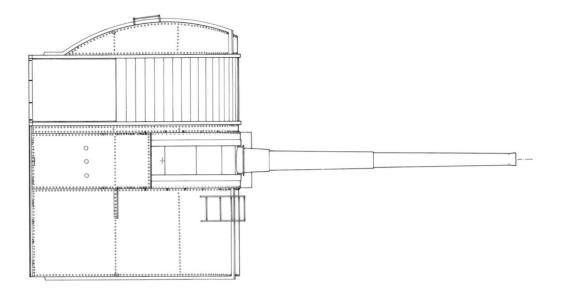

E9/4

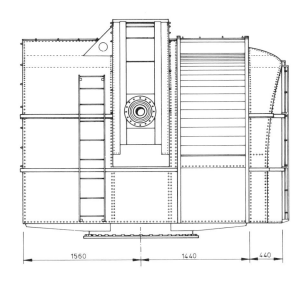

E9/2

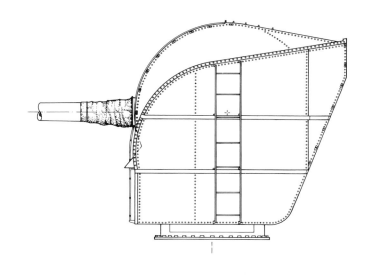

E9/3

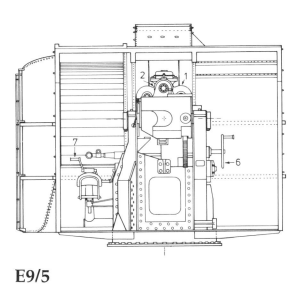

E9/5

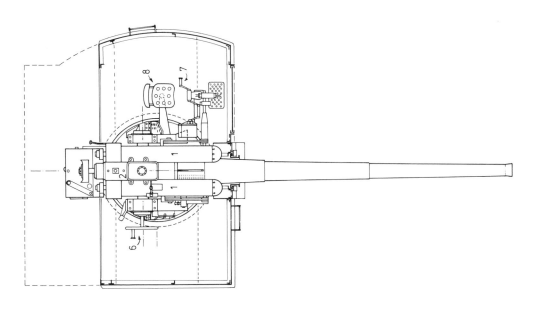

E9/6

E Armament

1   Recoil cylinders
2   Recuperator
3   Trunnion
4   Elevating arc (toothed quadrant)
5   Support
6   Elevating handle
7   Training handles
8   Trainer's seat

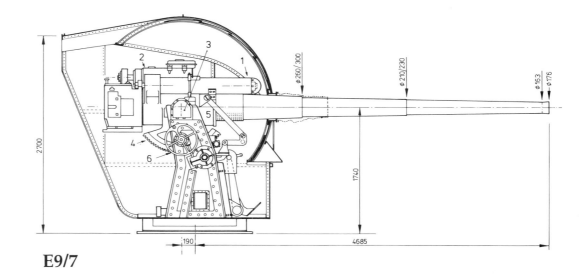

E9/7

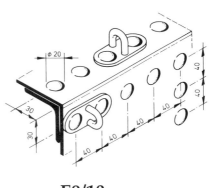

E9/8

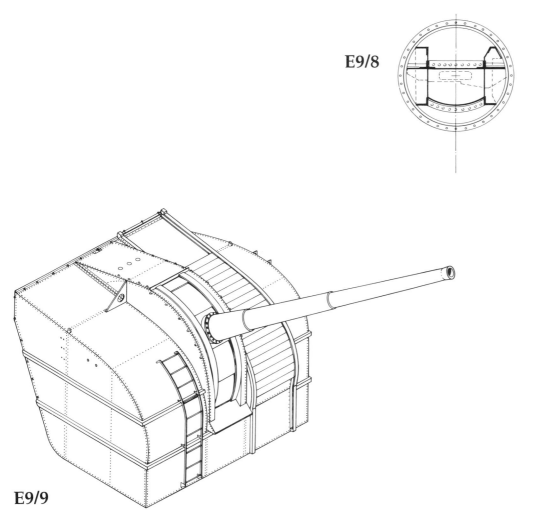

E9/9

E9/10

150

E10   12.7cm 40cal AA GUN–89
       SHIKI, MODEL A-1, FITTED
       MARCH 1942 (scale 1/50)
E10/1   *Right profile*
E10/2   *Front elevation*
E10/3   *Plan*
E10/4   *Rear view*

       See following page for key

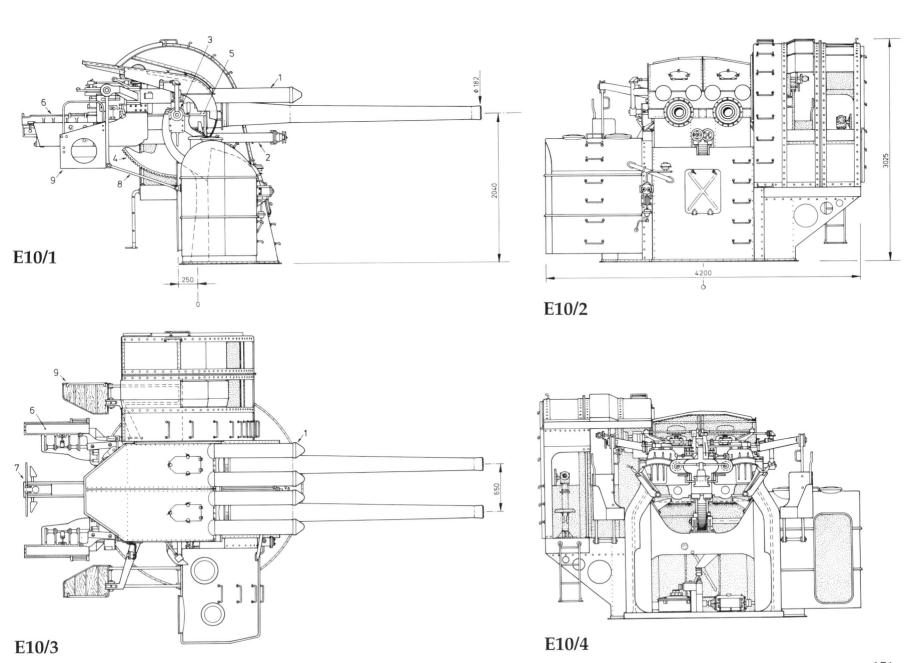

E10/1

E10/2

E10/3

E10/4

E Armament

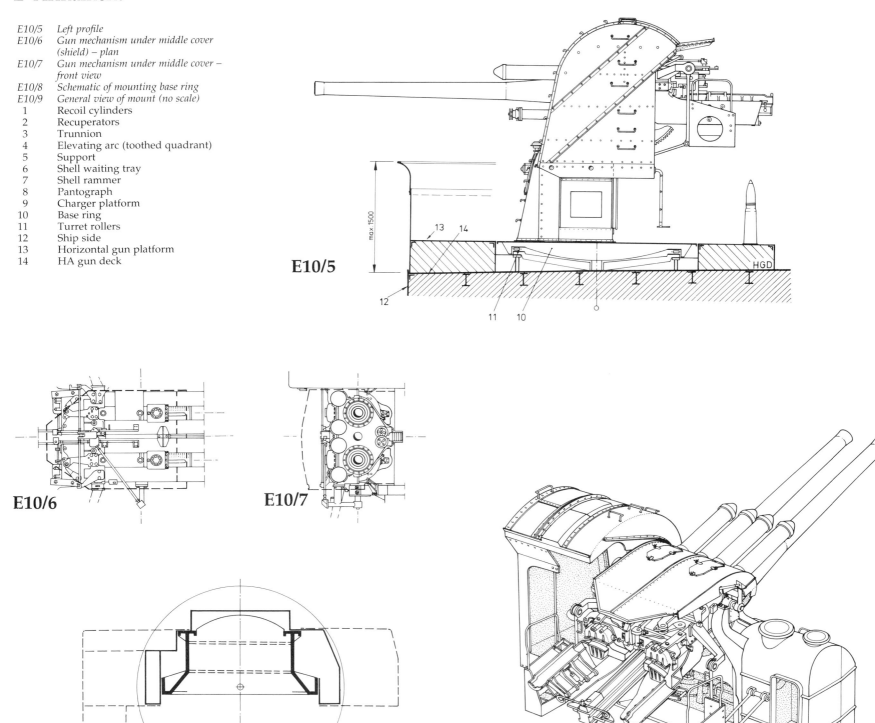

E10/5

E10/6

E10/7

E10/8

E10/9

E11   40mm 62cal SINGLE
       MACHINE-GUN – *'HI' SHIKI
       KIJU* (VICKERS MK VIII)
       (scale 1/25)
E11/1 *Right profile*
E11/2 *Left profile*
E11/3 *Plan*

       See following page for key

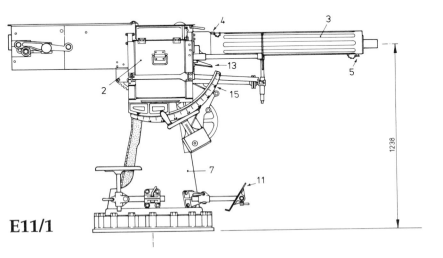

E11/1

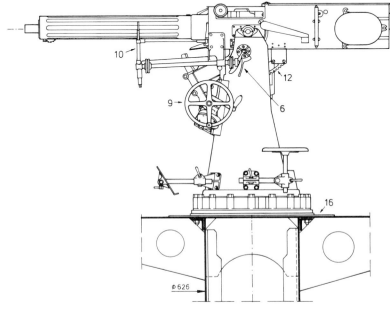

E11/2

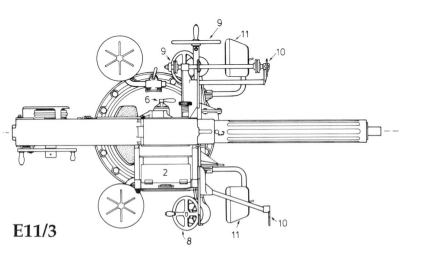

E11/3

E Armament

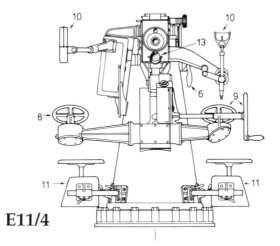

E11/4

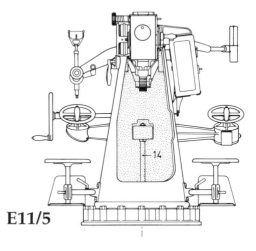

E11/5

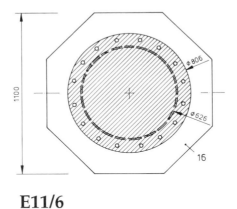

E11/6

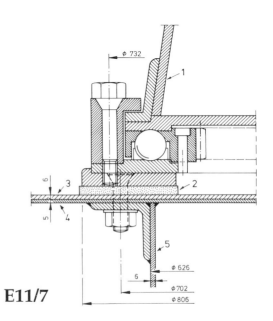

E11/7

E12   25mm TWIN MAG MOUNTING
TYPE 96 FITTED AUGUST 1939
(FOUR MOUNTS) AND
AUTUMN 1941 (TWO MOUNTS)
(scale 1/25)

E12/1   *Right profile*
E12/2   *Left profile*
E12/3   *Plan*

See following page for key

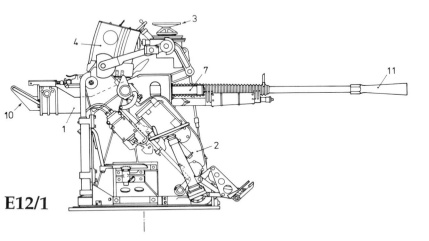

E12/1

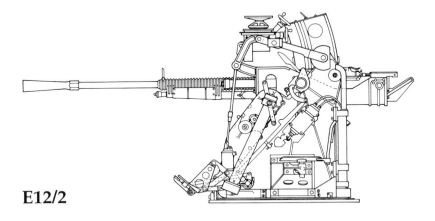

E12/2

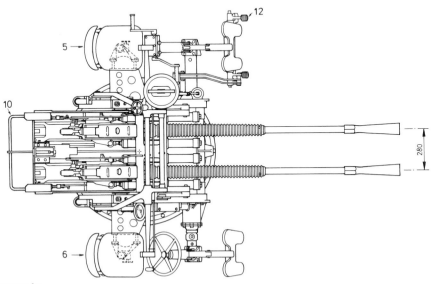

E12/3

E Armament

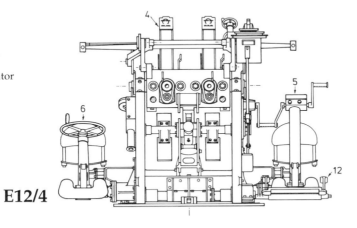

E12/4

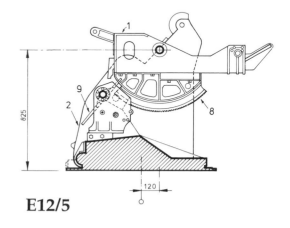

E12/5

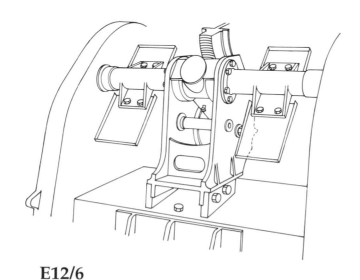

E12/6

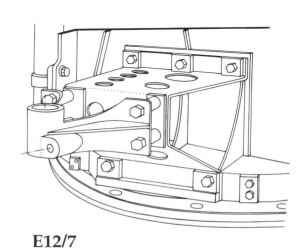

E12/7

E13   25mm TRIPLE MG MOUNTING
       TYPE 96 FITTED AUGUST 1943
       (TWO MOUNTS) AND
       SEPTEMBER 1944 (FOUR
       MOUNTS) (scale 1/25)
E13/1   *Right profile*
E13/2   *Left profile*
E13/3   *Plan*

See following page for key

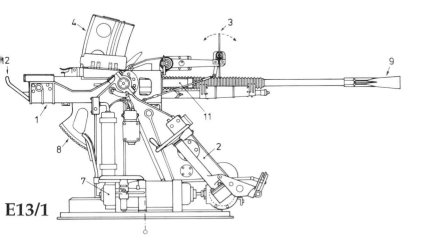

E13/1

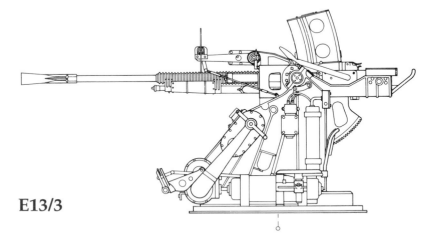

E13/3

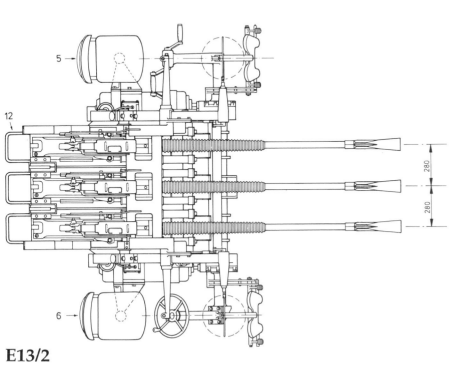

E13/2

E Armament

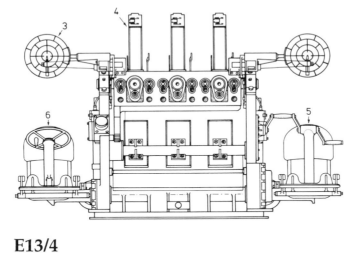

E13/4

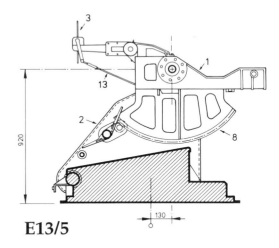

E13/5

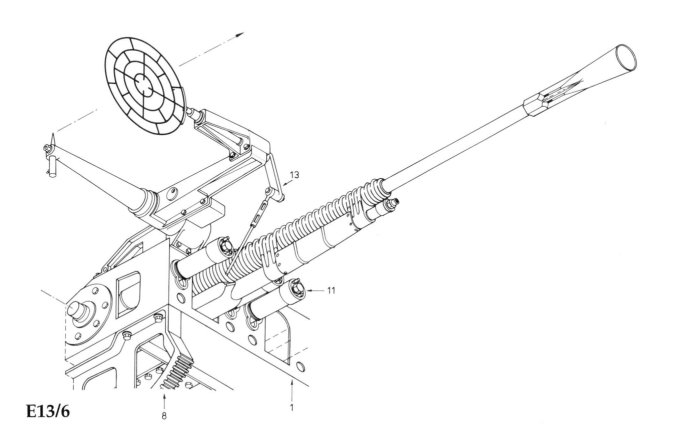

E13/6

E14   25mm SINGLE MG MOUNTING
       TYPE 96 FITTED JANUARY 1944
       (EIGHT MOUNTS) AND
       SEPTEMBER 1944 (TWENTY-TWO
       MOUNTS) (scale 1/25)
E14/1 *Right profile*
E14/2 *Left profile*
E14/3 *Plan*
E14/4 *Front elevation*

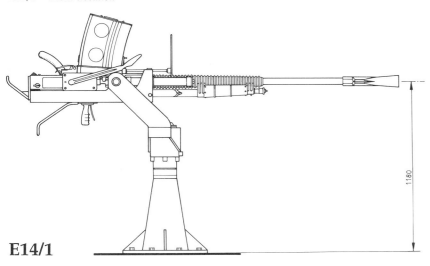

E14/1

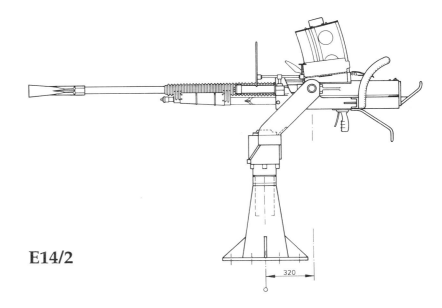

E14/2

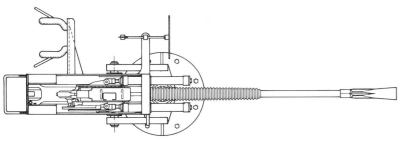

E14/3

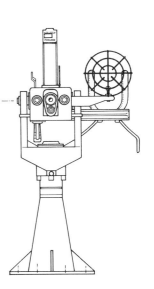

E14/4

E Armament

E15   TYPE 96 25mm GUN BARREL
       WITH BREECH BLOCK
E15/1   *Profile (scale 1/12½)*
E15/2   *Plan (scale 1/12½)*

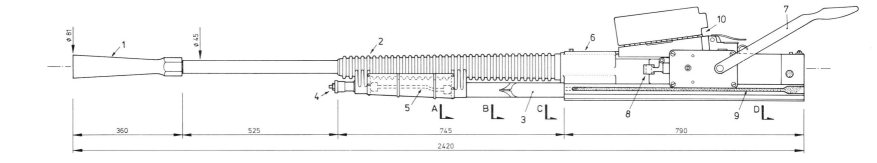

E15/1

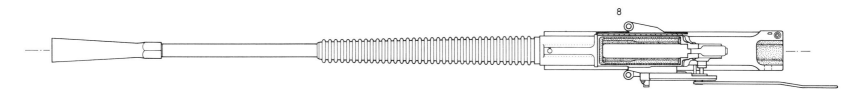

E15/2

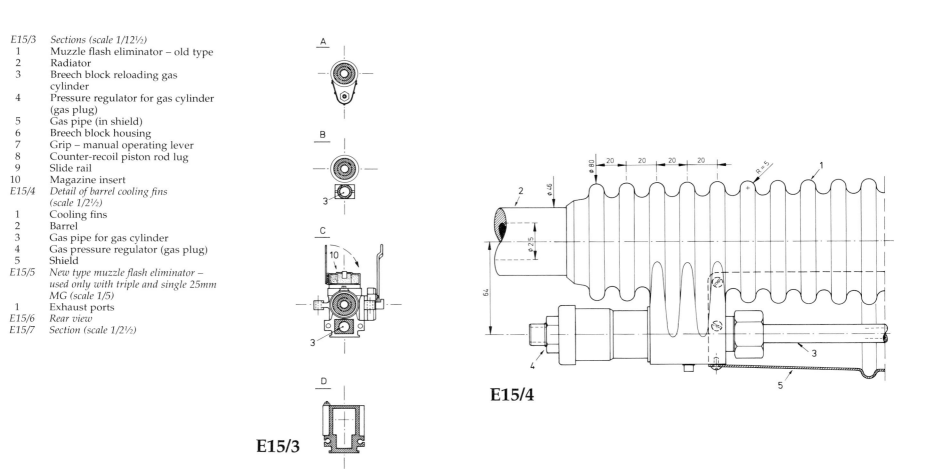

E15/3

E15/4

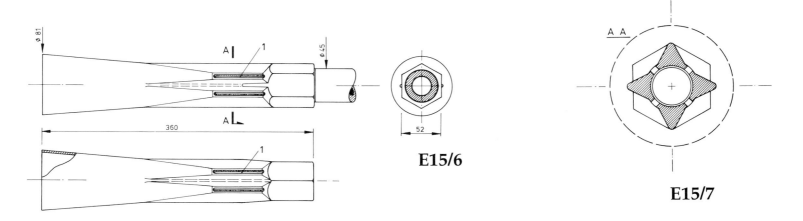

E15/5

E15/6

E15/7

E Armament

E16   13mm TWIN MG MOUNTING
        TYPE 93, FITTED AUGUST 1939
E16/1   Right profile (scale 1/25)
E16/2   Front elevation (scale 1/25)
E16/3   Left profile (scale 1/25)
E16/4   Plan (scale 1/25)
1   Mounting
2   Trunnion bracket
3   Top carriage
4   Sight
5   Pantograph
6   Training wheel
7   Elevation wheel
8   Magazine for 30 rounds
E16/5   Detail of assembly – A washer
*   (scale 1/5)*

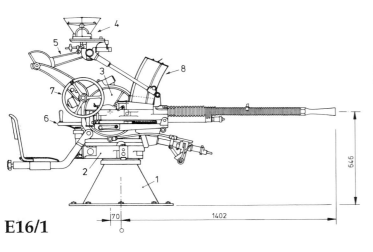

E16/1

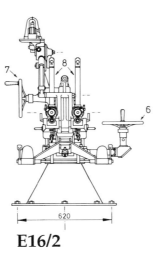

E16/2

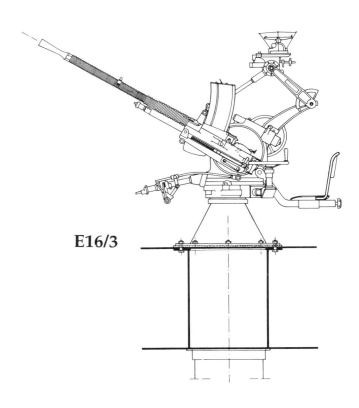

E16/3

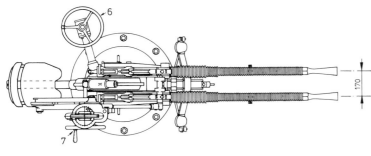

E16/4

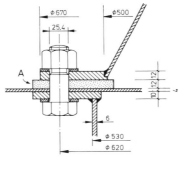

E16/5

162

E17   TYPE 93 13mm MG BARREL
        WITH BREECH BLOCK
        (scale 1/10)
E17/1   *Profile*
E17/2   *Plan*
E17/3   *Sections*
1   Muzzle flash eliminator
2   Muzzle sight (foresight)
3   Radiator
4   Gas cylinder (chamber)
5   Pressure regulator (gas plug)
6   Barrel catch
7   Breech block
8   Breech block handle
9   Magazine insert
10   Rear sight
11   Breech block catch (pawl)
12   Firing lock
13   Grip

E17/1

E17/2

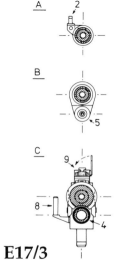

E17/3

E Armament

E18   7.7mm LEWIS TYPE MG
       (scale 1/12½)
E18/1   Profile
E18/2   Front view
E18/3   Plan
E18/4   View (plan) of mounting upper part
E18/5   Mounting height stopper
E18/6   Section – flash eliminator and air
         cooling (scale 1/2)
E18/7   Elevation protractor (scale 1/2)
E18/8   Bearing protractor (scale 1/2)

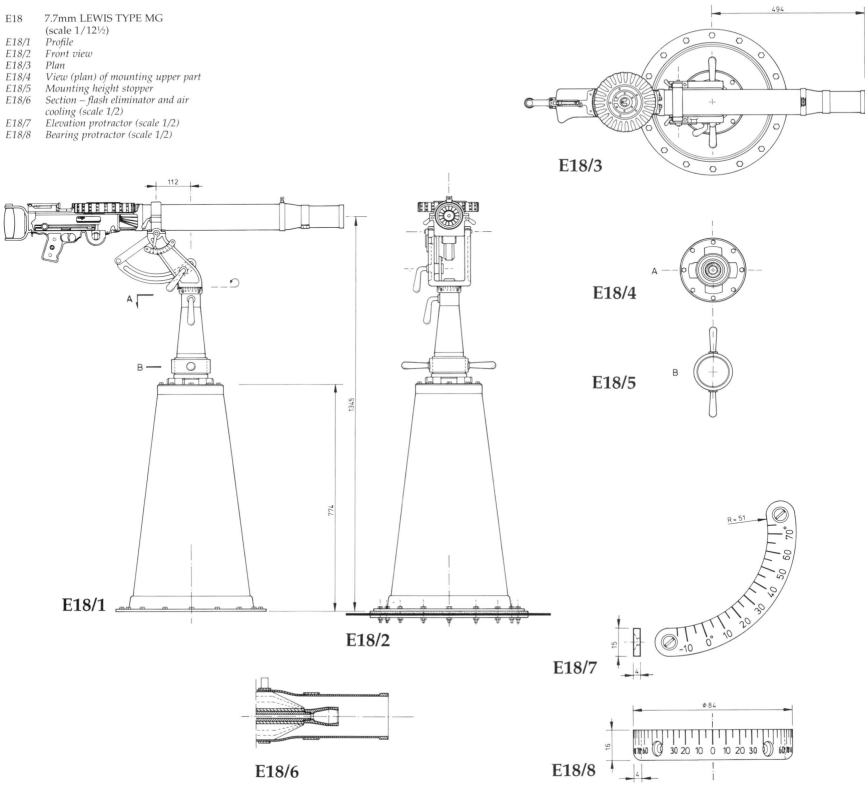

E18/3

E18/1

E18/2

E18/4

E18/5

E18/6

E18/7

E18/8

E19   25mm AMMUNITION BOX FOR
       240 ROUNDS, FITTED ON UPPER
       DECK AND STANDBY ROOMS
       (scale 1/25)
E19/1   *Profile*
E19/2   *Front view*
E19/3   *Plan*
E19/4   *Box with open cover*

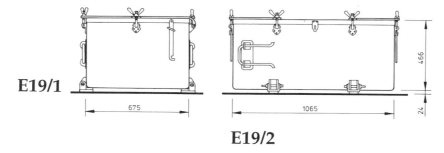

E19/1

E19/2

E19/3

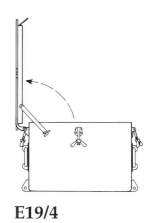

E19/4

E20   25mm AMMUNITION BOX FOR
       240 ROUNDS, FITTED ON
       PLATFORMS AROUND
       FUNNELS (scale 1/25)
E20/1   *Profile*
E20/2   *Front view*
E20/3   *Plan*
E20/4   *Box with open cover (fragment)*

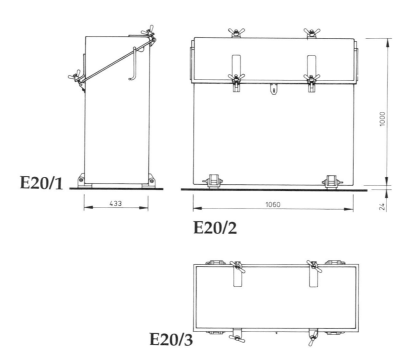

E20/1

E20/2

E20/3

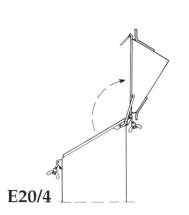

E20/4

165

E Armament

E21   13mm AMMUNITION BOX FOR
        960 ROUNDS (scale 1/25)
E21/1   Profile
E21/2   Front view
E21/3   Plan

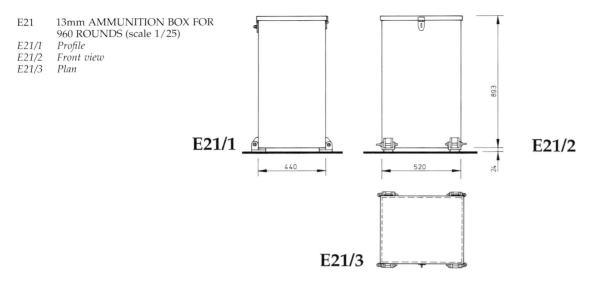

E21/1   E21/2   E21/3

E22   BOX DECK FIXTURE
E22/1   Profile (scale 1/2½)
E22/2   Plan (scale 1/2½)
E22/3   Perspective view (no scale)
  1   Ammunition box
  2   Box assembly jig
  3   Deck assembly jig
  4   Pin
  5   Washer
  6   Cotter pin
  7   Square washer

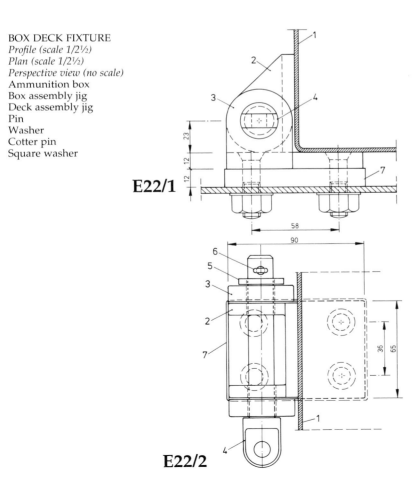

E22/1

E22/2

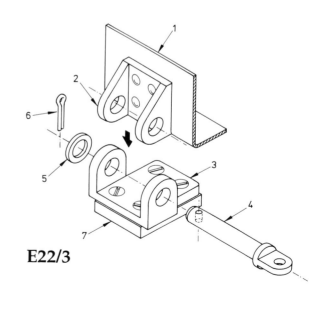

E22/3

E23 TWIN TORPEDO TUBE *89 SHIKI*
MOUNTING (1932–38)
E23/1 *Right elevation (scale 1/75)*
E23/2 *Front elevation with section of ship*
structure (scale 1/75)
E23/3 *Plan (scale 1/75)*
E23/4 *61cm 90 Shiki torpedo (scale 1/75)*
E23/5 *Section of ship side opening framing*
(scale 1/40)
1 Base of the opening (sponson)
2 Upper part – gutter
3 Eye for canvas shield

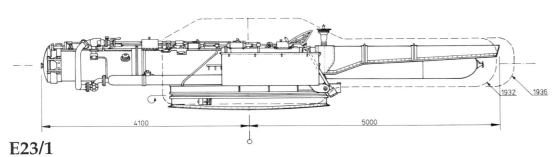

E23/1

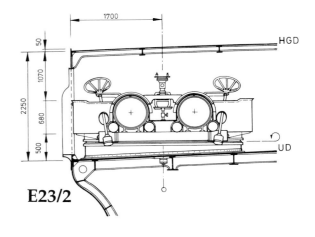

E23/2

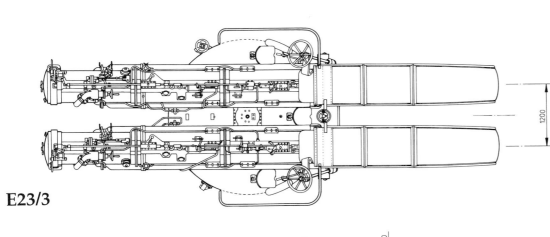

E23/3

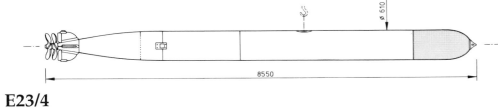

E23/4

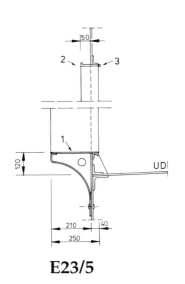

E23/5

E Armament

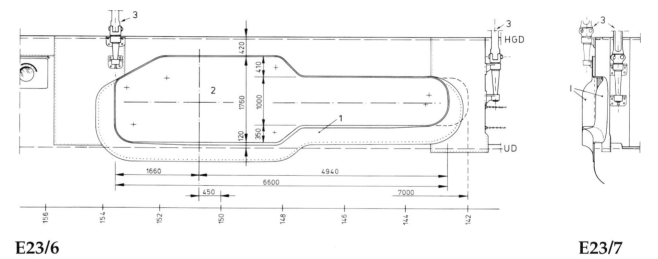

E23/6

E23/7

E23/8

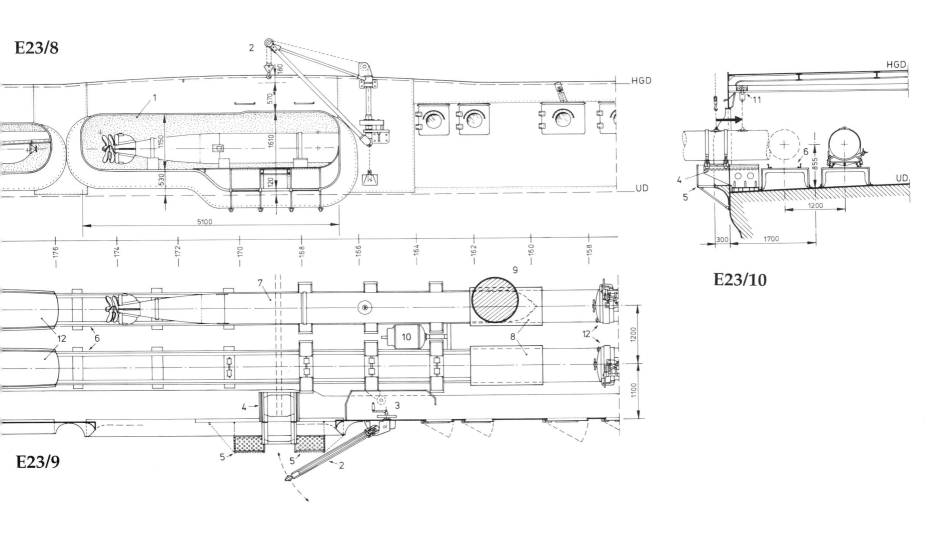

HGD

UD

2

180

570

1

1150

1610

530

120

5100

HGD

11

6

855

4

5

1200

300   1700

E23/10

176   174   172   170   168   166   164   162   160   158

9

7

10

8

12   6

1200

12

1100

4   3

5   5   2

E23/9

E Armament

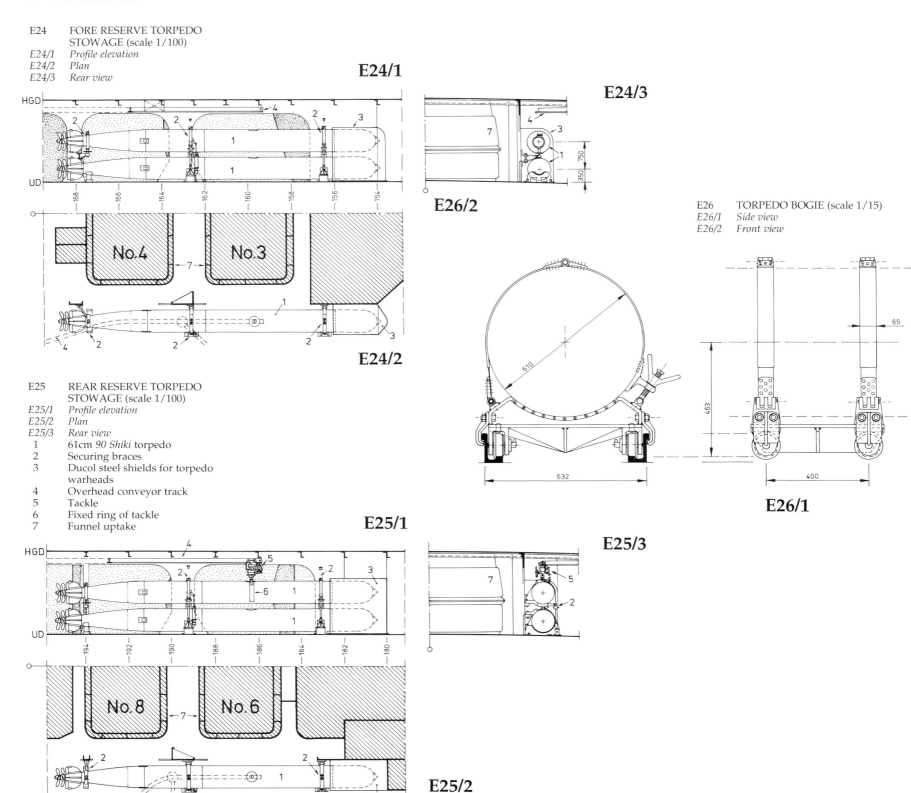

E24   FORE RESERVE TORPEDO
          STOWAGE (scale 1/100)
E24/1   *Profile elevation*
E24/2   *Plan*
E24/3   *Rear view*

E24/1

E24/3

E26/2

E26   TORPEDO BOGIE (scale 1/15)
E26/1   *Side view*
E26/2   *Front view*

E24/2

E25   REAR RESERVE TORPEDO
          STOWAGE (scale 1/100)
E25/1   *Profile elevation*
E25/2   *Plan*
E25/3   *Rear view*
1   61cm *90 Shiki* torpedo
2   Securing braces
3   Ducol steel shields for torpedo
     warheads
4   Overhead conveyor track
5   Tackle
6   Fixed ring of tackle
7   Funnel uptake

E26/1

E25/1

E25/3

E25/2

E27   TORPEDO DECK (UPPER DECK 1932–38) – PLAN (scale 1/200)

1   Twin torpedo type mounting *89 Shiki*
2   Loading rail
3   61cm *90 Shiki* torpedo
4   Ducol steel protection of torpedo warheads
5   Overhead conveyor track provided with tackle to move torpedoes
6   Overhead conveyor track for loading torpedoes aboard ship
7   Derrick to load torpedoes
8   Electric motor drive for loading track
9   Derrick control position
10   Reserve torpedo stowage for eight torpedoes
11   Pillar of 12cm HA gun
12   Workshop
13   Ventilation cowls of forced draught fans
14   Casting
15   Donkey boiler
16   Hangar
17   Heads

No 2 to No 9 – Funnel uptakes of boiler rooms

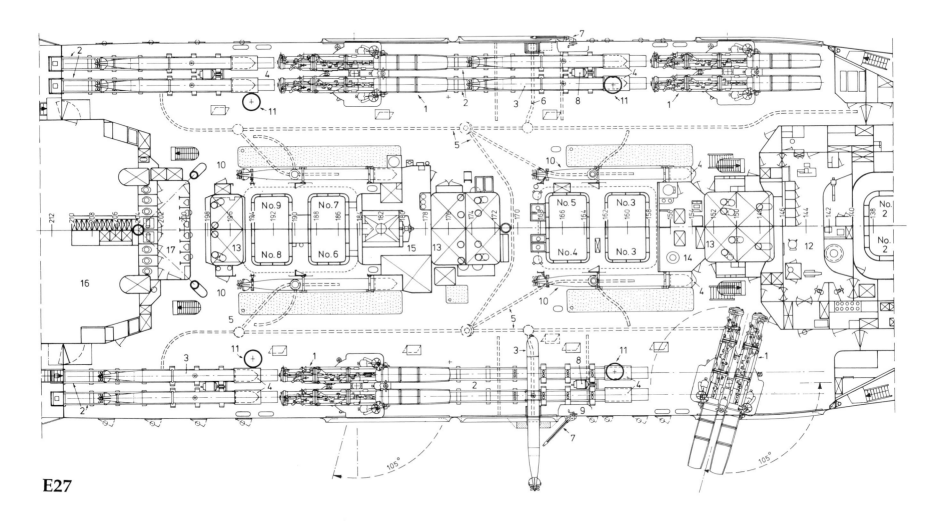

E27

171

E Armament

E28   OPENING OF NO 3 QUADRUPLE
       TORPEDO TUBE TYPE 92,
       AUGUST 1939 (scale 1/75)

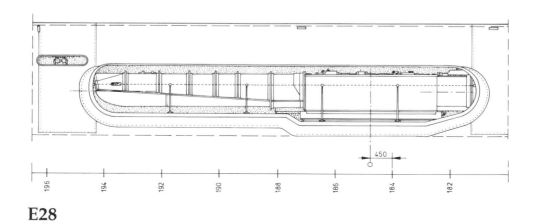

E28

E29   TORPEDO EMBARKATION
       OPENING AND DERRICK,
       AUGUST 1939 (scale 1/75)

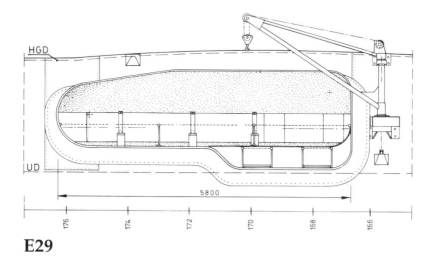

E29

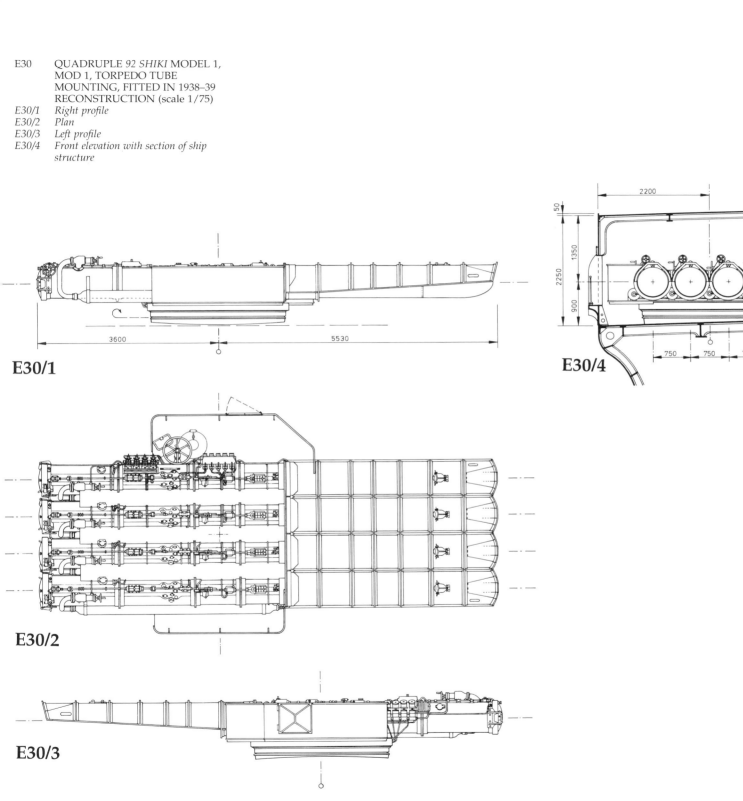

E30 QUADRUPLE *92 SHIKI* MODEL 1,
     MOD 1, TORPEDO TUBE
     MOUNTING, FITTED IN 1938–39
     RECONSTRUCTION (scale 1/75)
E30/1 *Right profile*
E30/2 *Plan*
E30/3 *Left profile*
E30/4 *Front elevation with section of ship*
       structure

E30/1

E30/4

E30/2

E30/3

E Armament

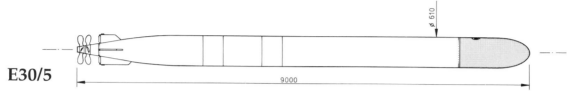

E30/5

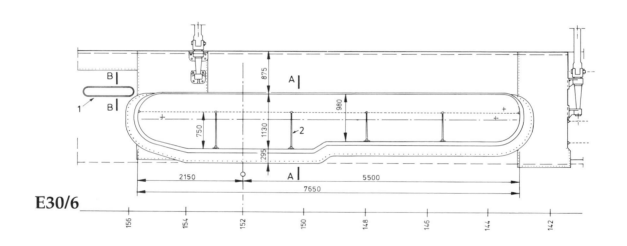

E30/6

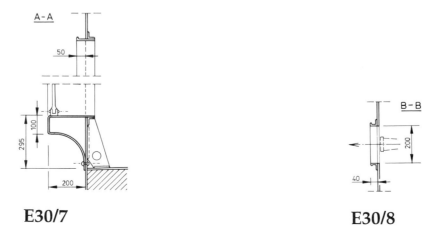

E30/7   **E30/8**

E31   TORPEDO DECK – UPPER DECK AFTER RECONSTRUCTION, AUGUST 1939 (scale 1/200)

1	Quadruple *92 Shiki* torpedo tube mounting	9	Pillar of 12cm HA gun (12.7cm HA gun after March 1942)
2	Loading rails	10	Workshop
3	61cm *93 Shiki* torpedoes	11	Casting
4	Conveyor track provided with tackle to move torpedoes	12	Ventilation cowls of forced draught fans
5	Torpedo loading overhead track	13	Heads
6	Derrick	14	Aviation store
7	Reserve torpedo stowage – eight torpedoes	15	Aircraft department
8	Torpedo lookout position	16	Distillation gear
		17	Drying machine
		18	Washing machine

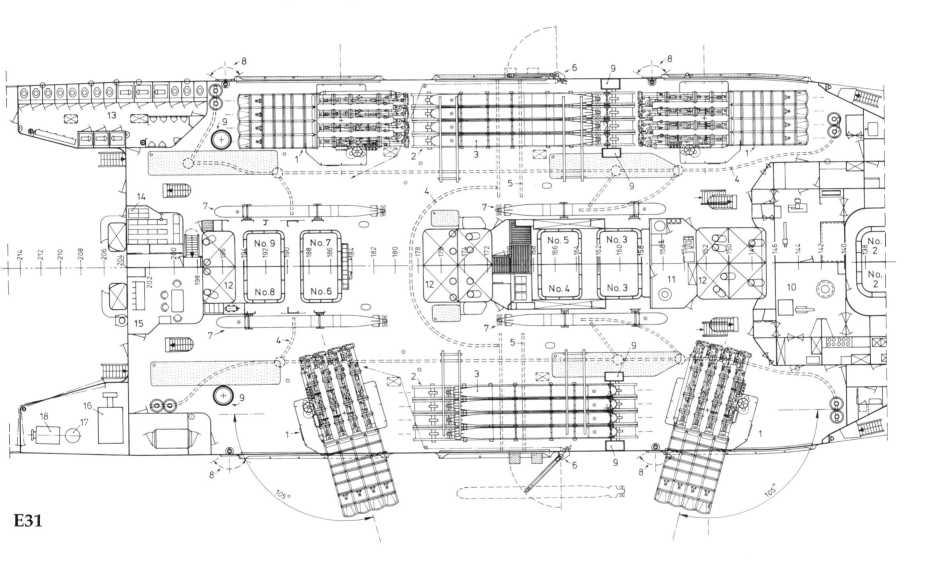

E31

F Fire control

F1   TOP OF TOWER BRIDGE
STRUCTURE – MAIN
ARMAMENT FIRE CONTROL
PLATFORM, 1932 (scale 1/50)
F1/1   *Starboard elevation*
F1/2   *Plan*

F1/3   *Fore view of survey telescope tower*
F1/4   *Fore view of* 14 Shiki *main director
control tower*
1   4.5m *14 Shiki* rangefinder
2   Main director control tower
3   Survey telescope tower

4   Movable shield
5   Ventilator
F1/5   *Starboard elevation, 1937*
F1/6   *Fore view of main director control
tower with new shield, 1937*
1   4.5m *14 Shiki* rangefinder tower
2   Main *14 Shiki* director control
tower
3   Survey telescope tower
4   Ventilators

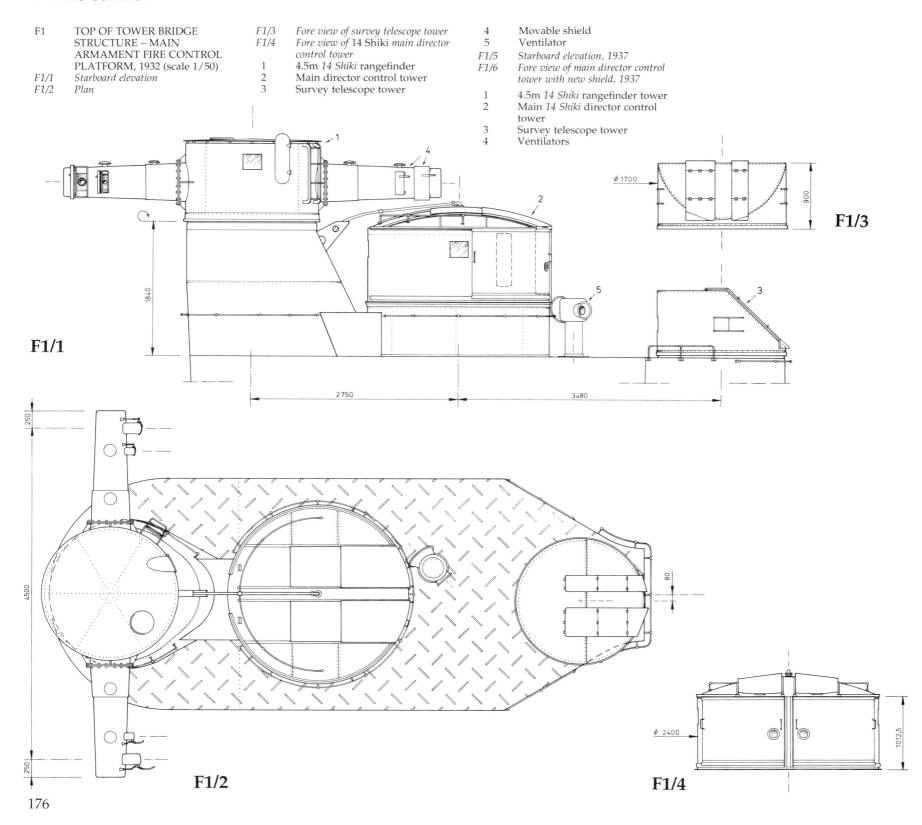

F1/1

F1/2

F1/3

F1/4

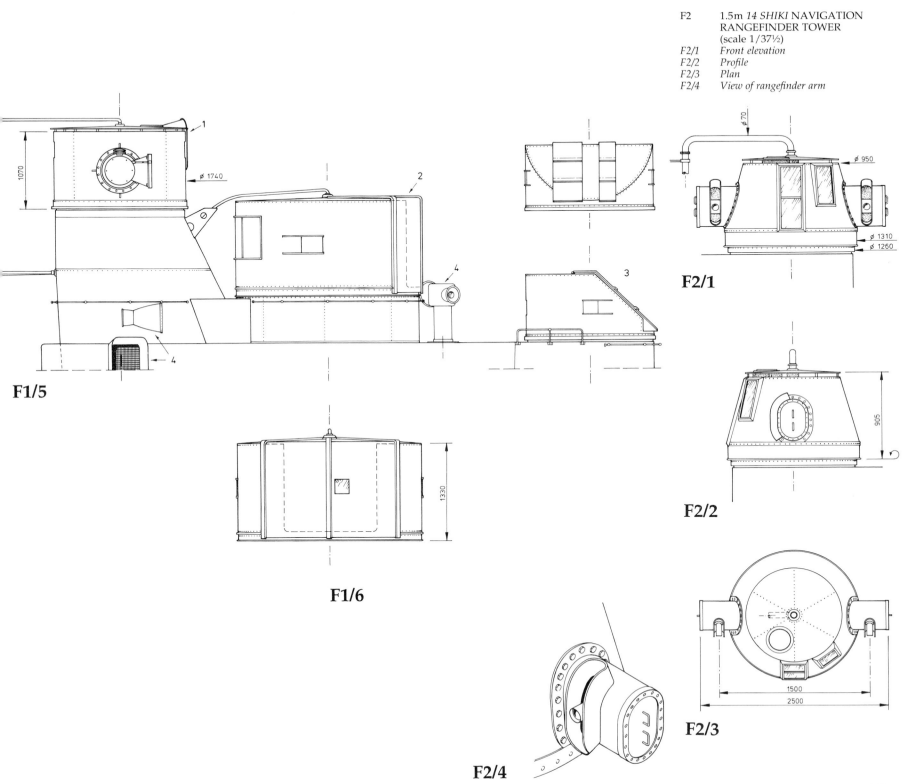

F2   1.5m *14 SHIKI* NAVIGATION
         RANGEFINDER TOWER
         (scale 1/37½)
F2/1   *Front elevation*
F2/2   *Profile*
F2/3   *Plan*
F2/4   *View of rangefinder arm*

F1/5

F1/6

F2/1

F2/2

F2/3

F2/4

177

F Fire control

F3   TOP OF TOWER BRIDGE
STRUCTURE – MAIN
ARMAMENT FIRE CONTROL
PLATFORM AFTER
RECONSTRUCTION, AUGUST
1939 (scale 1/62½)

F3/1   *Starboard elevation*
F3/2   *Plan*
F3/3   *Fore elevation*
1   6m *14 Shiki* rangefinder tower –
rangefinder from No 1 20.3cm gun
turret
2   Low angle director tower – *94 Shiki
Hoiban Shageki Sōchi*
3   Aerials tripod
4   Box for sighting-training
equipment
5   Voice pipe
6   Periscope tower
7   Hatch
8   Lamp

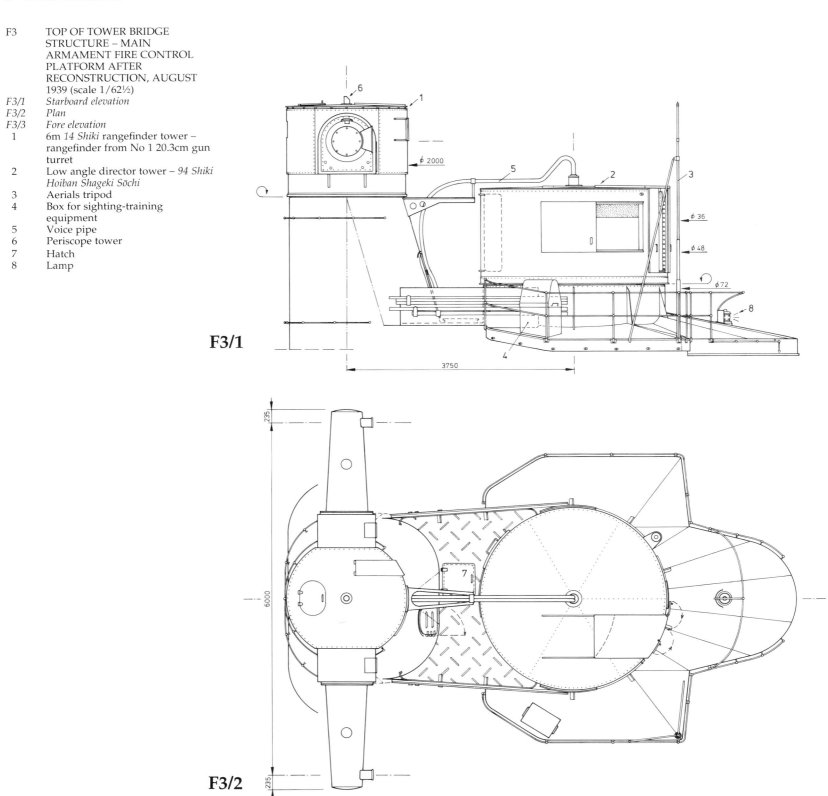

F3/1

F3/2

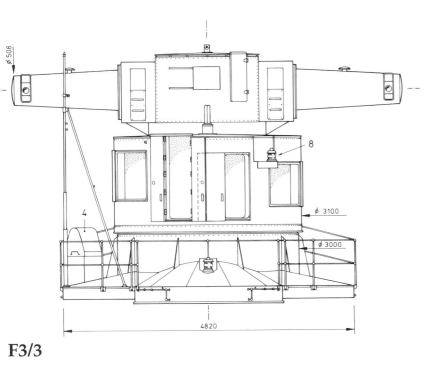

F3/3

F4   4.5m HA RANGEFINDER – *94 SHIKI* (scale 1/50)

F4/1   *Profile with mount from hangar structure, frame 222, 1932–38*

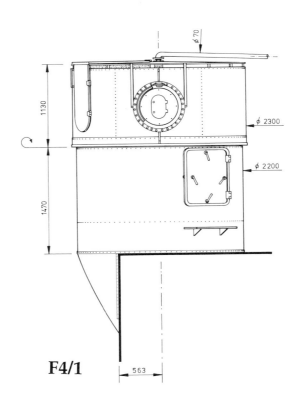

F4/1

F Fire control

F5   4.5m HA RANGEFINDER
      TRANSFERRED TO SIDE OF
      TOWER BRIDGE, FRAME 150,
      AUGUST 1939
F5/1 *Front elevation – on bridge structure*
      side (scale 1/50)
F5/2 *Profile (scale 1/50)*
F5/3 *Plan (scale 1/50)*
F5/4 *Section of supporting sponson*
      (scale 1/75)
F5/5 *View of arm (no scale)*

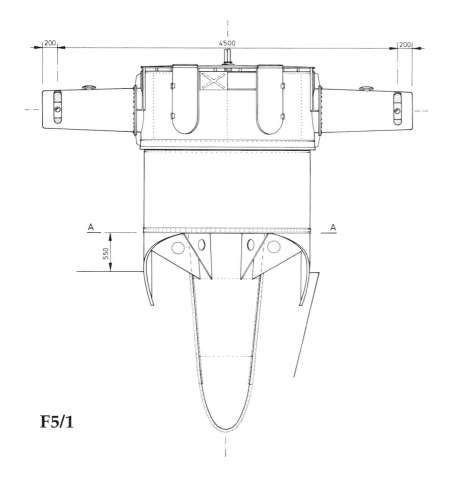

F5/1

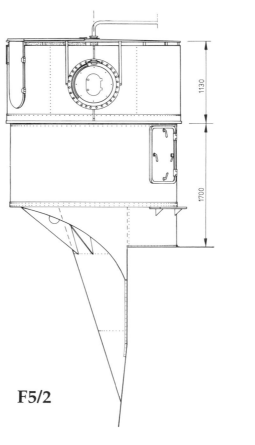

F5/2

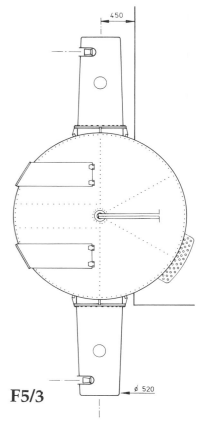

F5/3

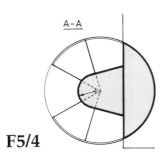

A–A

F5/4

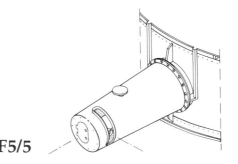

F5/5

F6   3.5m *14 SHIKI* RANGEFINDER
         FRAME 138 (scale 1/50)
F6/1   *Front elevation*
F6/2   *Left profile*
F6/3   *Plan*
F6/4   *Section of supporting sponson*

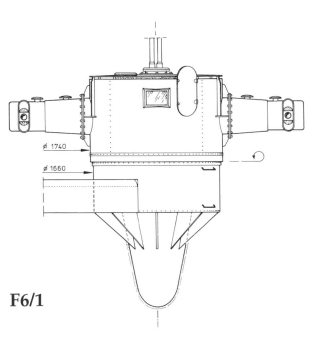

F6/1

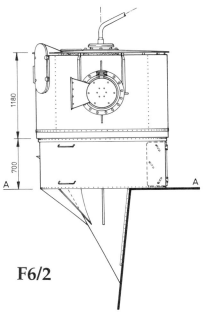

F6/2

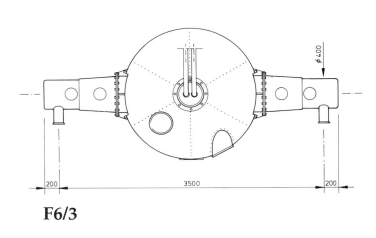

F6/3

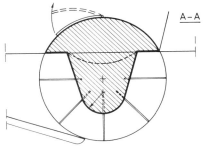

F6/4

F Fire control

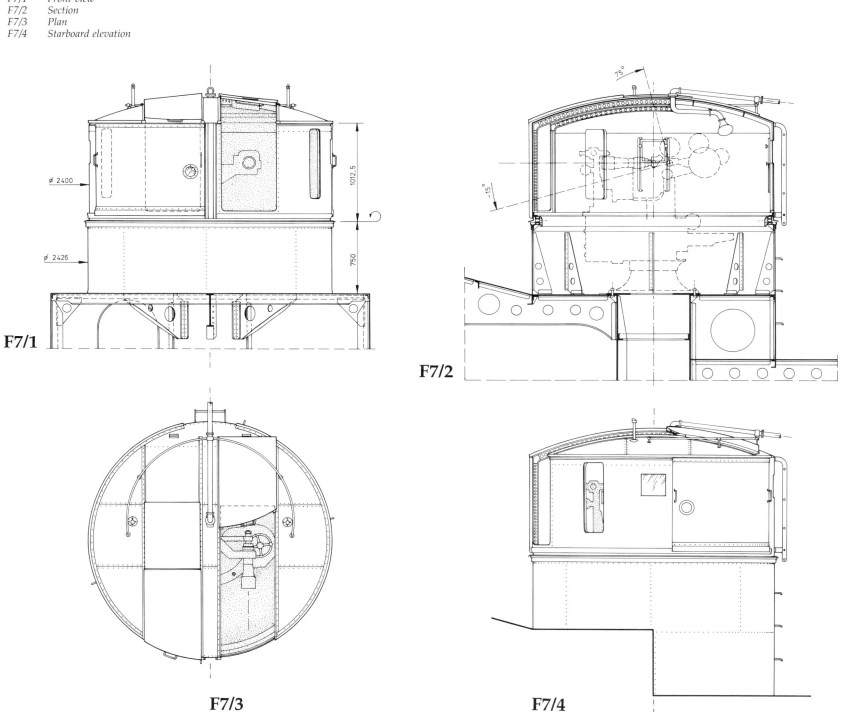

F7/1

F7/2

F7/3

F7/4

F8   HA DIRECTOR – *91 SHIKI*
               KOSHA SOCHI, FRAME 146,
               SHIELD 1932–36 (scale 1/50)
F8/1   *Front elevation*
F8/2   *Profile*
F8/3   *Plan*

F8/4   *HA director in new type shield, frame*
           146, 1937–38, starboard profile

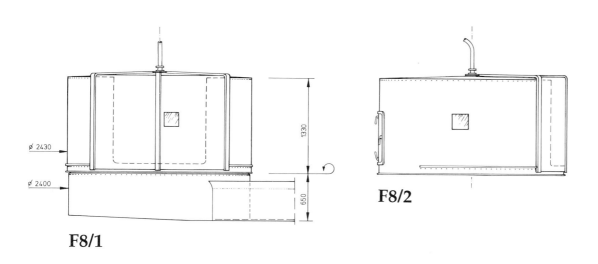

F8/1

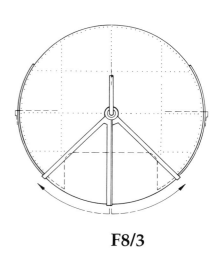

F8/2

F8/3

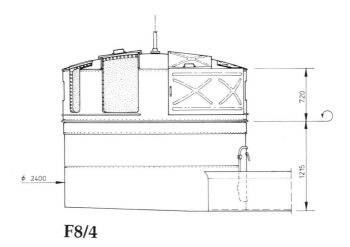

F8/4

183

F Fire control

F9   HA DIRECTOR IN NEW SHIELD
            TRANSFERRED TO FRAME 140,
            AUGUST 1939 (scale 1/50)

F9/1   *View from forward*
F9/2   *Starboard elevation*
F9/3   *Plan*
F9/4   *Section of support (sponson)*

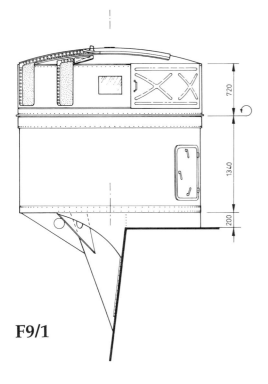

F9/1

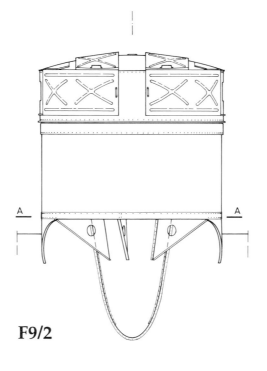

F9/2

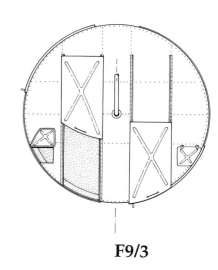

F9/3

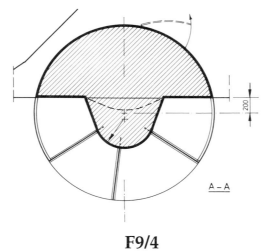

F9/4

F10　　MACHINE-GUN FIRE CONTROL
　　　　TOWER – *95 SHIKI KIJU SHAGEKI*
　　　　SOCHI, FITTED IN 1939
F10/1　Front view (scale 1/37½)
F10/2　Left profile (scale 1/37½)
F10/3　Plan (scale 1/37½)
F10/4　Section AA – roller bearing and
　　　　windows (scale 1/3.75)
F10/5　Section of roller bearing in rear of
　　　　tower (scale 1/3.75)

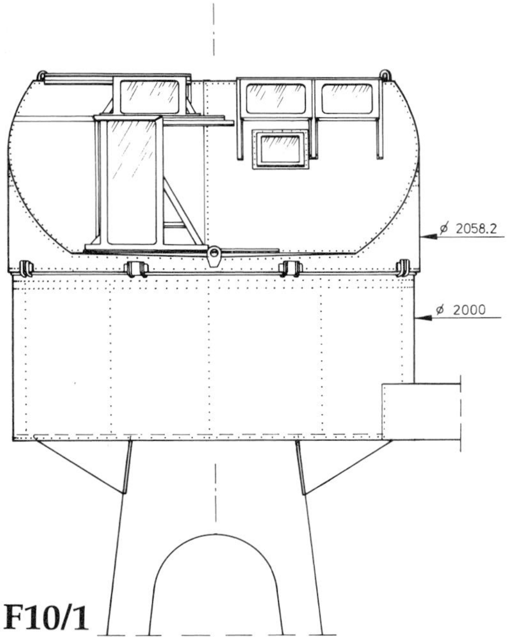

ø 2058.2

ø 2000

F10/1

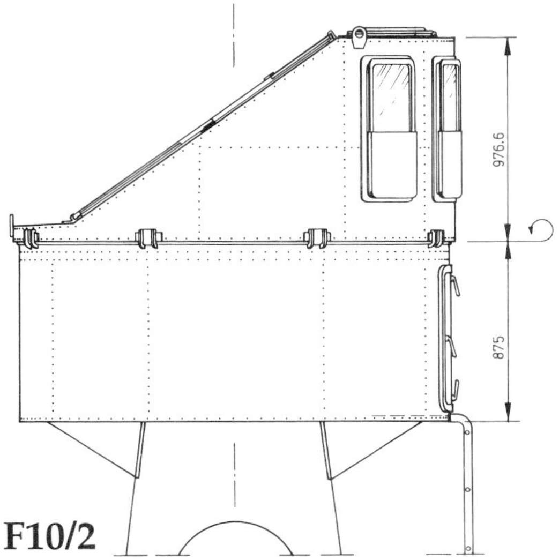

F10/2

976.6

875

A – A

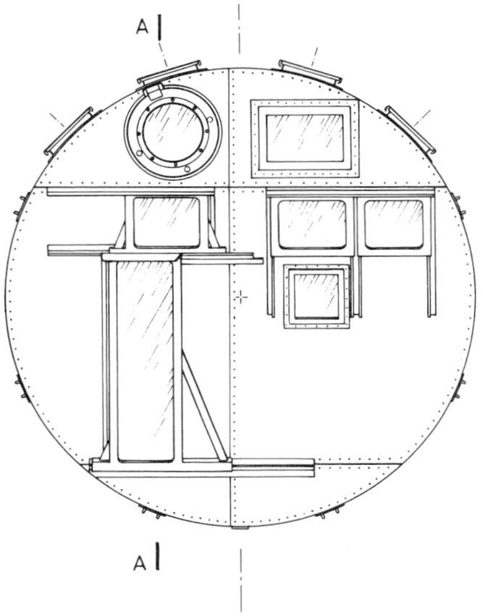

F10/3

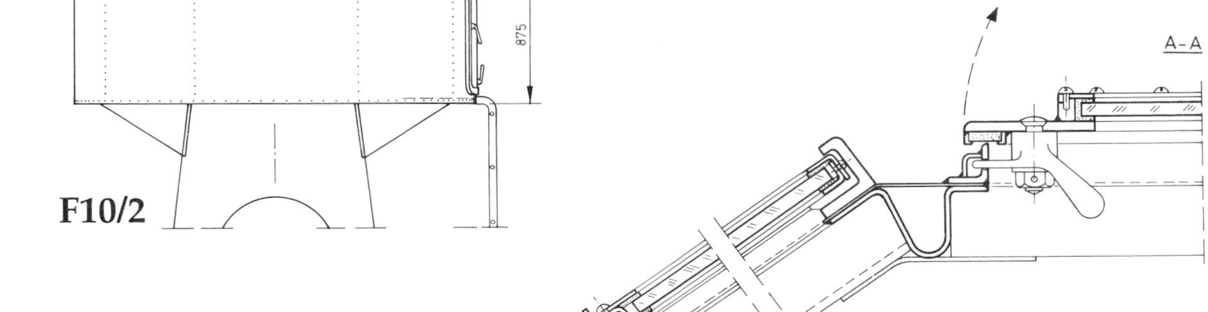

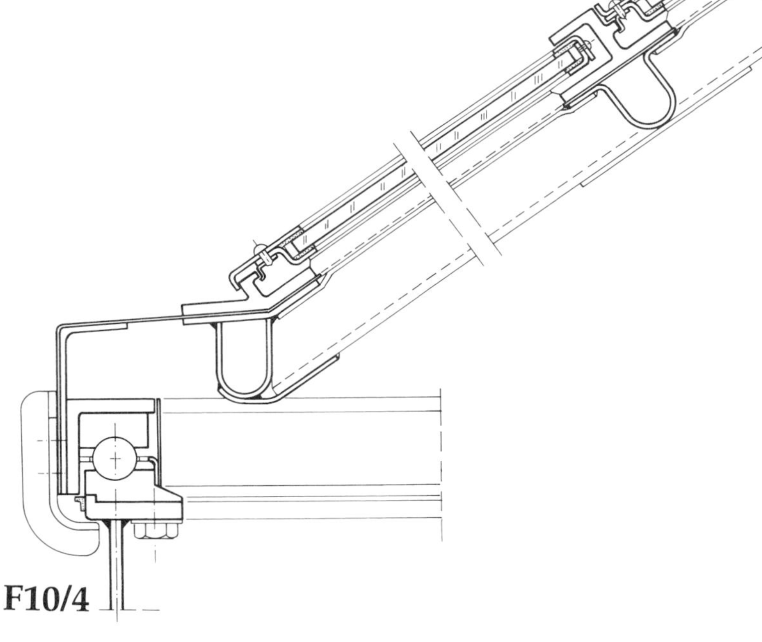

F10/4

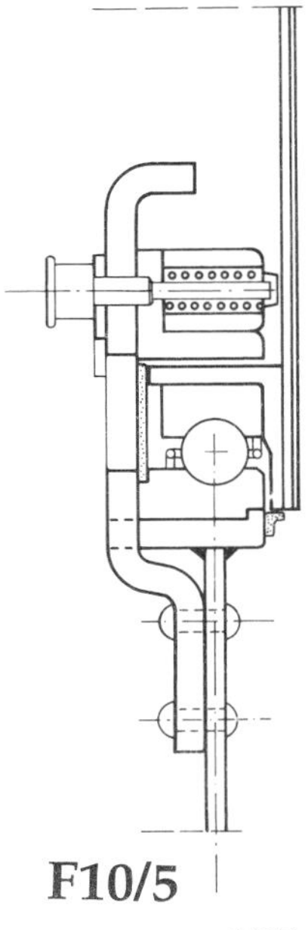

F10/5

F Fire control

F11   SEARCHLIGHT CONTROL
TOWER, FOUR TOWERS FITTED
ON REAR PART OF FIRE
CONTROL PLATFORM – DECK
VI, PROTECTIVE SHIELDS
REMOVED IN 1936–37 REFIT
(scale 1/50)
F11/1   *Front elevation*
F11/2   *Profile*
F11/3   *Plan*

F12   SEARCHLIGHT CONTROL
TOWER FROM HANGAR
STRUCTURE FRAME 214
(scale 1/50)
F12/1   *Front view*
F12/2   *Profile*
F12/3   *Plan*

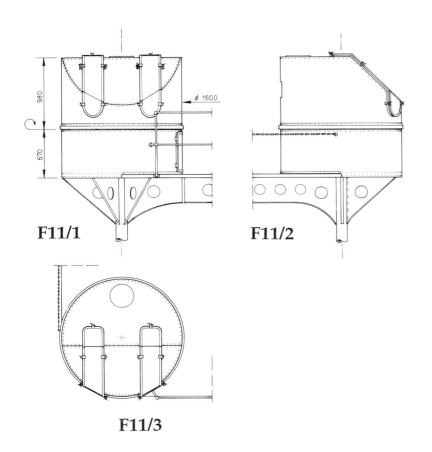

F11/1

F11/2

F11/3

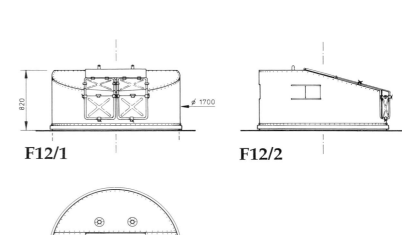

F12/1

F12/2

F12/3

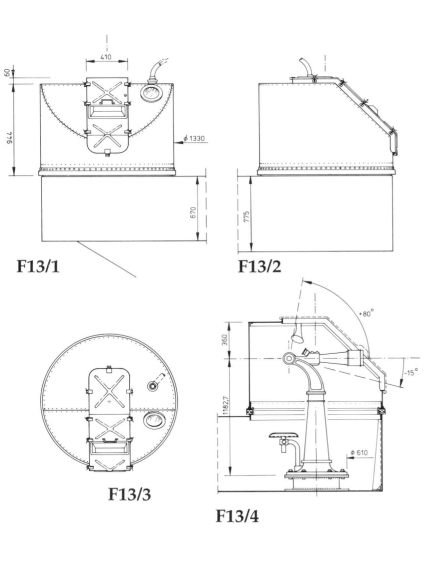

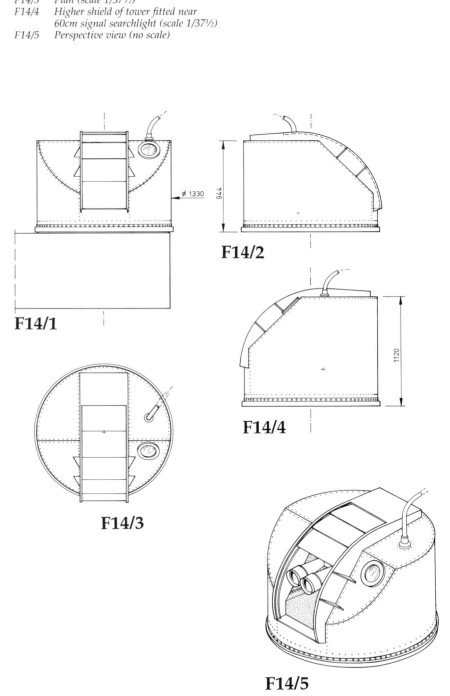

F13 PROTECTED LOOKOUT
     POSITION EQUIPPED WITH
     BINOCULARS (scale 1/37½)
F13/1   *Front elevation*
F13/2   *Profile*
F13/3   *Plan*
F13/4   *Section*

F14 PROTECTED LOOKOUT
     POSITION – NEW TYPE FITTED
     TO 1936–37 REFIT
F14/1   *Front view (fitted on port side of*
        compass platform (scale 1/37½)
F14/2   *Profile (scale 1/37½)*
F14/3   *Plan (scale 1/37½)*
F14/4   *Higher shield of tower fitted near*
        60cm signal searchlight (scale 1/37½)
F14/5   *Perspective view (no scale)*

F13/1

F13/2

F13/3

F13/4

F14/1

F14/2

F14/3

F14/4

F14/5

F Fire control

F15 LOWER DIRECTION LOOKOUT
POSITION, NOTE WIND
BAFFLES ON FORE PART,
FITTED AUGUST 1939, FRAME
134 (scale 1/37½)

F15/1 *Plan*
F15/2 *Front view*
F15/3 *Profile*

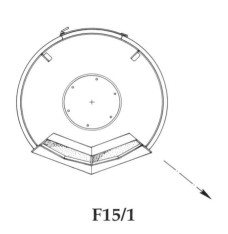

F15/1

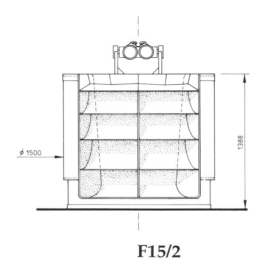

F15/2

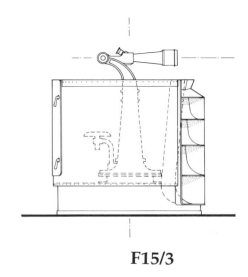

F15/3

F16   HA FIRE CONTROL
INSTALLATION – *94 SHIKI
KOSHA SOCHI* INSTALLATION:
94 SHIKI 4.5m RANGEFINDER
AND *94 SHIKI KOSHA
SHAGEKIBAN* COMPUTER
LOCATED UNDER BRIDGE
BELOW ARMOURED DECK IN
FIRE CONTROL ROOM
(scale 1/37½)

F16/1   *Front view*

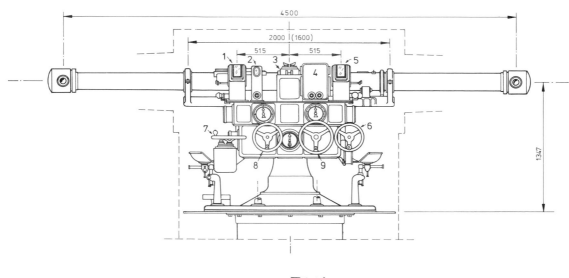

F16/1

F Fire control

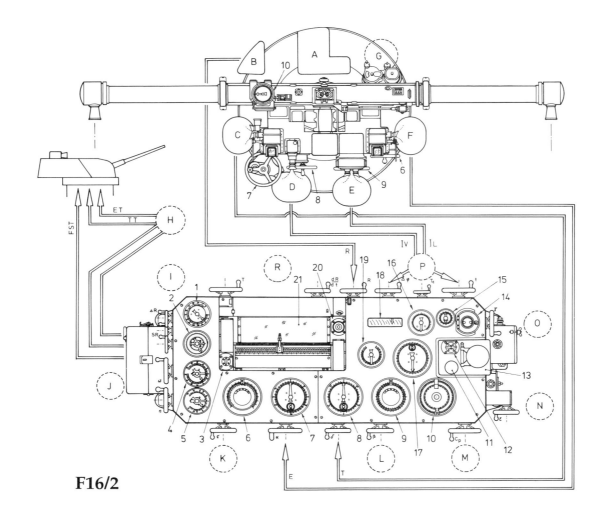

F16/2

F17 MACHINE-GUN CONTROL
   TOWER – *95 SHIKI KIJU SHAGEKI*
   SOCHI (scale 1/37½)
F17/1 *Internal profile*
F17/2 *Plan*

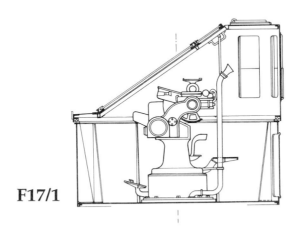

F17/1

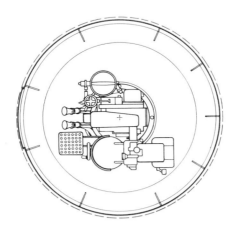

F17/2

F Fire control

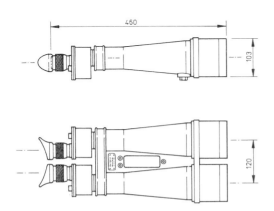

F18/1

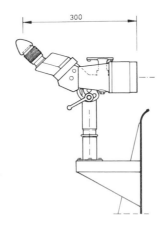

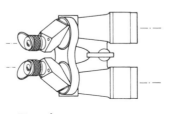

F18/2

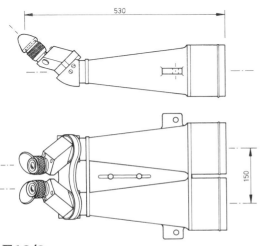

F18/3

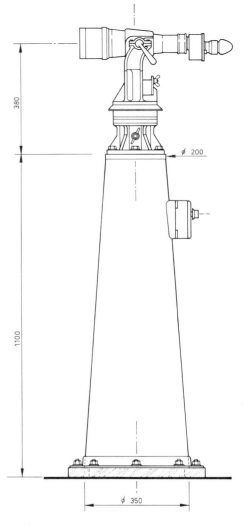

F18/4

F19   12cm BINOCULARS WITH
        SIGNALLING LAMP
        (scale 1/12½)
F19/1   *Profile*
F19/2   *Rear view*
  1   900mm high railing

F20   12cm BINOCULARS WITH
        INFRA-RED MESSAGE
        TRANSMITTER (scale 1/12½)
F20/1   *Profile*
F20/2   *Rear view with section of binocular*

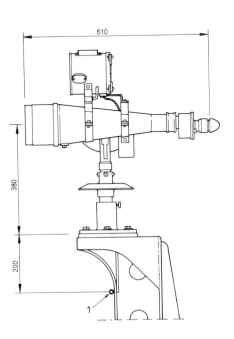

F19/1

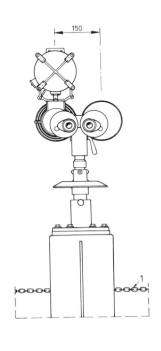

F19/2

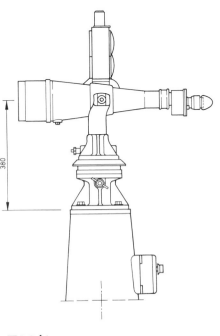

F20/1

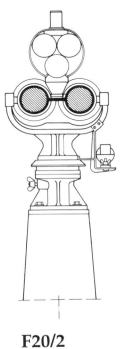

F20/2

193

F Fire control

F21   WIND STRENGTH
       TRANSMITTER (scale 1/6¼)
F21/1 *Front view*
F21/2 *Profile*
F21/3 *Plan*
  1   Robinson cup
  2   Casing

F22   WIND DIRECTION INDICATOR
       (scale 1/6¼)
F22/1 *Front view*
F22/2 *Profile*
F22/3 *Plan*
  1   Revolving vane
  2   Casing

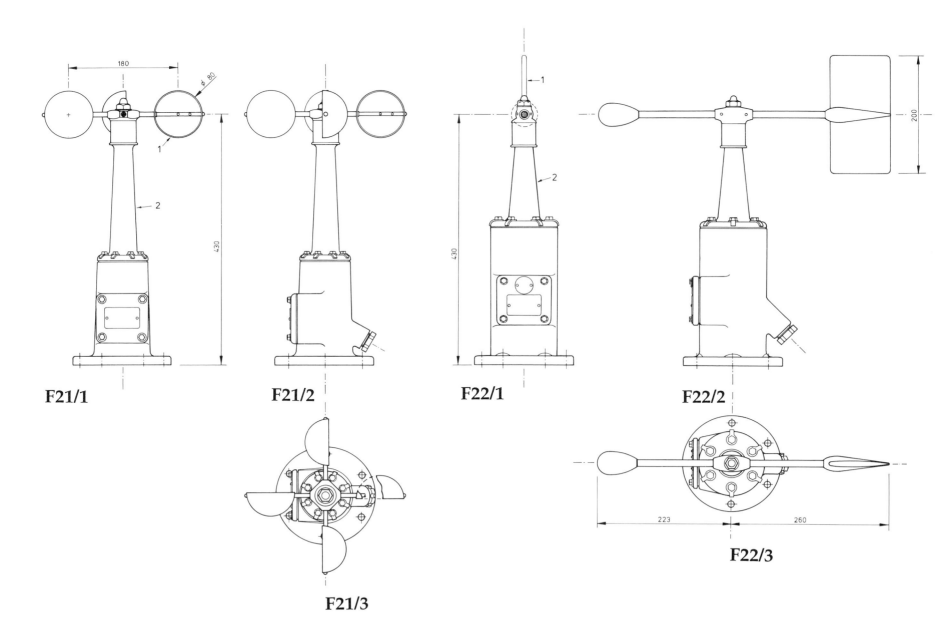

F21/1 **F21/2** **F22/1** **F22/2**

F21/3 **F22/3**

F23 *21 ĜO DENTAN KAI 2* AIR
SEARCH RADAR MATTRESS
TYPE ANTENNA, FITTED IN
JULY–AUGUST 1943

The antenna consisted of combined transmitting
and receiving arrays of 10mm diameter copper
bars

F23/1 *Front elevation (scale 1/37½)*
F23/2 *Profile (scale 1/37½)*
F23/3 *Plan (scale 1/37½)*
F23/4 *Rear elevation (scale 1/37½)*
F23/5 *Section in detail (scale 1/10)*

1 Receiving array (10mm diameter bar)
2 Transmitting array
3 Antenna frame
4 Insulators
5 Wire screen grid, 48mm × 48mm module
6 Support plates for insulators
7 Mounting

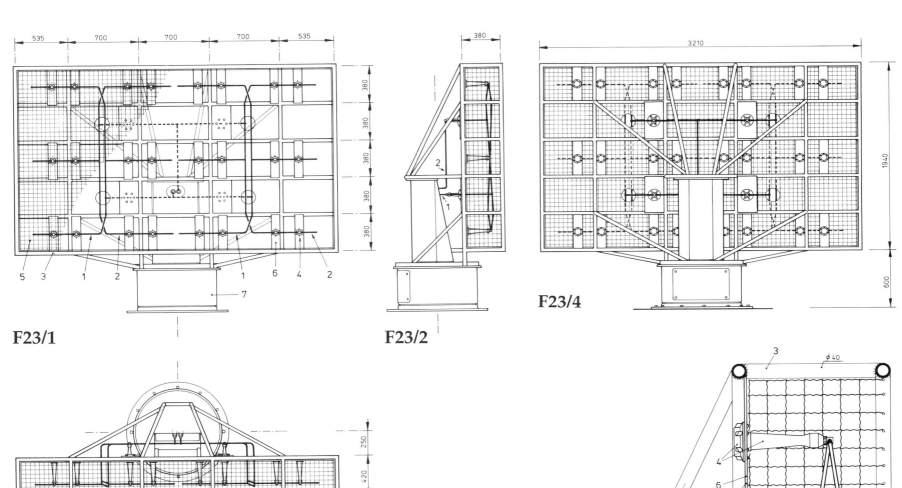

F23/1

F23/2

F23/4

F23/3

F23/5

195

F Fire control

F24 *13 ĜO TYPE AIR SEARCH RADAR* F24/1 *Profile (scale 1/37½)* F24/5 *Section of pillar (scale 1/18¾)*
   ANTENNA 3 SHIKI 1 ĜO DENPA F24/2 *Front elevation (scale 1/37½)* 1 Receiving array (10mm diameter
   TANSHINGI 3 GATA TYPE 3, MK F24/3 *Rear elevation (scale 1/37½)*   bar)
   1 RADAR MODEL 3) F24/4 *Plan (scale 1/37½*   2 Transmitting array (10mm
Installed in June–July 1944 back of foremast   diameter bar)

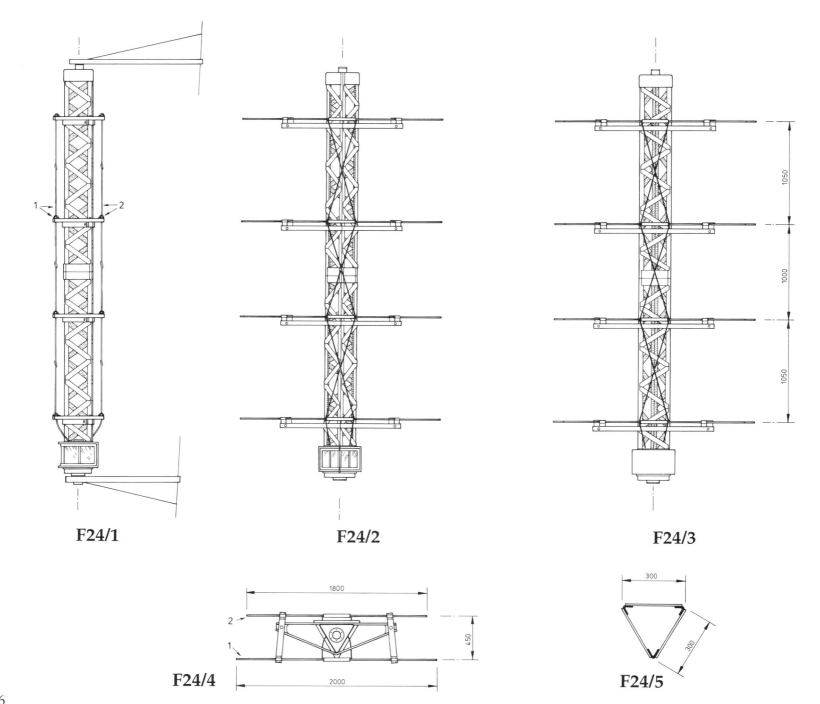

F24/1   **F24/2**   **F24/3**

F24/4   **F24/5**

F25 *22 ĜO DENTAN KAI 4 (2 ĜO DENPA TANSHINGI 2 GATA KAI 4)* – SURFACE SEARCH RADAR HORNS ANTENNA, FITTED JANUARY 1944, ON BOTH SIDES BELOW 6M RANGEFINDER (scale 1/37½)

F25/1   *Starboard profile*
F25/2   *Front view – starboard mount*
F25/3   *Plan – starboard mount*
F25/4   *Section of horn*
1   Receiving horn (upper)
2   Transmitting horn (lower)

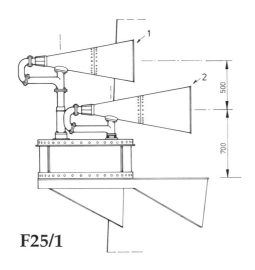

F25/1

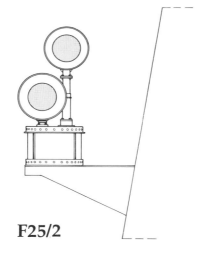

F25/2

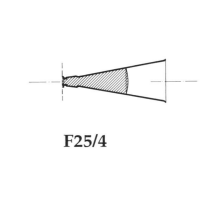

F25/4

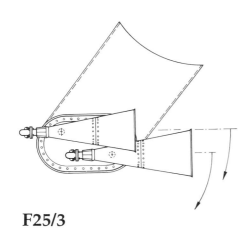

F25/3

197

G Ground tackle

G1 FORECASTLE, FRAMES FP – 66
G1/1 Side view – starboard (scale 1/200)
G1/2 Plan (scale 1/200)

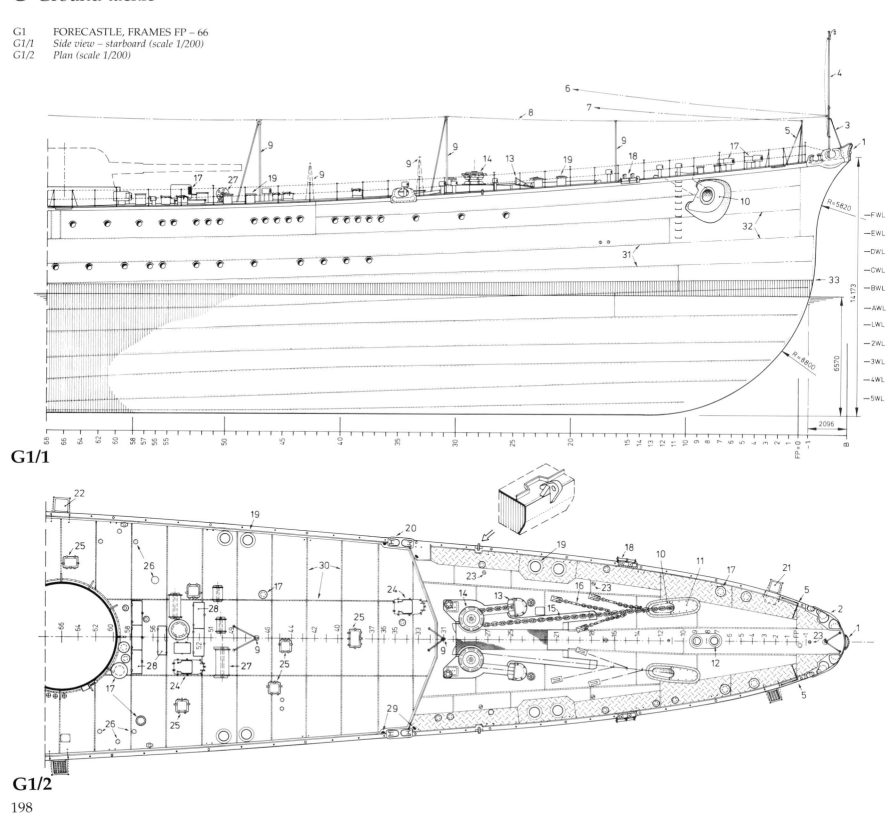

G1/1

G1/2

G1/3   *Front view (scale 1/200)*
1   Gold chrysanthemum crest
2   Towing fairlead
3   Tripod – jackstaff stanchion and
        support for dressing line and
        awning lines
4   Jackstaff – folding part (removable)
5   Tripod stanchion for aerials (both
        sides)
6   Dressing line
7   Aerials (antenna)
8   Awning line
9   Awning stanchion – (higher on
        centreline)
10   Hawse pipe
11   Hawse pipe cover
12   Bollard
13   Navel pipe
14   Cable holder with brake handle
15   Anchor cable
16   Stopper
17   Mushroom vents
18   Paravane roller fairlead
19   Bollards
20   Fairlead
21   Leadsman's platform
22   Sounding platform
23   Eye plate
24   Hatch
25   Skylight
26   Closed deck holes
27   Reels
28   Wash deck locker
29   Scupper
30   Brass strips – support of linoleum
        joints
31   Riveted side plates
32   Welded side plates
33   Upper limit of red-brown colour
        (note rise towards bow and stern)
G1/4   *Chrysanthemum crest – dimensions*
        for 'A' class cruisers (scale 1/25)

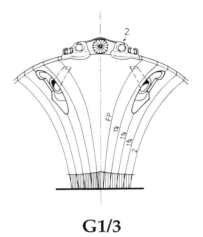

G1/3

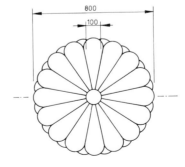

G1/4

G Ground tackle

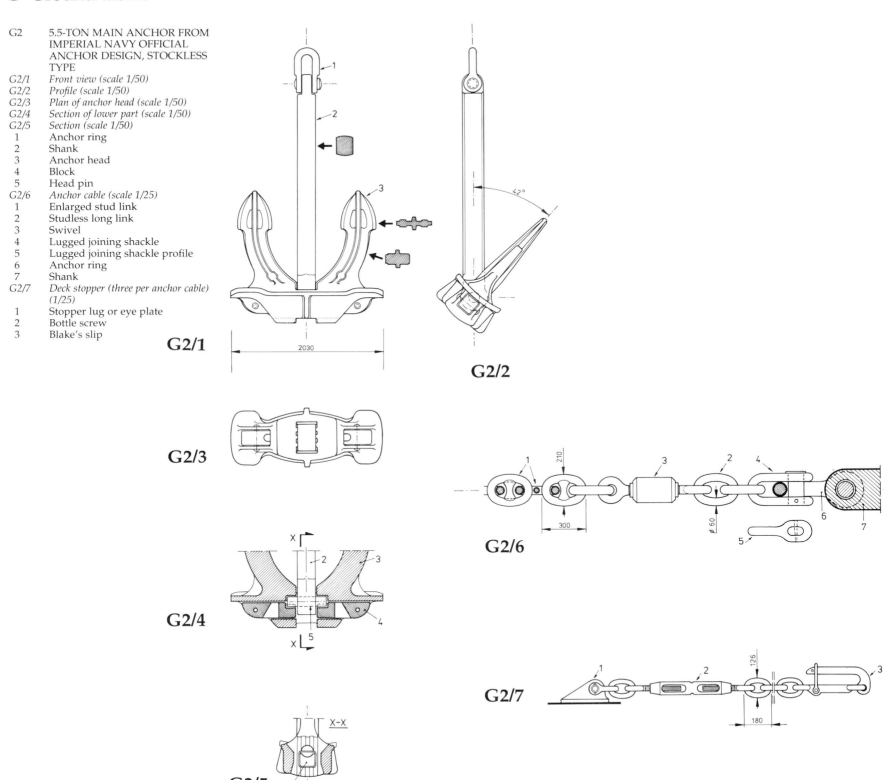

G2   5.5-TON MAIN ANCHOR FROM IMPERIAL NAVY OFFICIAL ANCHOR DESIGN, STOCKLESS TYPE
G2/1   *Front view (scale 1/50)*
G2/2   *Profile (scale 1/50)*
G2/3   *Plan of anchor head (scale 1/50)*
G2/4   *Section of lower part (scale 1/50)*
G2/5   *Section (scale 1/50)*
1   Anchor ring
2   Shank
3   Anchor head
4   Block
5   Head pin
G2/6   *Anchor cable (scale 1/25)*
1   Enlarged stud link
2   Studless long link
3   Swivel
4   Lugged joining shackle
5   Lugged joining shackle profile
6   Anchor ring
7   Shank
G2/7   *Deck stopper (three per anchor cable) (1/25)*
1   Stopper lug or eye plate
2   Bottle screw
3   Blake's slip

G2/1

G2/2

G2/3

G2/4

G2/5

G2/6

G2/7

G3   ELECTRIC CAPSTAN
G3/1   Profile (scale 1/50)
G3/2   Hood plate (scale 1/50)
G3/3   Cover over brake (no scale)
1   Scroll plate
2   Hood plate
3   Hole for portable capstan bars
4   Sprocket and snugs
5   Brake handwheel
6   Ramp to navel pipe
7   Ramp to chaffing plate

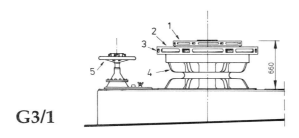

G3/1

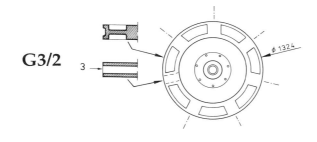

G3/2

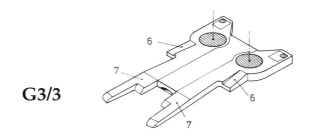

G3/3

H Fittings

H1   FORECASTLE DECK FITTINGS,
      FRAMES 66–144
H1/1   *Plan (scale 1/200)*
H1/2   *Starboard view (scale 1/200)*
1   Skylight
2   Hatch
3   Mushroom vents
4   Electric winch
5   Fore accommodation ladder
6   Ladder davit
7   Accommodation ladder stowed for sea
8   Upper platform – wooden grating
9   Foot plate
10   Lower platform
11   Paravane – deck stowage
12   Davit
13   Closed deck holes
14   Brass strips – support for linoleum
15   Scupper
16   Torpedo room
17   61cm twin type 89 torpedo tube
18   Passage
19   No 1 boiler room vent
20   Workshop
21   (Bend) line of side surface bending

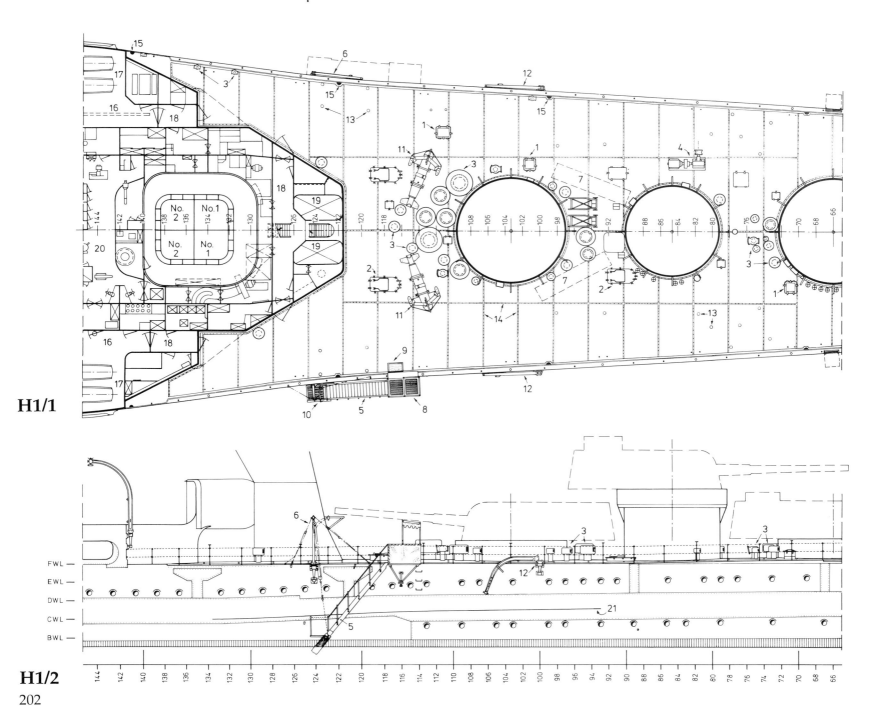

H1/1

H1/2

202

*H1/3   Accommodation ladder and side
        plating (no scale)*

H2   TYPICAL SKYLIGHT (scale 1/25)
H2/1   Profile
H2/2   Plan

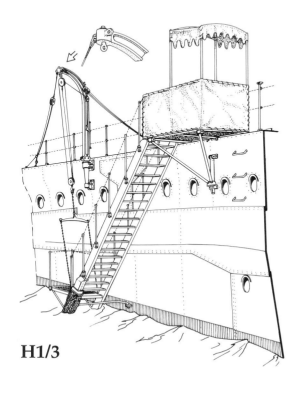

H1/3

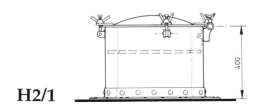

H2/1

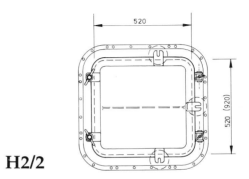

H2/2

H Fittings

H3   GUARD RAILS (scale 1/25)
H3/1   *Front view*
H3/2   *Profile*
H3/3   *Guard rail stanchion used as lower*
          part of awning stanchion – front view
H3/4   *Profile*
H3/5   *Azonometric (no scale)*
1   Guard rail stanchion
2   Guard rail of chain
3   Spurnwater
4   Waterway
5   Brass stripe
6   Linoleum
7   Scupper
H3/6   *Detail of brass strip – support of*
          linoleum joints (no scale)

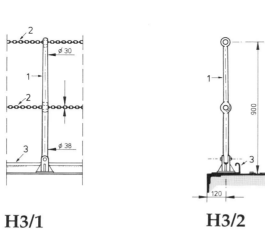

H3/1

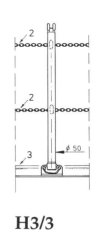

H3/2

H3/3

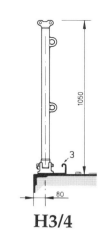

H3/4

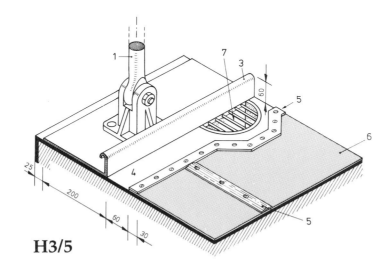

H3/5

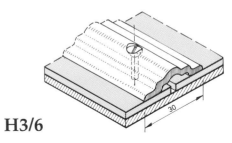

H3/6

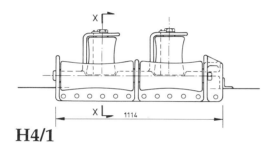

H4/1

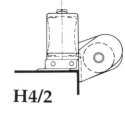

H4/2

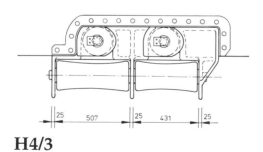

H4/3

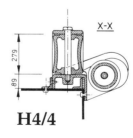

H4/4

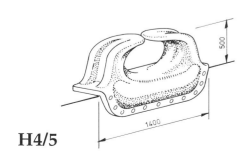

H4/5

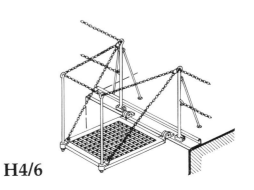

H4/6

H Fittings

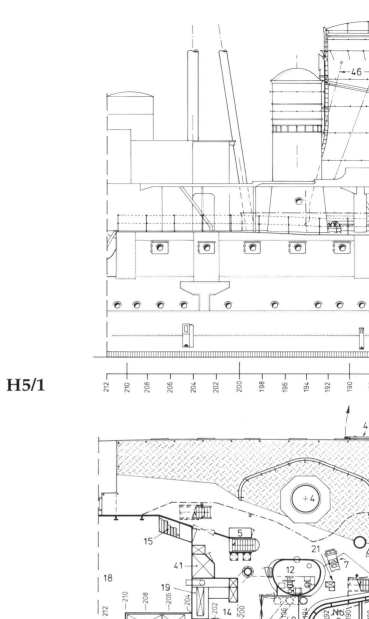

H5/1

H5/2

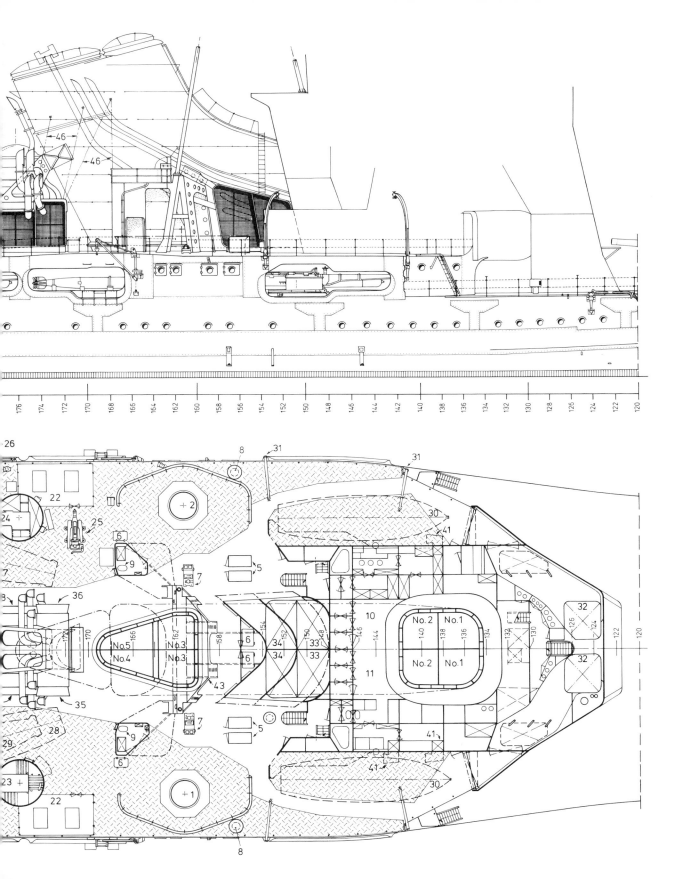

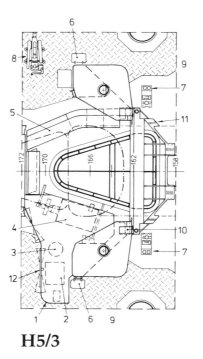

H5/3

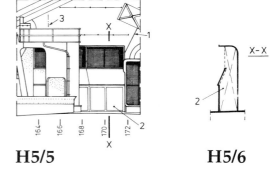

H5/5

H5/6

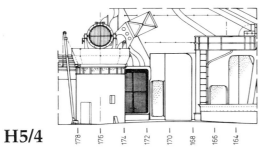

H5/4

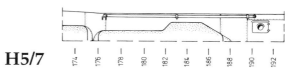

H5/7

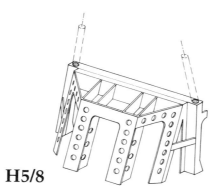

H5/8

H6 MIDSHIP HULL AND HA GUN DECK FITTINGS, 1942, FRAMES 140–216

H6/1 *Starboard elevation (scale 1/200)*

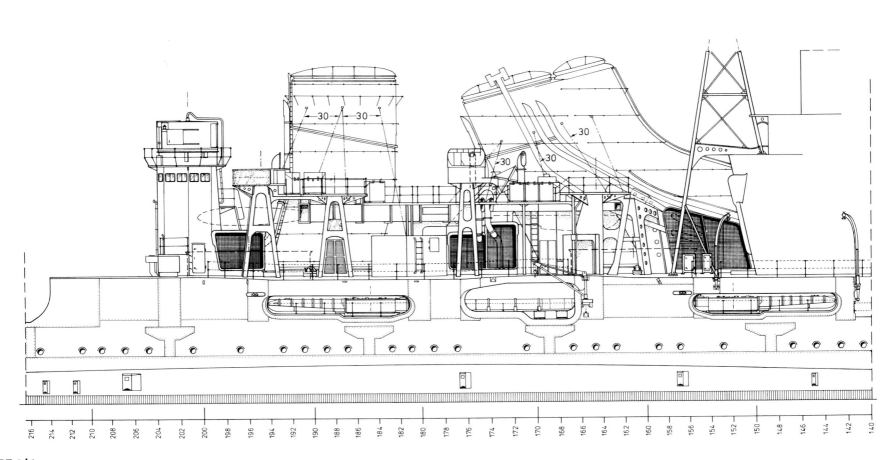

H6/1

H Fittings

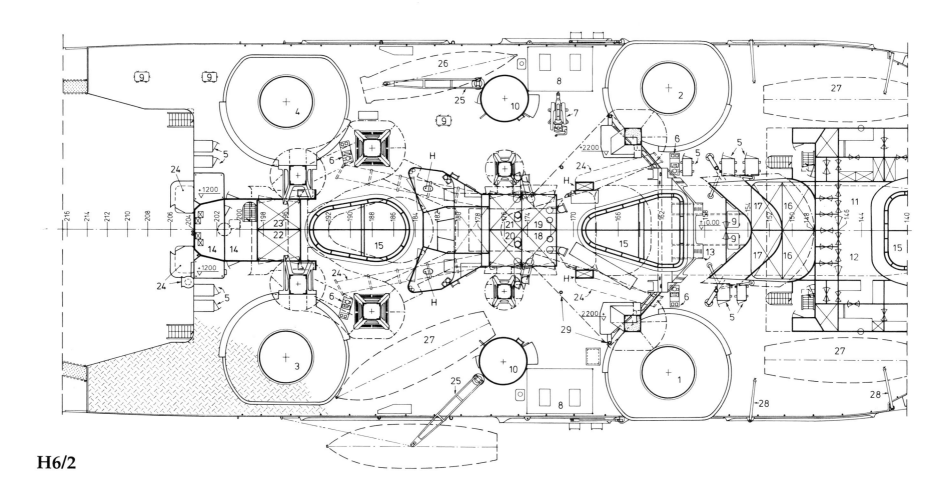

H6/2

19	No 5 boiler room ventilation fans	25	6m derrick (for boats)	31	25mm twin MG platforms	36	Intake (ventilators)
20	No 6 boiler room ventilation fans	26	27ft (8.2m) sampan position	32	25mm ammunition box	37	Auxiliary low angle director
21	No 7 boiler room ventilation fans	27	9m cutter position	33	110cm searchlight *92 Shiki* platform		platform (*94 Shiki Hoiban Shōjun*
22	No 8 boiler room ventilation fans	28	9m cutter davits		with circular wood grating		*Sōchi*)
23	No 9 boiler room ventilation fans	29	Pillar	34	Communication platform	H	Hoist
24	Ventilators	30	Funnel stay	35	MG fire control tower – *95 Shiki*	H6/4	*Intakes behind fore funnel (scale 1/200)*

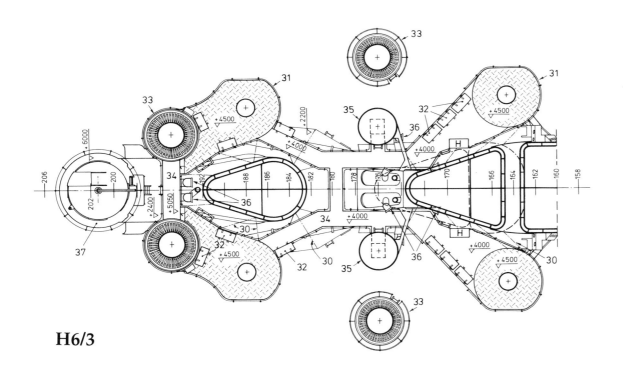

H6/3

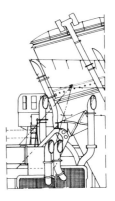

H6/4

211

H Fittings

H7	MIDDLE STRUCTURE AND PLATFORMS, SEPTEMBER 1944 (scale 1/200)	2	25mm triple MG post, frame 202 in July–August 1943, frame 186 and on stern deck in June–September 1944	5	MG fire control tower – *95 Shiki Kiju Shageki Sōchi*. Note 80cm higher level than in 1939
H7/1	*Elevation*			6	110cm searchlight *92 Shiki* platform
H7/2	*Plan*	3	25mm single MG post, fitted in frame 180 in June–September 1944	7	Standby room of AA fire crew, 1943
H7/3	*Section frame 182*			8	Standby room of AA fire crew, September 1944
1	25mm twin MG post, August 1939	4	25mm ammunition box		

9	Funnel
10	Auxiliary fire control room
11	Ventilator intake
12	Gangway with wood grating
13	4.5m rangefinder tower on bridge superstructure (94 shiki)
14	Hoist

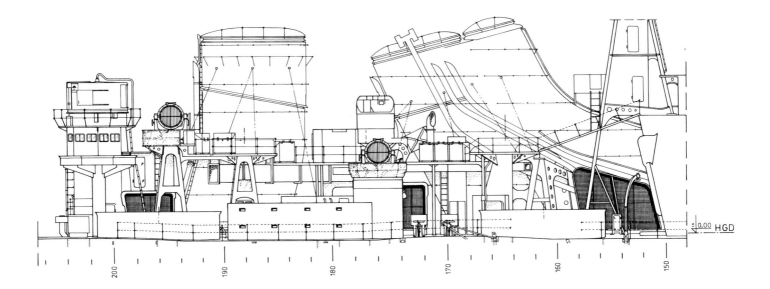

H7/1

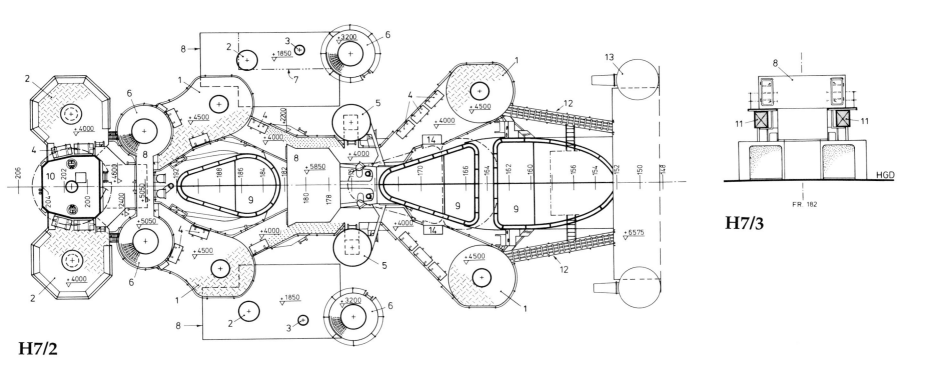

H7/2

H7/3

H Fittings

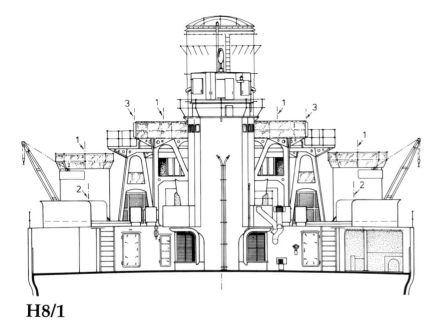

H8/1

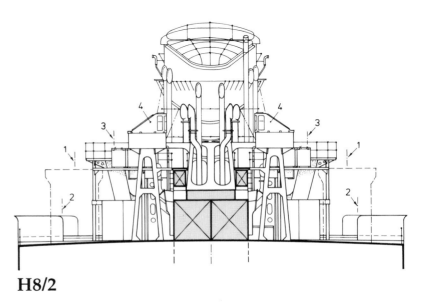

H8/2

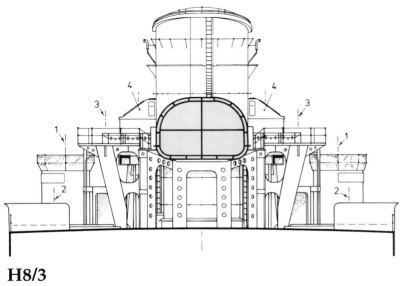

H8/3

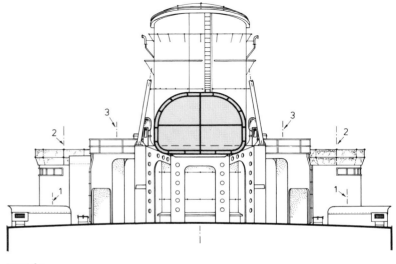

H8/4

H9 SECTION OF SUPERSTRUCTURE,
AUGUST 1932, VIEW FROM
FRAMES 178–160 (scale 1/200)
1   7.7mm MG stand
2   110cm searchlight tower with anti-
    blast shield and canvas roof
3   5m derrick for moving boats

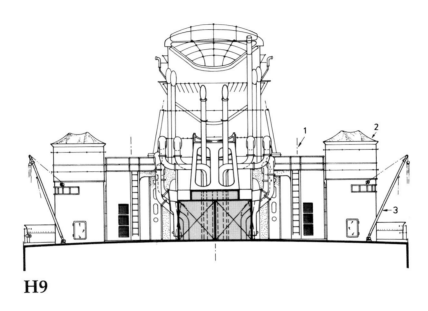

H9

H Fittings

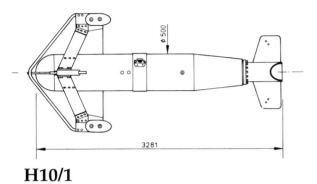

H10/1

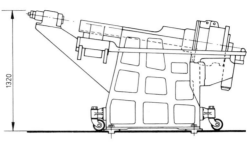

H11/1

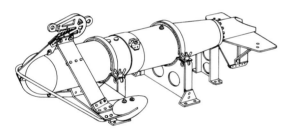

H10/2

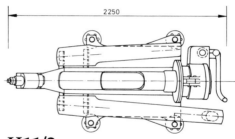

H11/2

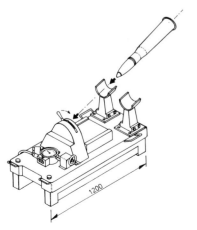

H10/3

H12   9m CUTTER ON RADIAL
      DAVITS (BOTH SIDES OF SHIP)
      FRAMES 140–152 (scale 1/100)
H12/1   *Elevation*
H12/2   *Front view*
1   Radial davit
2   Blocks
3   Jackstay
4   Lifelines
5   Jacob's ladder
6   Gripes
7   Fairlead
8   Griping spar
9   Cleat
10   Hinged seating
11   Working guy
12   Boat cruth on HGD (high angle
      deck)

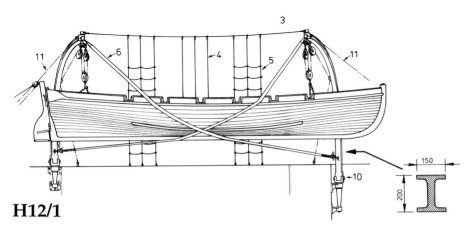

H12/1

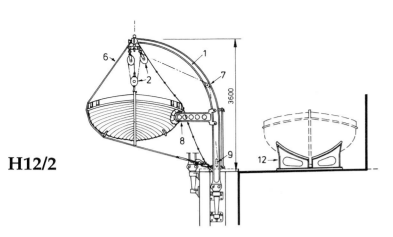

H12/2

H13   TYPICAL REELS
H13/1   *85cm reel (scale 1/50)*
H13/2   *85cm reel (from aircraft deck 1939–*
      45) (scale 1/50)
H13/3   *60cm reel (scale 1/50)*

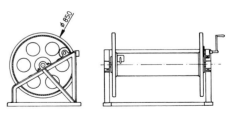

H13/1

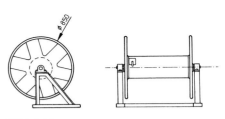

H13/2

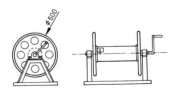

H13/3

H14   ARMOURED DEGAUSSING
      CABLE, SEE GENERAL PROFILE
      1944 (scale 1/25)

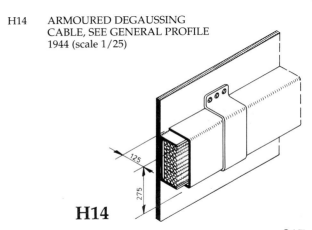

H14

H Fittings

H15   TYPICAL SCUPPER PIPES
        (no scale)

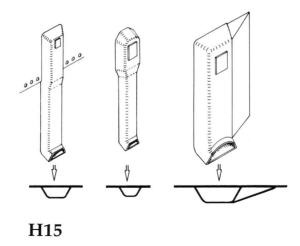

H15

H16   FORE FUNNEL WHITE BANDS –
        USED ONLY IN PEACE TIME
        (scale 1/200)

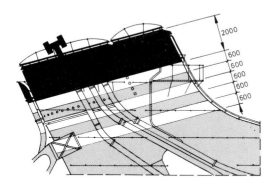

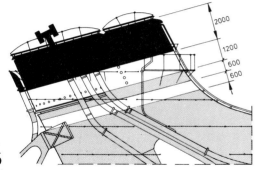

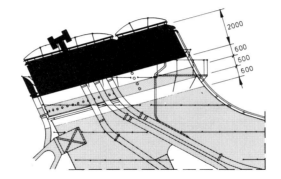

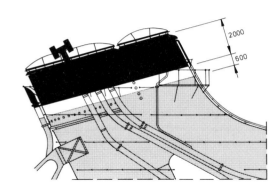

H16

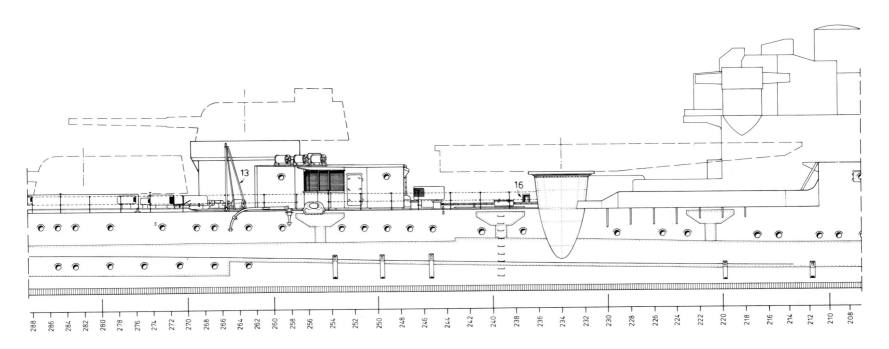

H17/1

H Fittings

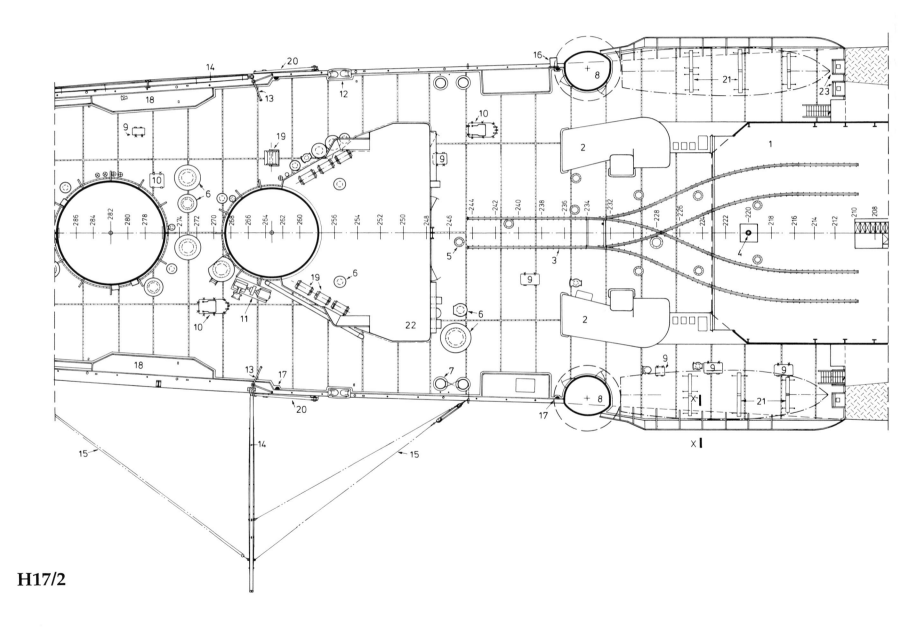

H17/2

220

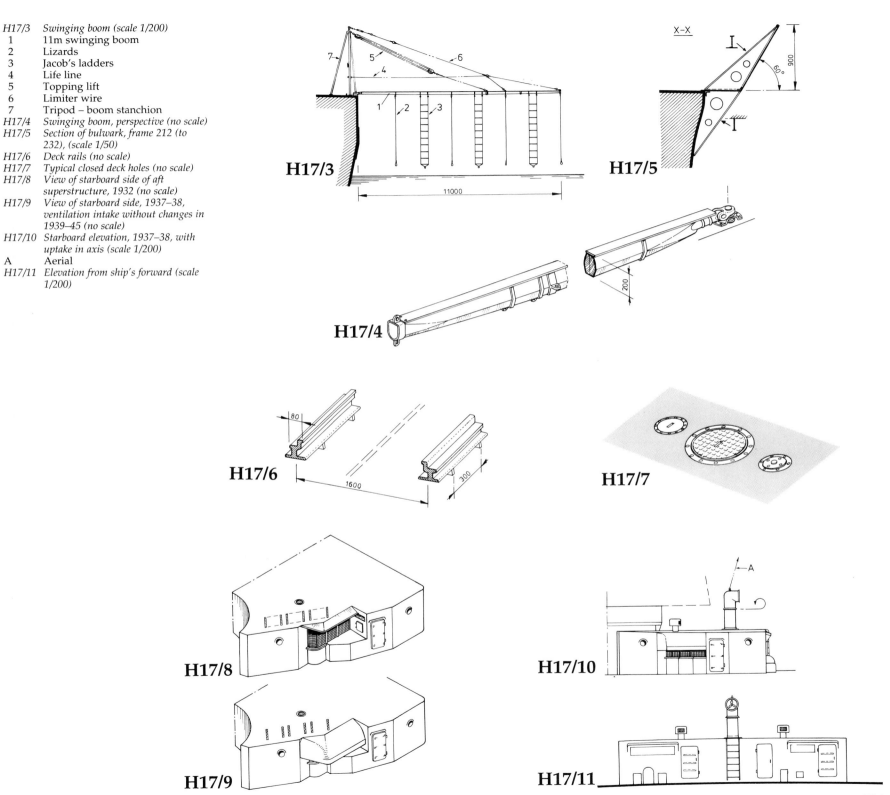

H17/3

H17/5

H17/4

H17/6

H17/7

H17/8

H17/9

H17/10

H17/11

221

H Fittings

H18 AIRCRAFT DECK AND BOAT
     DECK AFTER REBUILD, AUGUST
     1939, FRAMES 200–270
H18/1 *Starboard elevation (scale 1/200)*
H18/2 *Plan of upper deck level (boats deck)*
       (scale 1/200)

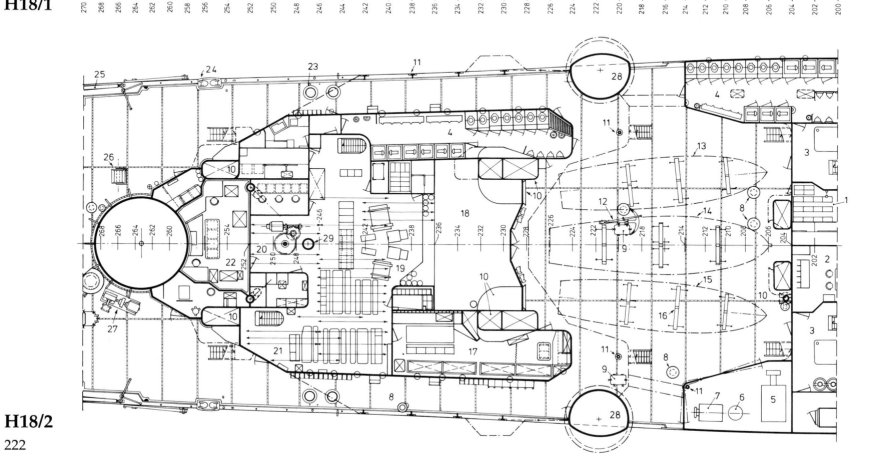

H18/1

H18/2

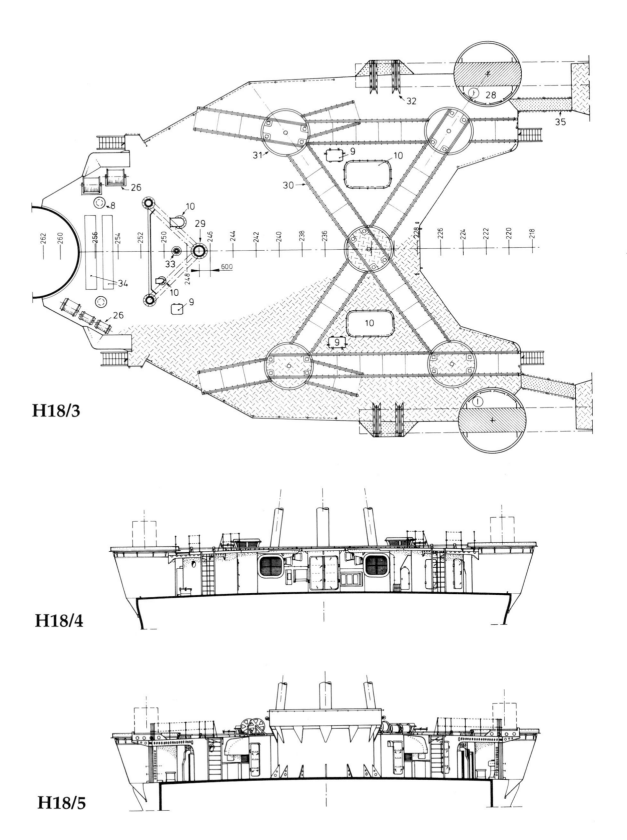

H18/3

H18/4

H18/5

H Fittings

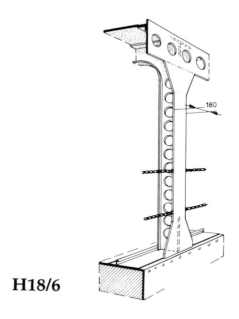

H18/6

H18/7

H19 STERN PART OF HULL AND
DECK FITTINGS, FRAMES 282–
358

*H19/1 Starboard profile, after part of hull,
1932 (scale 1/200)*

1 Hatch
2 Wash-deck locker
3 Reels
4 Mushroom type ventilators
5 Closed deck holes
6 Skylight
7 11m swinging boom
8 Scupper
9 Deck washer
10 Life buoy
11 Outer propeller folding limiter
(boom)
12 Inner propeller limiter
13 Awning stay
14 After capstan
15 Deck eye plate

16 Bollards
17 Screen smoke
18 Fairlead (towing)
19 Ensign staff tripod – stanchion
(and dressing line and awning line
support)
20 Ensign staff – folding
21 Gold *hiragana* (ship name)
22 After anchor
23 Admirality pattern anchor (after
August 1939 on boat deck)
24 Admirality pattern anchor derrick
(davit)
25 Hatch to magazines
26 Aerial antennae stanchion (1934–38
and September 1944–45)
27 Aerial antennae support with radio
equipment, August 1939–June 1944
28 Dressing line to top of mainmast
29 Antenna aerials to both sides of
main mast top wireless yard
30 Dept charges projector
31 Brass stripes – support of linoleum
32 12ft 9in (3886mm) diameter
propeller
33 Rudder

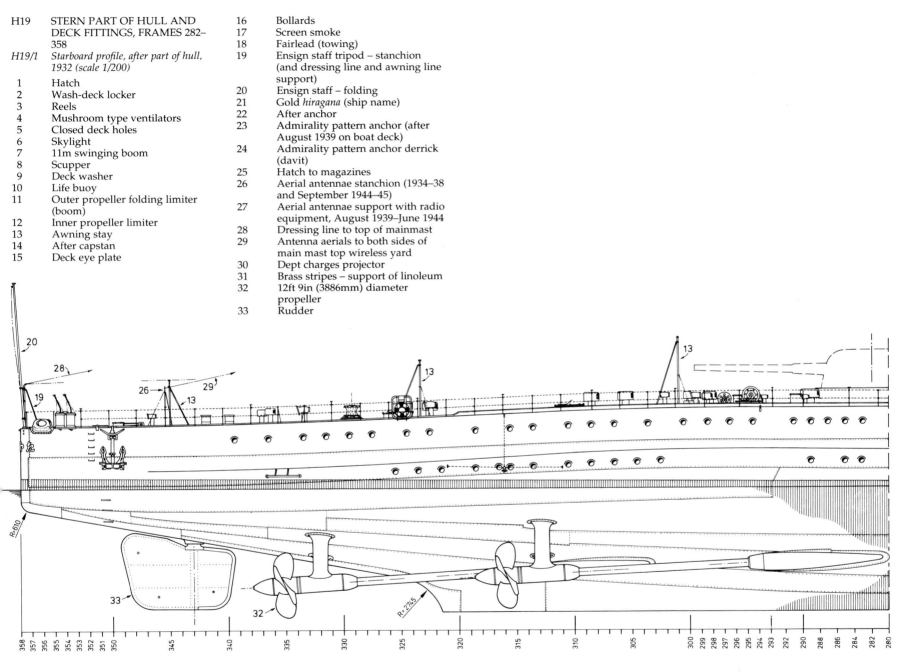

H19/1

H Fittings

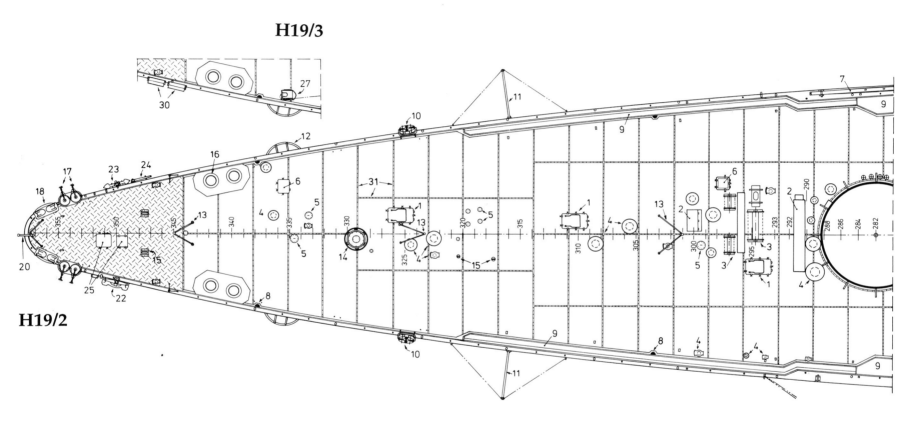

H19/3

H19/2

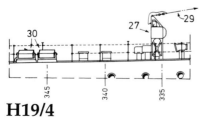

H19/4

H19/5   *Port side profile, 1932–38 (fragment)*
        (scale 1/200)

H19/6   *Gold* hiragana *inscription on stern –*
        development of stern side surface
        (scale 1/50)
H19/7   *Stern anchor (scale 1/50)*
H19/8   *Admiralty pattern anchor (scale 1/50)*

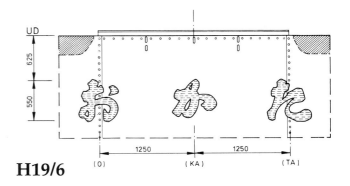

H19/6

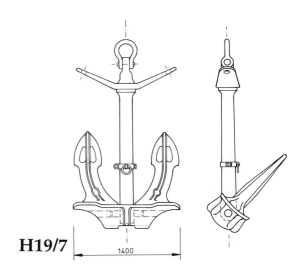

H19/7

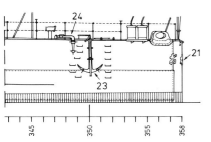

H19/5

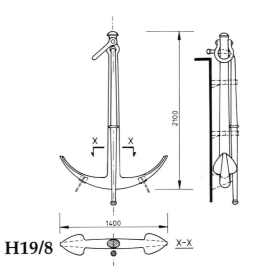

H19/8

H Fittings

H19/9   *Life buoy – front view (scale 1/50)*
H19/10 *Life buoy – profile (scale 1/50)*
H19/11 *Perspective (no scale)*
H19/12 *Deck washer rear part (note brass stripes on linoleum surface) (no scale)*
H19/13 *Deck washer – section (scale 1/20)*

H20   ANTENNA AERIALS SUPPORT WITH RADIO EQUIPMENT – FRAME 335 (AUGUST 1939–JUNE 1944) – PORT SIDE SUPPORT *(scale 1/50)*
H20/1 *Profile view from ship axis*
H20/2 *View from ship forward*
H20/3 *Plan*
H20/4 *View from ship side*

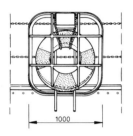

H19/9

H19/10

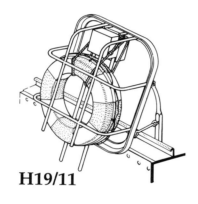

H19/11

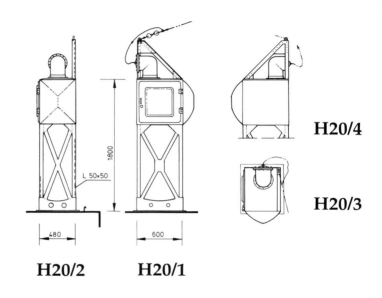

H20/4

H20/3

H20/2   **H20/1**

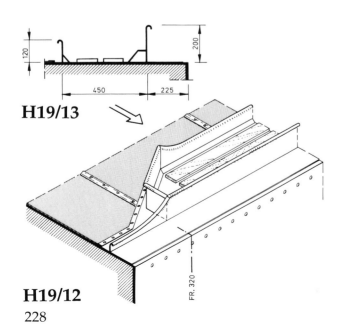

H19/13

H19/12

H21   PROPELLERS
H21/1 *12ft 9in = 3886mm propeller (scale 1/100)*
H21/2 *Scheme of propellers' rotation (no scale)*

H21/1

H21/2

228

H22   VENTILATORS
*H22/1 Mushroom type ventilators – profiles
       and plans (scale 1/50)*
*H22/2 Mushroom type ventilators – detail of
       deck assembly (no scale)*
1   Leg of ventilator

2   Circular stripe
3   Linoleum
4   Deck plate
*H22/3 Detail of mushroom type ventilator
       wire gird (no scale)*

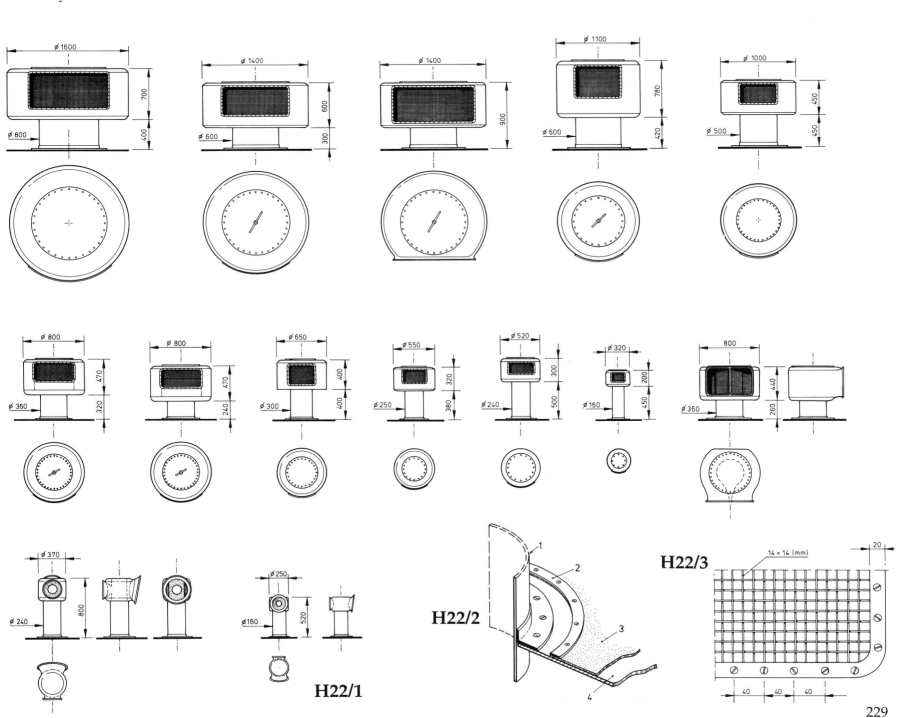

H22/1

H22/2

H22/3

229

H Fittings

H23 DECK HATCH – TYPE USED IN
   FORE DECKS
H23/1 *Plan (scale 1.25)*
H23/2 *Profile (scale 1/25)*
H23/3 *Profile with open hatch (scale 1/25)*
H23/4 *Front view (scale 1/25)*

H23/1

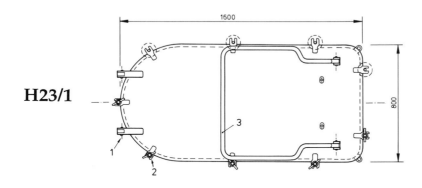

H23/2

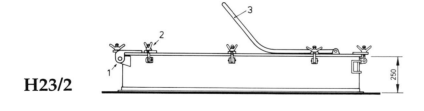

H23/4

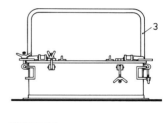

H23/3

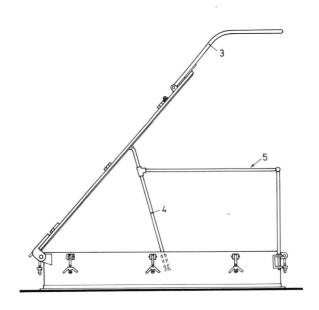

H24   DECK HATCH – TYPE USED ON
           REAR DECK
H24/1 Plan (scale 1/25)
H24/2 Profile (scale 1/25)
  1   Hinge
  2   Butterfly nut
  3   Handle
H24/3 Detail of deck assembly (no scale)
  1   Hatch side
  2   Angle bar
  3   Flat bar
  4   Linoleum
  5   Deck plate
  6   Brass strip – holder for linoleum
H24/4 Detail of chequer plate (scale 1/12½)

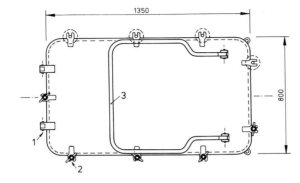

H24/1

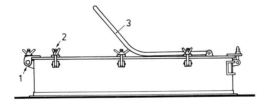

H24/2

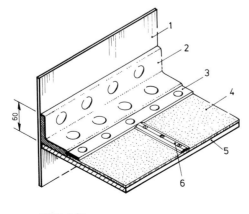

H24/3

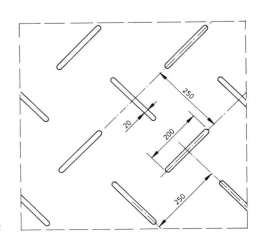

H24/4

H Fittings

H25   110cm *92 SHIKI* SEARCHLIGHT
        (scale 1/37½)
H25/1   *Left profile*
H25/2   *Front view*
H25/3   *Right profile*
H25/4   *Rear view*
H25/5   *Plan*

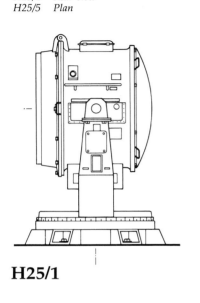

H25/1

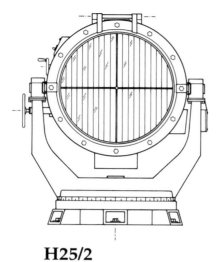

H25/2

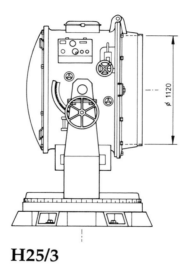

H25/3

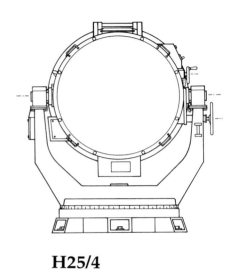

H25/4

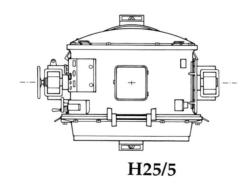

H25/5

H26   60cm SIGNALLING
        SEARCHLIGHT (scale 1/37½)
H26/1   *Left profile*
H26/2   *Front view*
H26/3   *Right profile*
H26/4   *Plan*

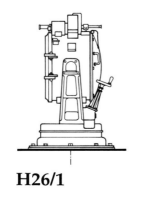

H26/1

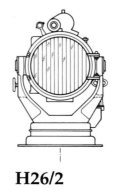

H26/2

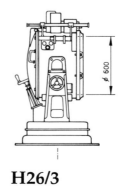

H26/3

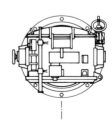

H26/4

H27   30cm DECK LAMP (scale 1/25)
H27/1   *Front view*
H27/2   *Right profile*
H27/3   *Plan*
H27/4   *Section*

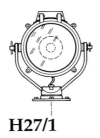 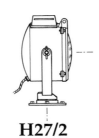 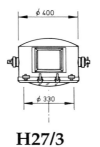 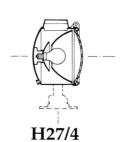

H27/1   **H27/2**   **H27/3**   **H27/4**

H28   30cm SIGNALLING LAMP
       (scale 1/25)
H28/1   *Front view*
H28/2   *Profile*

 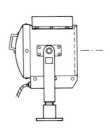

H28/1   **H28/2**

H29   2kw DAYLIGHT SIGNAL
       LANTERN
Fitted 1932–35 – rear of main fire control platform
– both sides below 4.5m rangefinder, 1935–45 one
lantern on foremast and one on mainmast.
H29/1   *Rear view (scale 1/20)*
H29/2   *Plan (scale 1/20)*
H29/3   *Typical lantern (scale 1/20)*

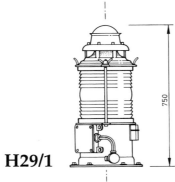 

H29/1   **H29/3**

H29/2

H Fittings

H30   SIDE SCUTTLE (scale 1/20)
H30/1   *Side scuttle*
H30/2   *Front view of side scuttle from ship*
         sides and superstructure
H30/3   *Front view of side scuttle from tower*
         bridge fore wall
H30/4   *Front view of side scuttle from tower*
         bridge fore wall
1   Scuttle or port
2   Scuttle frame
3   Deadlight
4   Rubber sealing ring
5   Sidelight glass
6   Sidelight frame
7   Butterfly clips
8   Clip lug
9   Save-all
10   Hinge
11   Back of deadlight
12   Rigol
13   Ship side plating
14   Arrow indicating direction of bow

H31   WATERTIGHT DOOR FROM
         BOTH SIDES OF TOWER BRIDGE
         – FORECASTLE DECK LEVEL
         (UD)
H31/1   *Open door (scale 1/37½)*
H31/2   *Section (scale 1/37½)*
H31/3   *Outer surface and plan (scale 1/37½)*
H31/4   *Section of clip (scale 1/5)*
H31/5   *View of clip (scale 1/5)*
H31/6   *Section of hinge (scale 1/5)*
H31/7   *View of hinge (scale 1/5)*

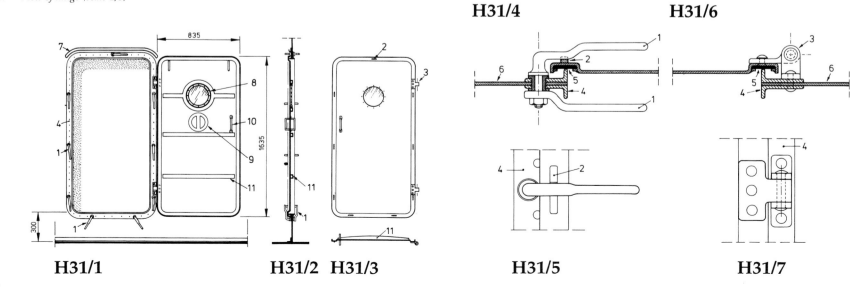

H30/2

H30/3

H30/4

H30/1

H31/4   **H31/6**

H31/1   **H31/2**   **H31/3**   **H31/5**   **H31/7**

H32 TYPICAL WATERTIGHT DOOR FROM UPPER PARTS OF SUPERSTRUCTURE
H32/1 *Open door (scale 1/37½)*
H32/2 *Section (scale 1/37½)*
H32/3 *Outer surface (scale 1/37½)*
H32/4 *Section of clip – note alternative clip (scale 1/5)*
H32/5 *View of clip (scale 1/5)*
H32/6 *Water-tight door from rear part of torpedo deck (scale 1/37½)*
  1 Clip
  2 Wedge on face of door
  3 Hinge
  4 Angle bar door frame (both sides of bulkhead)
  5 Rubber seal
  6 Bulkhead
  7 Rigol
  8 20cm diameter door scuttle
  9 Colour sign (white)
 10 Door handle – both sides
 11 Inner reinforcement
 12 Stamping reinforcement – note: middle inner, upper and lower – outer

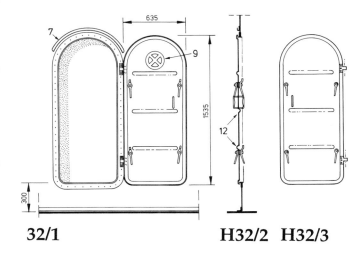

32/1 **H32/2 H32/3**

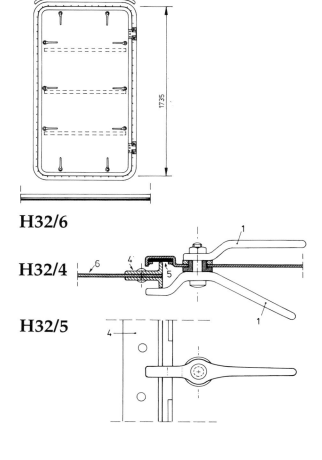

H32/6

H32/4

H32/5

H33 LADDERS (scale 1/37½)
H33/1 *Ladder from forecastle deck to HGD, rear part of HGD*
H33/2 *Ladder from superstructure*
H33/3 *Ladder from superstructure*
H33/4 *Ladder from masts, funnels, inner spaces*

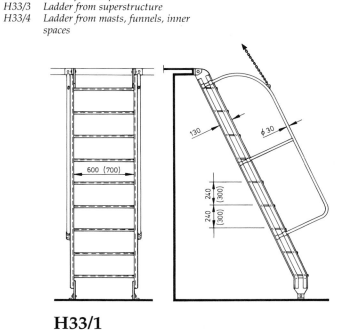

H33/1

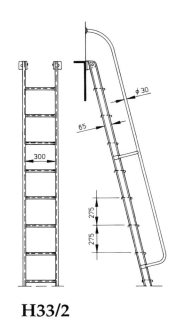

H33/2

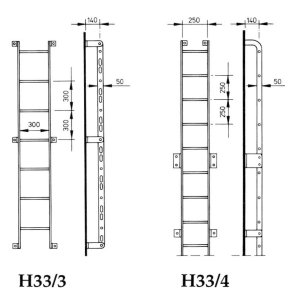

H33/3   **H33/4**

J Aircraft

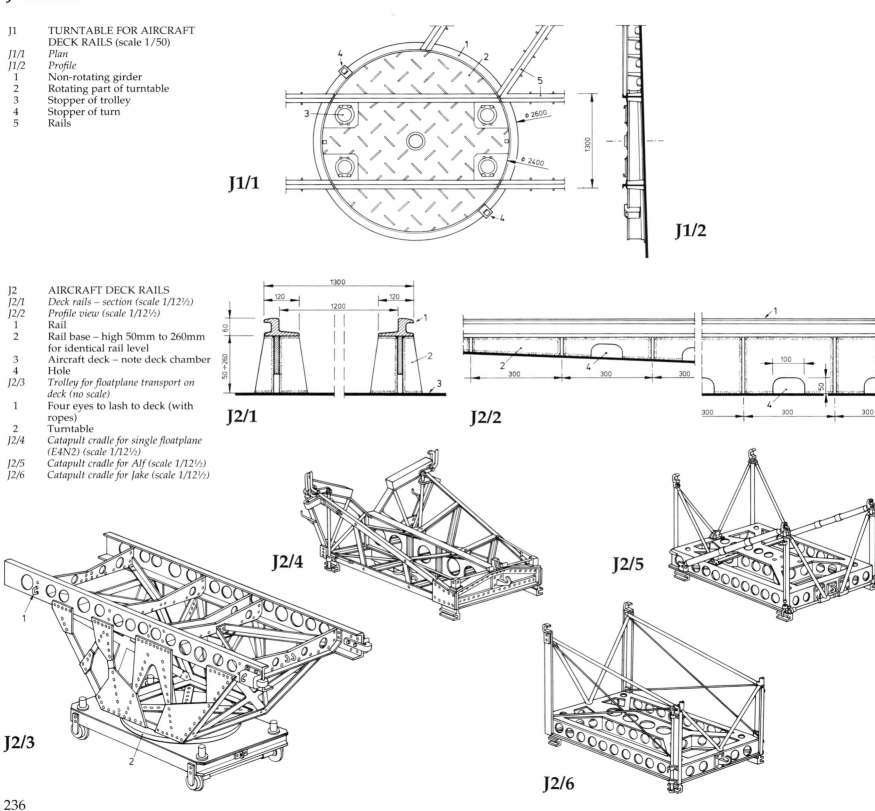

J1 TURNTABLE FOR AIRCRAFT
DECK RAILS (scale 1/50)
J1/1 *Plan*
J1/2 *Profile*
1 Non-rotating girder
2 Rotating part of turntable
3 Stopper of trolley
4 Stopper of turn
5 Rails

J1/1

φ 2600

φ 2400

1300

J1/2

J2 AIRCRAFT DECK RAILS
J2/1 *Deck rails – section (scale 1/12½)*
J2/2 *Profile view (scale 1/12½)*
1 Rail
2 Rail base – high 50mm to 260mm
for identical rail level
3 Aircraft deck – note deck chamber
4 Hole
J2/3 *Trolley for floatplane transport on
deck (no scale)*
1 Four eyes to lash to deck (with
ropes)
2 Turntable
J2/4 *Catapult cradle for single floatplane
(E4N2) (scale 1/12½)*
J2/5 *Catapult cradle for Alf (scale 1/12½)*
J2/6 *Catapult cradle for Jake (scale 1/12½)*

J2/1

1300
120 120
1200
60
50 ÷ 260

J2/2

1
2 4
300 300 300
100
50
300 300 300

J2/4

J2/5

J2/3

J2/6

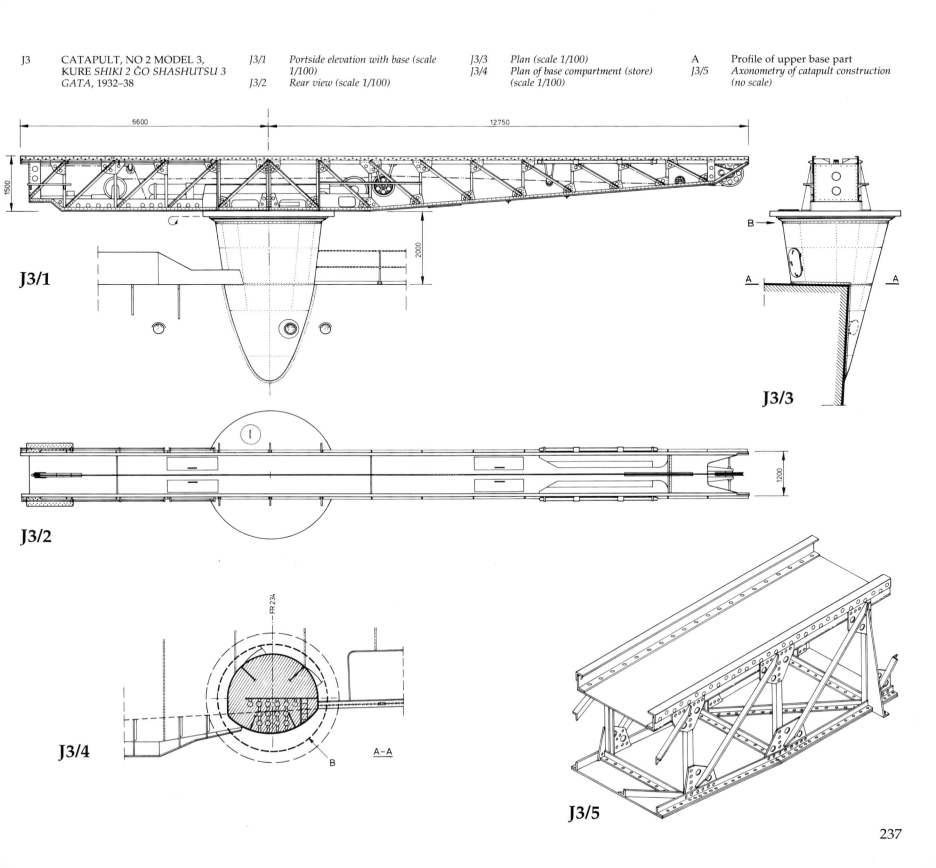

J3 CATAPULT, NO 2 MODEL 3, KURE *SHIKI 2 ĜO SHASHUTSU 3 GATA*, 1932–38

J3/1 *Portside elevation with base (scale 1/100)*
J3/2 *Rear view (scale 1/100)*
J3/3 *Plan (scale 1/100)*
J3/4 *Plan of base compartment (store) (scale 1/100)*
A *Profile of upper base part*
J3/5 *Axonometry of catapult construction (no scale)*

J3/1

J3/2

J3/3

J3/4

J3/5

J Aircraft

J4   CATAPULT, NO 2 MODEL 5, *SHIKI 2 GŌ 5 GATA, 1939–45*

J4/1   *Starboard elevation with base (scale 1/100)*

J4/2   *Rear view (scale 1/100)*

J4/3   *Plan (scale 1/100)*

J4/4   *Plan of base, section (scale 1/100)*
AA   Lower level
B   Upper level

J4/5   *Axonometry of structure (no scale)*

J4/6   *Perspective of fore part (no scale)*

J4/7   *View on catapult stay position*

support with rotation limiter on aircraft deck edge (no scale)

J4/8   *Equipment for floatplane moving, 1939–45 (scale 1/100)*

1   Deck rails for trolley

2   Deck trolley

3   Catapult cradle for floatplane

4   Rear part of catapult

5   Stoping ropes

6   Aircraft deck. Note chamber

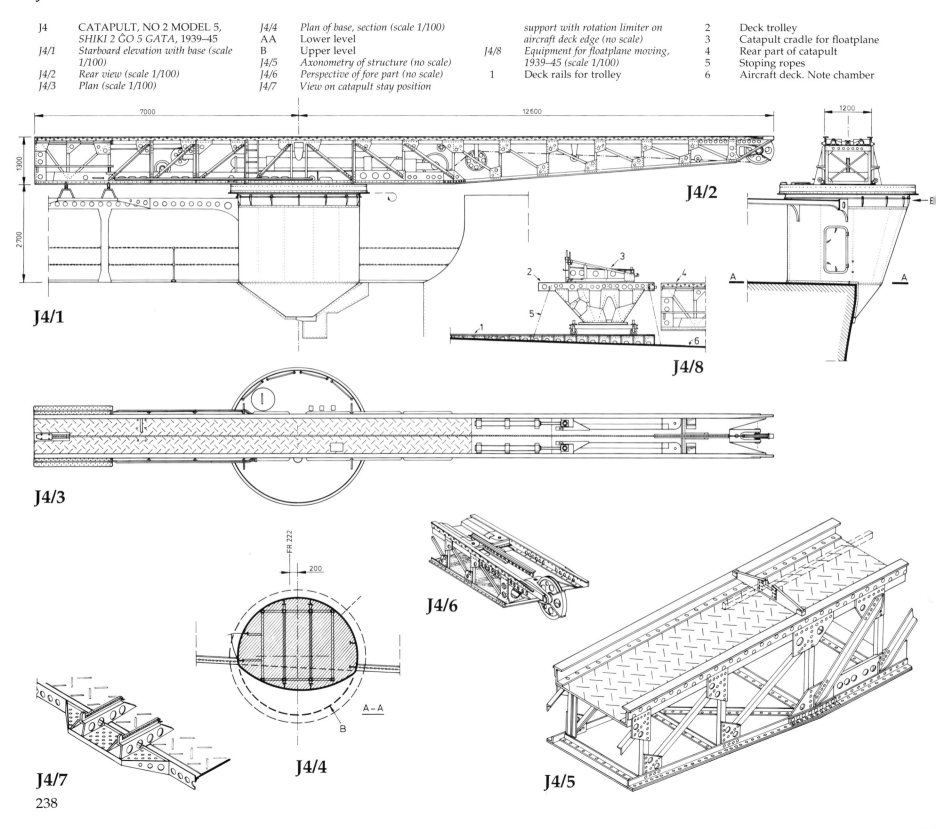

J4/1

J4/2

J4/8

J4/3

J4/6

J4/4

J4/7

J4/5

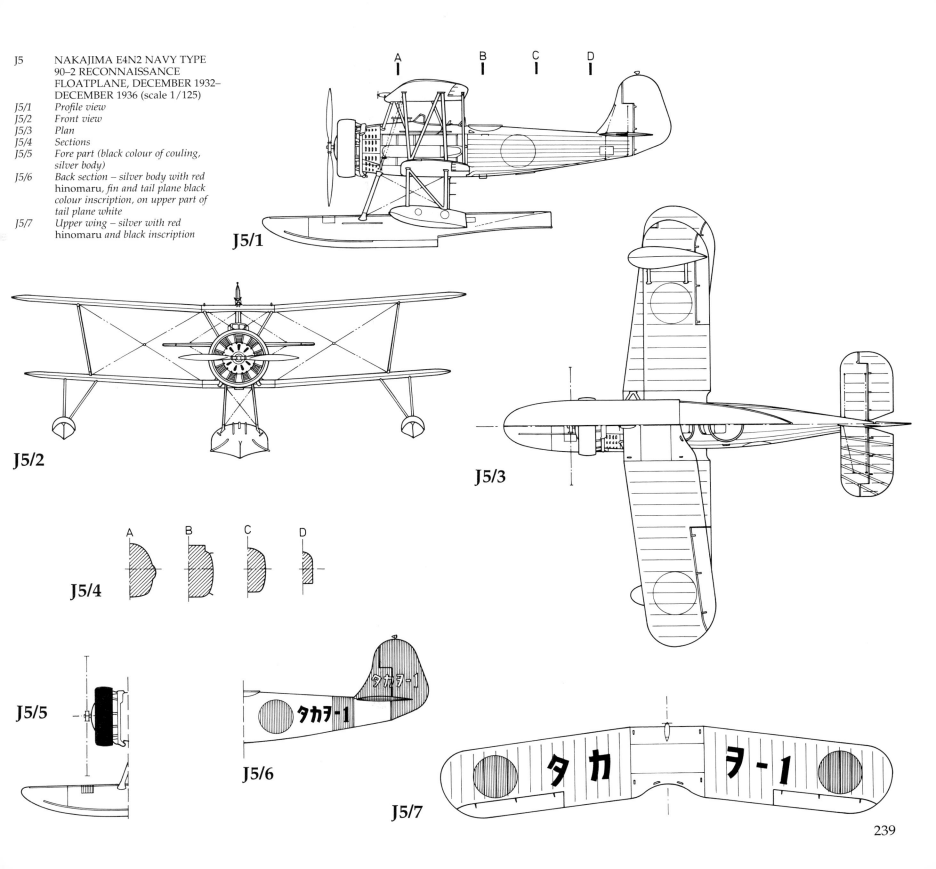

J5 NAKAJIMA E4N2 NAVY TYPE
90–2 RECONNAISSANCE
FLOATPLANE, DECEMBER 1932–
DECEMBER 1936 (scale 1/125)

J5/1   Profile view
J5/2   Front view
J5/3   Plan
J5/4   Sections
J5/5   Fore part (black colour of couling,
       silver body)
J5/6   Back section – silver body with red
       hinomaru, fin and tail plane black
       colour inscription, on upper part of
       tail plane white
J5/7   Upper wing – silver with red
       hinomaru and black inscription

J5/1

J5/2

J5/3

J5/4

J5/5

J5/6

J5/7

J Aircraft

J6   KAWANISHI E7K2 'ALF' NAVY
       TYPE 94 RECONNAISSANCE
       FLOATPLANE AUGUST 1939–
       NOVEMBER 1941 (scale 1/125)

J6/1   *Profile*
J6/2   *Front view*
J6/3   *Plan*
J6/4   *Sections*

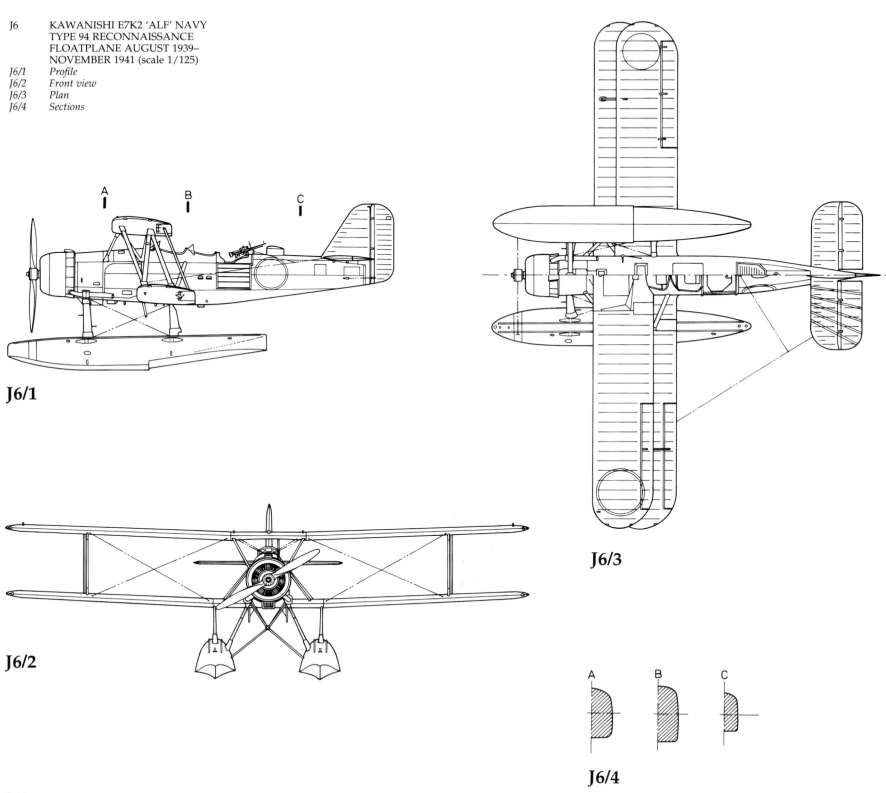

J6/1

J6/2

J6/3

J6/4

J7   KAWANISHI E7K1 'ALF' NAVY
TYPE 94 RECONNAISSANCE
FLOATPLANE, DECEMBER 1934–
1938 (scale 1/125)
J7/1   *Profile*
J7/2   *Front view (fragment)*
J7/3   *Plan (fragment) note 60kg bomb*
J7/4   *Four bladed propeller*
J7/5   *Section*

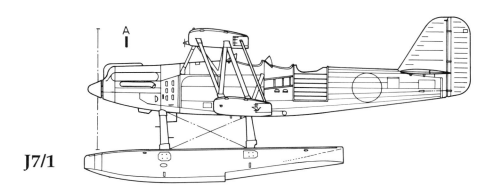

J7/1

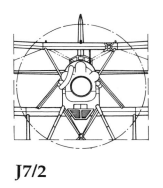

J7/2

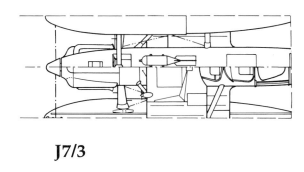

J7/3

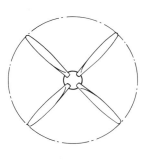

J7/4

J7/5

J Aircraft

J8 NAKAJIMA E8N2 'DAVE' NAVY
TYPE 95 RECONNAISSANCE
FLOATPLANE, DECEMBER 1936–
AUTUMN 1942 (scale 1/125)
J8/1 Profile
J8/2 Fore view
J8/3 Plan
J8/4 Sections

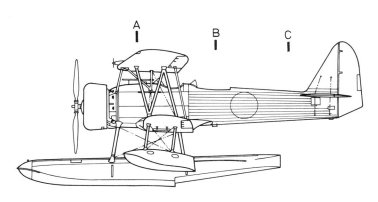

J8/1

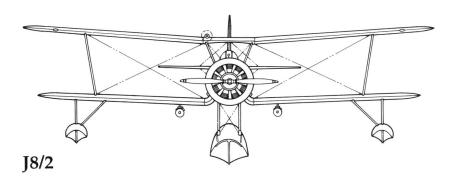

J8/2

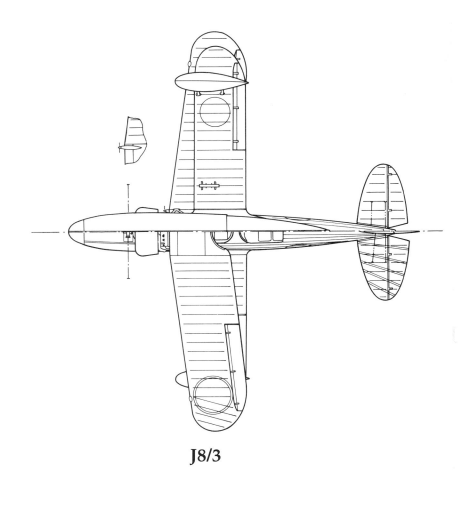

J8/3

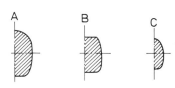

J8/4

J9   MITSUBISHI F1M2 'PETE' NAVY
      TYPE O RECONNAISSANCE
      FLOATPLANE, AUTUMN 1942–
      1945 (scale 1/125)
J9/1 Profile
J9/2 Fore view
J9/3 Plan
J9/4 Triple bladed propeller
J9/5 60kg bomb
J9/6 Sections

J9/1

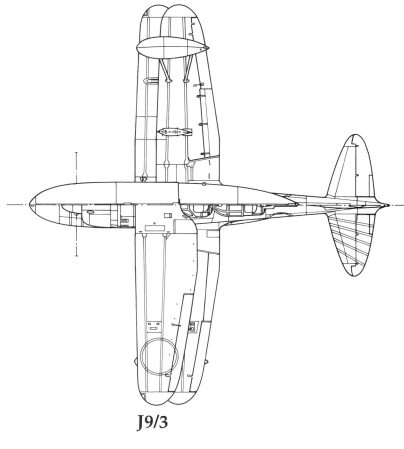

J9/3

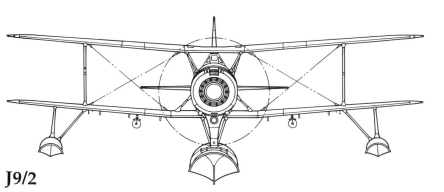

J9/2

J9/5

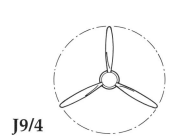

J9/4

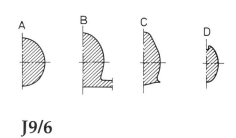

J9/6

J Aircraft

J10   AICHI E13A1 'JAKE' NAVY TYPE
O RECONNAISSANCE
FLOATPLANE AUTUMN 1942–45
(scale 1/125)
J10/1   *Profile*
J10/2   *Front view*
J10/3   *Plan*
J10/4   *Sections*

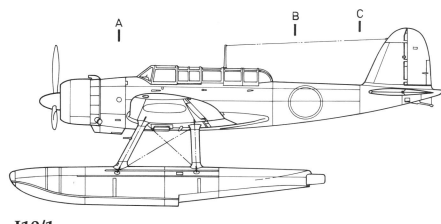

J10/1

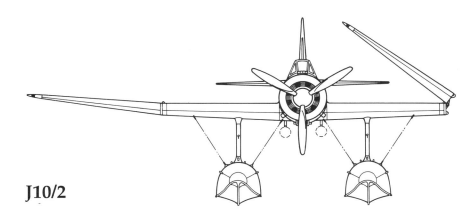

J10/2

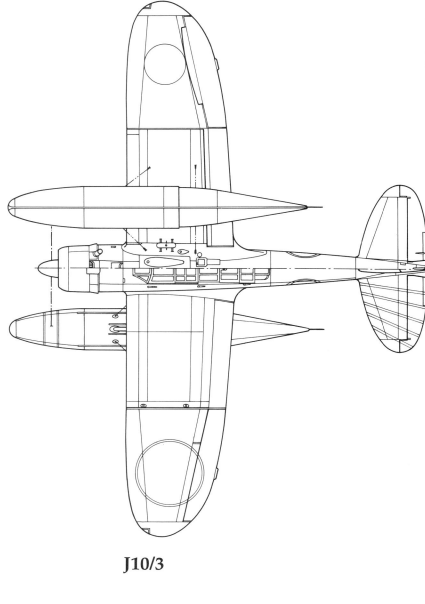

J10/3

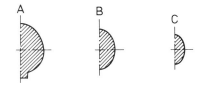

J10/4

K Boats

K1   11m 60hp MOTOR BOAT –
        CEREMONIAL BARGE
        (scale 1/75)
K1/1   *Side elevation*
K1/2   *Plan*

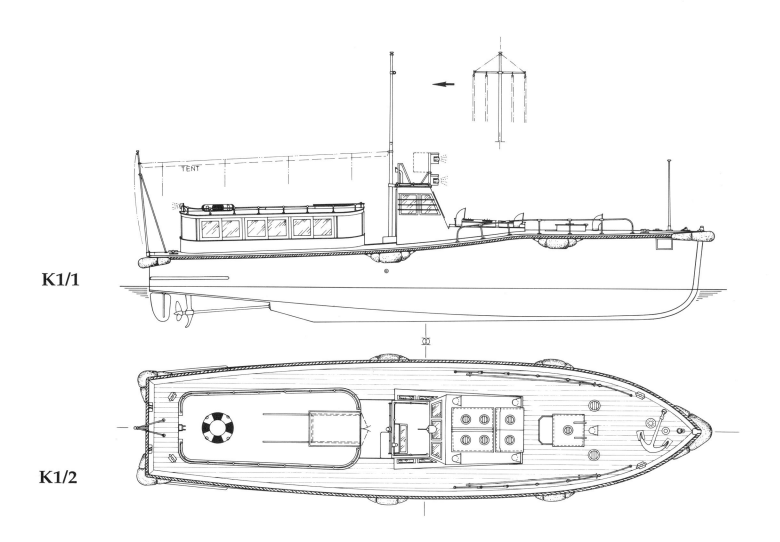

K1/1

K1/2

K

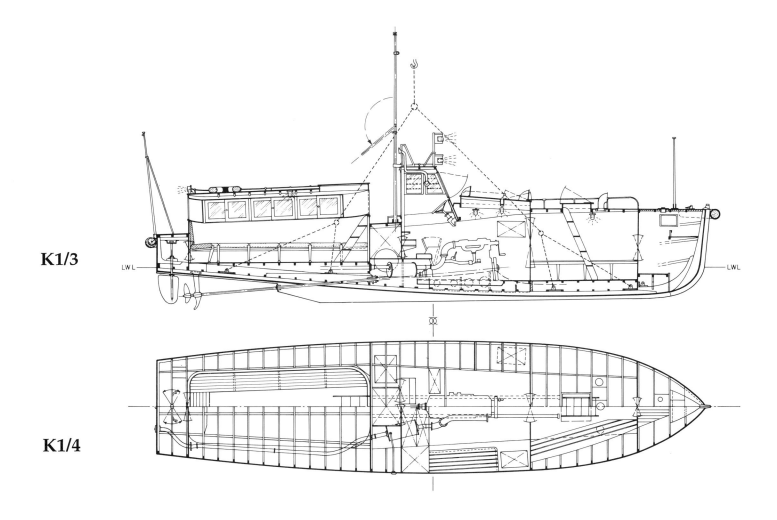

K1/3

LWL

LWL

K1/4

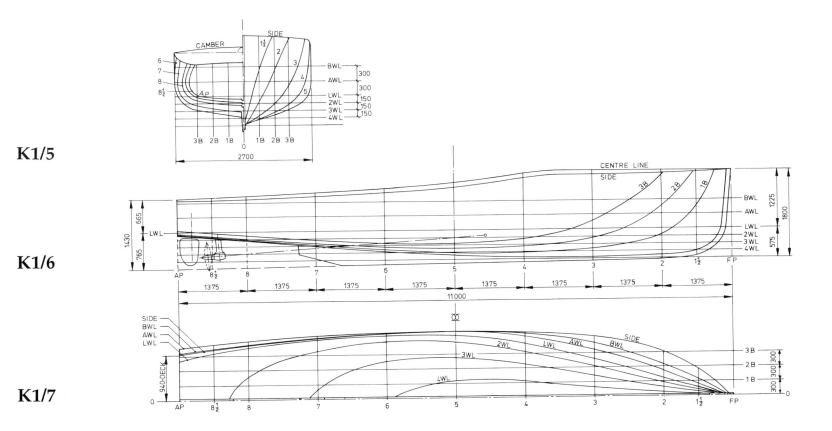

K1/5 Body plan
K1/6 Sheer elevation
K1/7 Waterline plan

K1/5

K1/6

K1/7

K Boats

K2   11m 60hp MOTOR BOAT
K2/1   Side elevation (scale 1/75)
K2/2   Plan (scale 1/75)
K2/3   Detail of canvas rack (no scale)

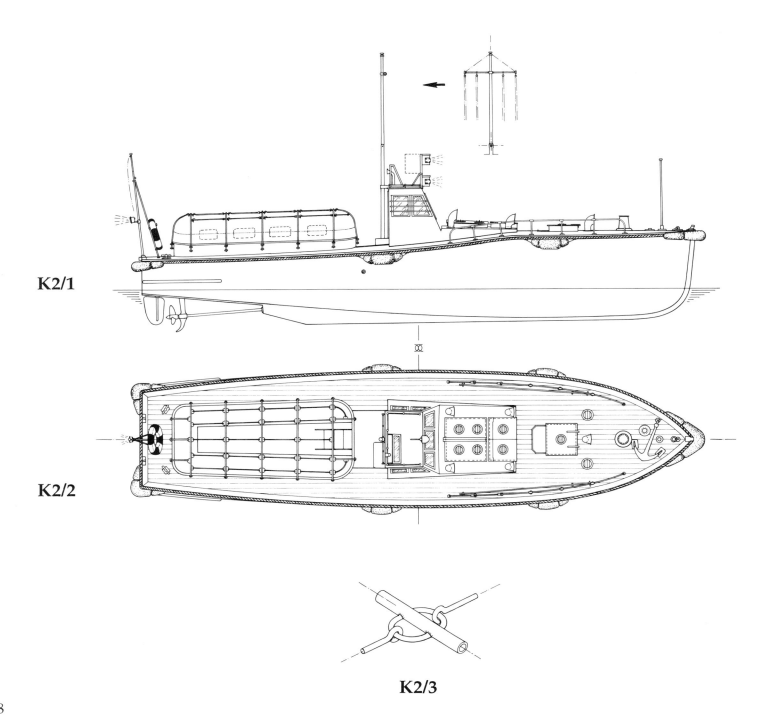

K2/1

K2/2

K2/3

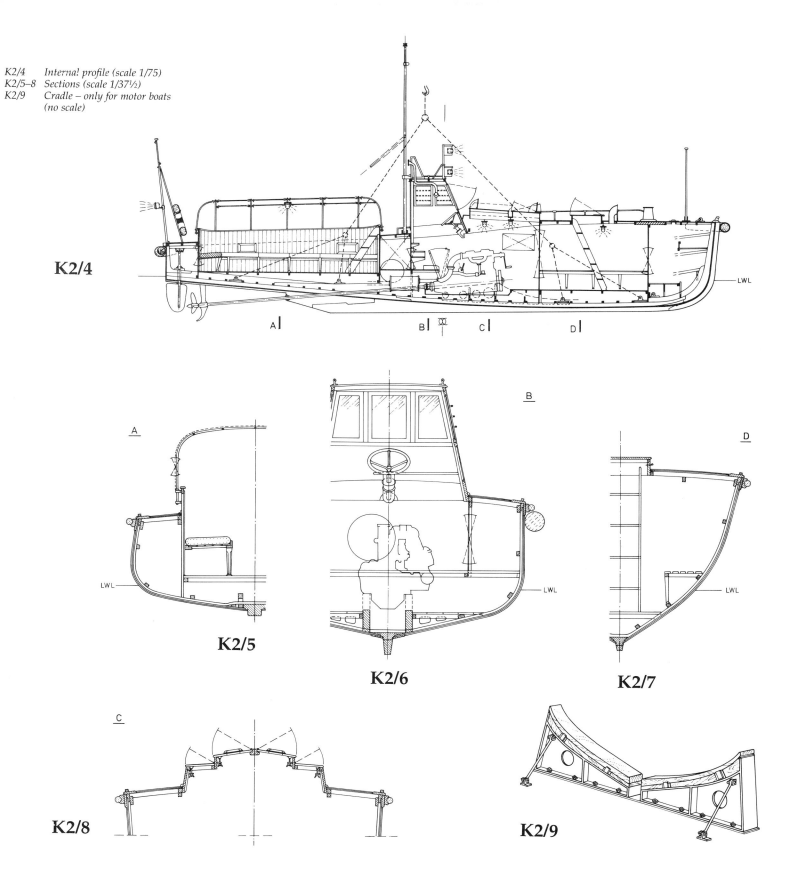

K2/4   *Internal profile (scale 1/75)*
K2/5–8   *Sections (scale 1/37½)*
K2/9   *Cradle – only for motor boats*
               (no scale)

K2/4

A   B   C   D

LWL

K2/5   **K2/6**   **K2/7**

K2/8   **K2/9**

K Boats

K3   12m 30hp MOTOR LAUNCH
(POST ON HANGAR – TWO
BOATS, AFTER 1939 ONE BOAT
ON BOAT DECK)

K3/1   *Internal profile – canvas rack was
fitted only sporadically (scale 1/75)*

K3/2   *Plan (scale 1/75)*

K3/3   *Typical cradle for 12m and 9m boats
(scale 1/75)*

K3/4   *Section of middle part (scale 1/37½)*

K3/5   *Detail of section – dolphin fender
(scale 1/18¾)*

K3/6   *Section B (scale 1/18¾)*

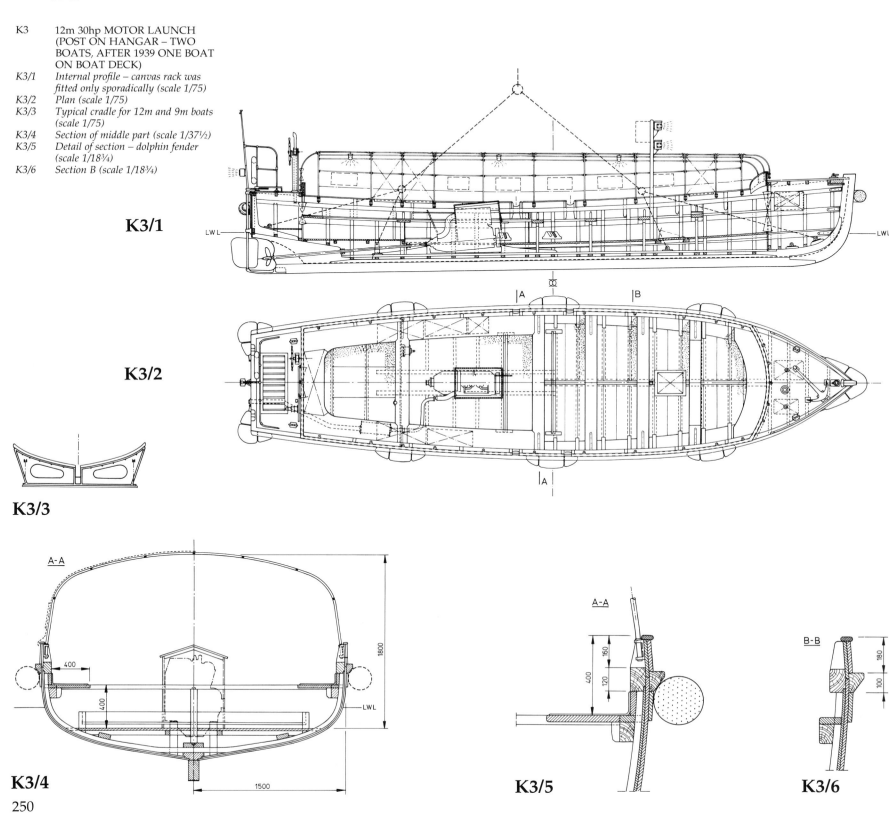

K3/1

K3/2

K3/3

K3/4

K3/5

K3/6

250

K3/7   Body plan (scale 1/75)
K3/8   Sheer elevation (scale 1/75)
K3/9   Waterline plan (scale 1/75)

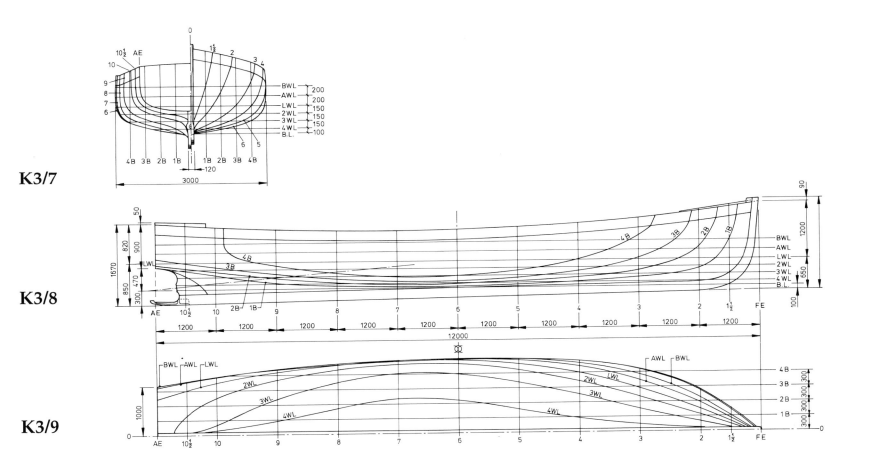

K3/7

K3/8

K3/9

251

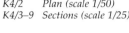

K Boats

K4   9m CUTTER
K4/1   *Internal profile (scale 1/50)*
K4/2   *Plan (scale 1/50)*
K4/3–9 *Sections (scale 1/25)*

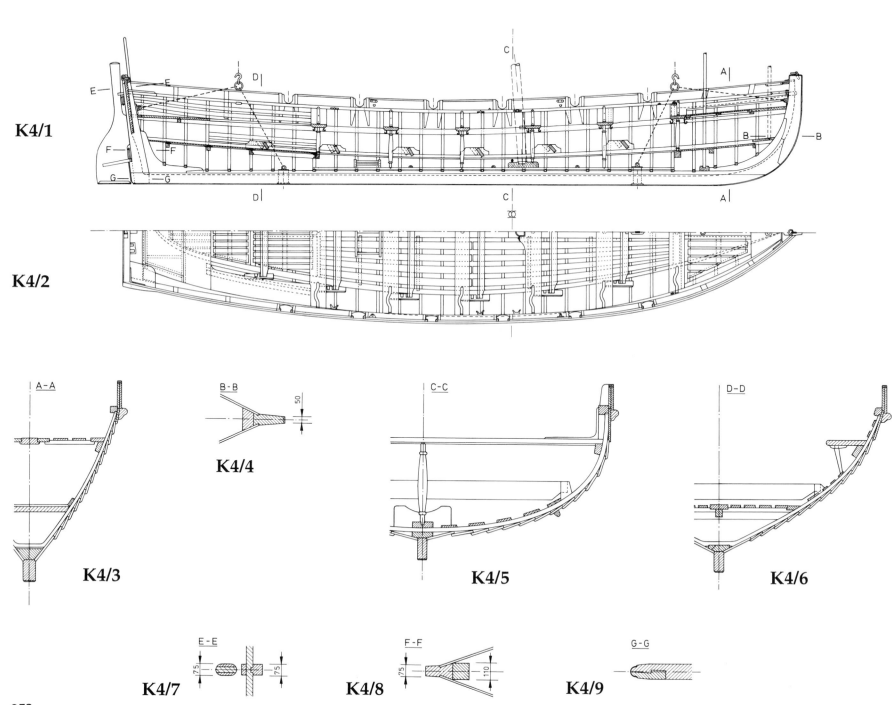

K4/1

K4/2

A–A   **K4/3**

B–B   **K4/4**

C–C   **K4/5**

D–D   **K4/6**

E–E   **K4/7**

F–F   **K4/8**

G–G   **K4/9**

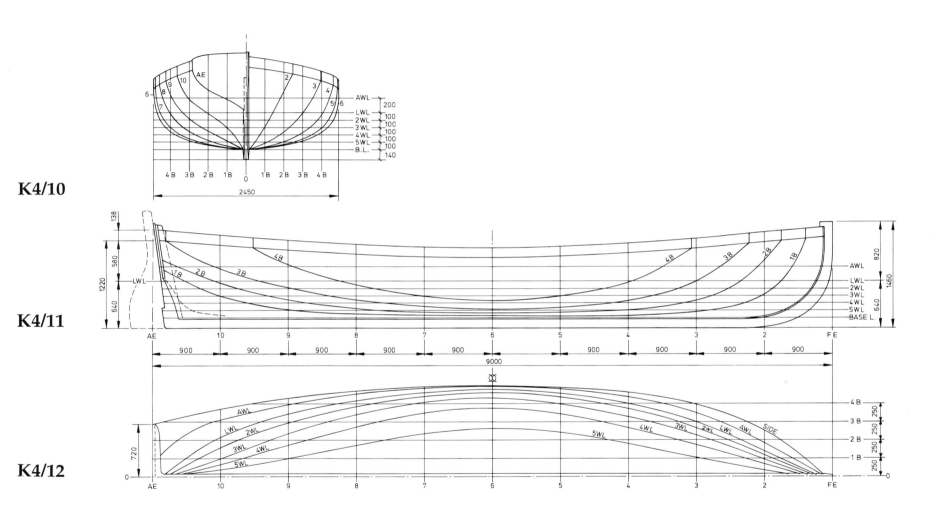

K4/10 Body plan (scale 1/50)
K4/11 Sheer elevation (scale 1/50)
K4/12 Waterline plan (scale 1/50)

K4/10

K4/11

K4/12

253

K Boats

K5   6m (20ft) SAMPAN (scale 1/50)
K5/1   *Profile view*
K5/2   *Internal profile*
K5/3   *Plan*
K5/4   *Section of middle part*
K5/5   *Rudder*

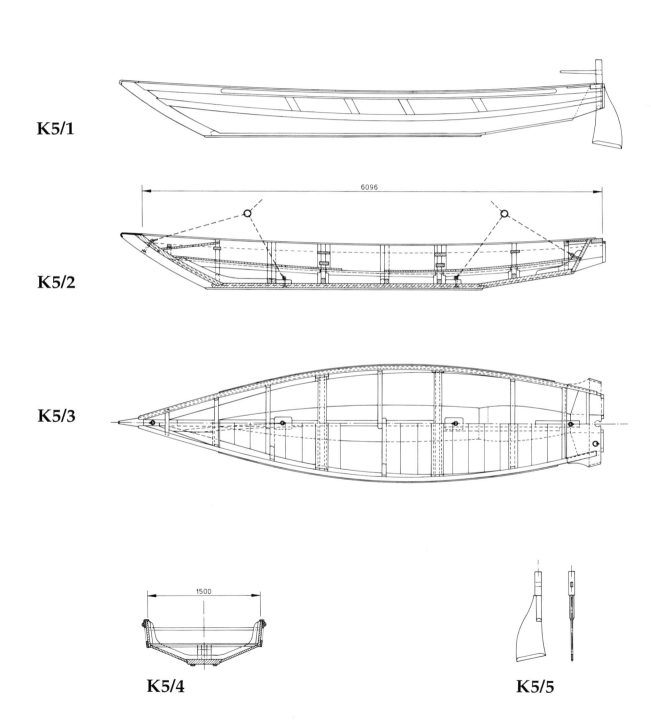

K5/1

6096

K5/2

K5/3

1500

K5/4

K5/5

K6   8m (27ft) SAMPAN (scale 1/50)
K6/1   Profile view
K6/2   Internal profile
K6/3   Plan
K6/4   Section of middle part
K6/5   Rudder

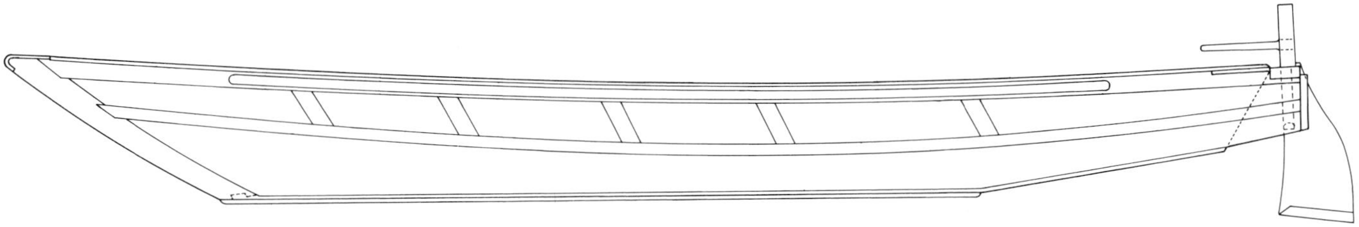

K6/1

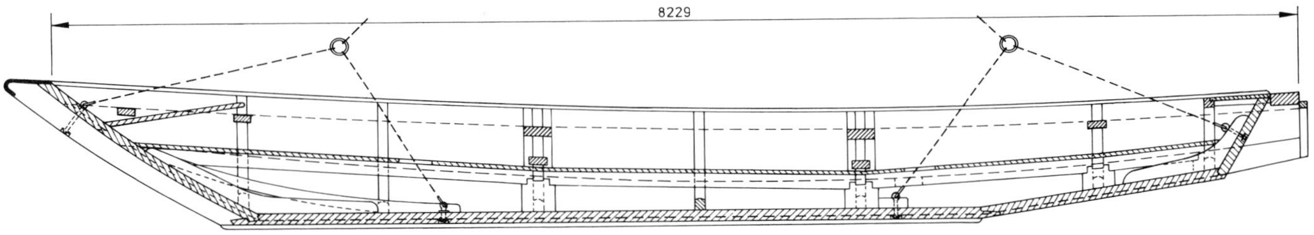

K6/2

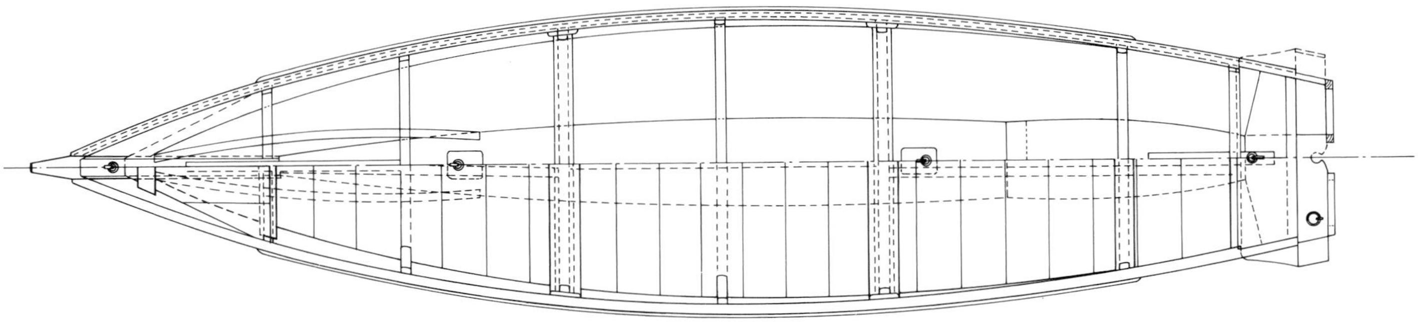

8229

K6/3

1900

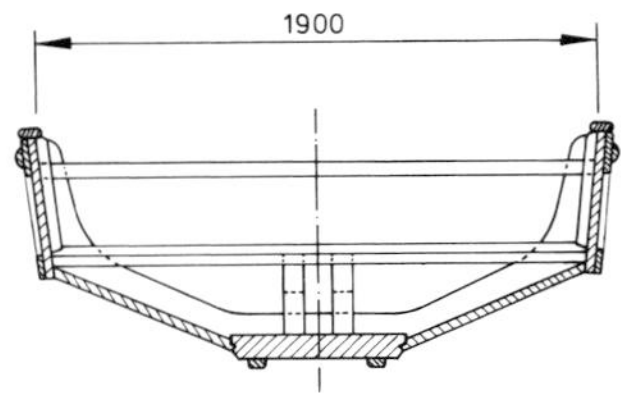

K6/4

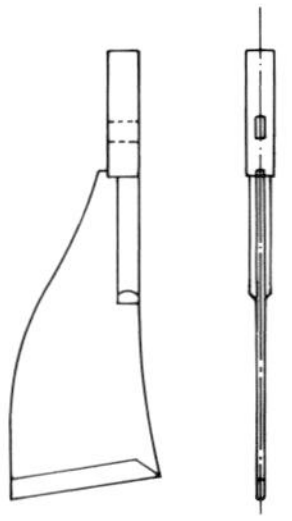

K6/5

L Flags

L1   IMPERIAL JAPANESE NAVY
ENSIGN – USED ONLY ON
ENSIGN STAFF (scale 1/50)

L2   VICE ADMIRAL'S FLAG
(scale 1/50)

L3   JACK (scale 1/50)

L4   IMPERIAL JAPANESE NAVY
ENSIGN (BATTLE ENSIGN)
FLAG WITH THESE
DIMENSIONS WERE FLOWN
FROM MAINMAST – SEE
SCHEME – IN THIS PURCHASE
WITHOUT FLAG ON ENSIGN
STAFF (scale 1/50)

L5   MAIN MAST FLAGS AS
1932–1938 (scale 1/150)

L6   MAIN MAST FLAGS AS
1939–1945 (scale 1/150)

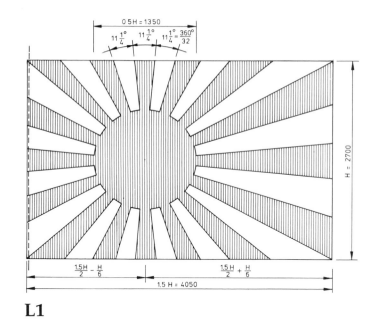

L1

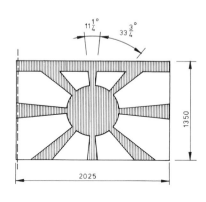

L2

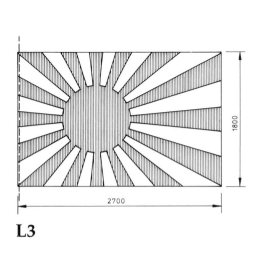

L3

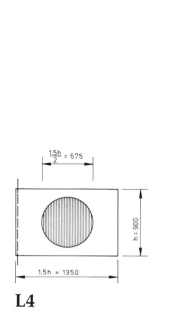

L4

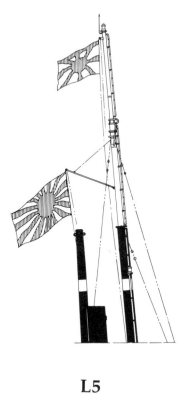

L5

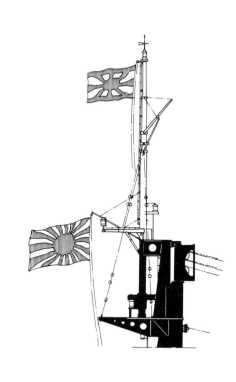

L6